Dear Readers:

The Pearls of Sharah series is about a mystical, ancient string of pearls and the magic it brings to the people into whose possession it temporarily falls. Or is it the people who make their own magic? You decide.

In **SAPPHIRE LIGHTNING** Toni Sinclair, a widow, falls in love with her husband's cousin, the one thing she did not want to do.

In **AMETHYST MIST** Marissa Berryman first has to forget her past before she can fall in love and begin her future.

All of these books explore the conflicts and heartaches, joys and passions that love can bring into the lives of two people who are meant for each other.

They are five of my favorite books and I am delighted that they are being reissued. It is my hope that you will enjoy reading them as much as I enjoyed writing them.

Sincerely,

Fayrene Preston

WHAT ARE *LOVESWEPT* ROMANCES?

They are stories of true romance and touching emotion. We believe those two very important ingredients are constants in our highly sensual and very believable stories in the *LOVESWEPT* line. Our goal is to give you, the reader, stories of consistently high quality that may sometimes make you laugh, sometimes make you cry, but are always fresh and creative and contain many delightful surprises within their pages.

Most romance fans read an enormous number of books. Those they truly love, they keep. Others may be traded with friends and soon forgotten. We hope that each *LOVESWEPT* romance will be a treasure—a "keeper." We will always try to publish

LOVE STORIES YOU'LL NEVER FORGET
BY AUTHORS YOU'LL ALWAYS REMEMBER

The Editors

LOVESWEPT® CLASSIC

Fayrene Preston
The Pearls of
Sharah III:
Leah's Story

BANTAM BOOKS
NEW YORK · TORONTO · LONDON · SYDNEY · AUCKLAND

THE PEARLS OF SHARAH III: LEAH'S STORY
A Bantam Book / Special Edition—Not for Sale

PUBLISHING HISTORY
Bantam edition published June 1989
Loveswept Classic edition / May 1995

If you would be interested in receiving protective vinyl covers for
your Loveswept books, please write to this address for
information:

Loveswept
Bantam Books
P.O. Box 985
Hicksville, NY 11802

ISBN 0-553-55022-5

Published simultaneously in the United States and Canada

PRINTED IN THE UNITED STATES OF AMERICA

OPM   10   9   8   7   6   5   4   3   2   1

The Pearls of Sharah series
is dedicated with all my love
to my sons,

Greg and Jeff,

two very special people.

Prologue

Far beneath the surface of the swelling waves, in the dark, mysterious, primordial depths of the sea, the pearls grew and waited.

Until . . .

King Darius was coming.

Princess Sharah sat by a pool of still water while a handmaiden ran a comb through the shimmering length of her black hair. Lotus blossoms floated on the pool that reflected the princess's serenely beautiful face. But just as the deep water hid the dark roots of the blossoms, so, too, did her serene countenance hide troubled thoughts.

With a wave of her hand she dismissed the

handmaiden. None of the servants had yet sensed their lord's approach, but Sharah did not need to see him or even to hear the soft tread of his footsteps to know he was near. She did not require Darius's presence to feel his every breath. She could not explain why this was, nor did she need to. She was a princess of the Karzana, a nomadic tribe, and she accepted that there were powers which could not be understood.

All she needed to know was that her blood sang when he strode through the halls of the great palace toward her private rooms here in the tower, and that the very air around her seemed to fill with excitement.

There was a stirring among her handmaidens. One of them tittered, then another. Ah, now they also knew he was coming.

Darius was drawing close.

On those nights when Darius came to her bedchamber, she accepted his attentions because circumstances had forced her to do so. She also writhed in pleasure beneath him, because he was a lover of great accomplishment. And afterward she held him through the night until dawn because, secreted within her heart, was a profound and deep love for him.

But she was also proud, and she refused to surrender her soul to him as he was determined she would. . . .

With the power of a great wind Darius strode into the chamber and clapped his hands. "Leave us."

The serving girls bowed and dispersed.

Sharah lifted her head and gazed at him. Every line of his strong body bespoke command and power. Even without the royal robes he wore he would have looked kingly. Nevertheless, his *candy* was of bluish-purple; his sash was of cloth of gold; and his shawl was ornamented with rubies, emeralds, sapphires, and diamonds.

The gods had bestowed all the manly graces on Darius, Sharah thought once again, and she knew that hearts beat fast within the breasts of all the fair young women upon whom he deigned to look.

But it was only she he wanted. And so she waited.

He held out his hand to her. "Come here, my love."

The dark blue silk of her full trousers and tunic murmured as she rose and moved with unconscious grace toward him. "My lord?"

He cupped his fingers around her chin and lifted her face to his. "Five years, Sharah. Why do you still insist upon calling me 'my lord' when we're alone? I've asked you not to."

She cast her eyes downward. "You are King Darius, ruler of all Persia. I am your concubine."

He stifled his impatience. "You are my beloved."

"I am your property, taken from my people as you swept through my country in your quest to expand your empire."

"How could I have left you?" he whispered roughly. "One look at that beautiful face of yours and my heart was lost."

Her dark eyes flashed fire at him. "Yet you keep me prisoner."

"Prisoner, Sharah? Gaze around you. What do you see? This is not a prison. This is one of the finest rooms in the palace." In anger and frustration he jerked the miter from his head and hurled it across the room. "No, I am *your* prisoner."

Darius's temper was legendary, and his action would be guaranteed to send brave men scurrying for cover.

Sharah simply met his hard gaze with a soft question. "Then I'm free to leave?"

"You know I cannot allow that. I cannot live without you. I will not."

She smiled sadly and turned away.

He caught her by the shoulders before she could put distance between them and brought her back against his body. "Is my presence in your bed so displeasing to you?" he murmured, his mouth at her ear.

She closed her eyes as pleasure shivered through her. "You know it is not. You are a very skilled lover. My body responds to you even when my mind wills differently. But the blood of the Karzana that runs in my veins demands I must be free to go to my people when they need me."

"*I* need you. Give me your love, Sharah."

"Gladly. When you give me my freedom."

He sighed heavily, and gradually his hands loosened on her shoulders until they dropped to his side.

The heat between their bodies disturbed her.

She took several steps away before she faced him again.

He pulled a red bag from the folds of his *candy*. "I have brought you a present that I have had made especially for you." She did not respond. Darius smiled inwardly. His Sharah—so stubborn, so proud. "Hold out your hands," he said softly, and when she did, he pulled the silken strings loose and upended the contents into her hand. Out spilled a long rope of large, matched pearls. The clasp was a pearl that had grown in the shape of a heart.

Unable to stop the gasp of admiration that rose naturally to her lips, she lifted the necklace to the light. Each pearl was an object of perfect loveliness, creamy white in color, blushed with a soft pink.

Darius took them from her hands and carefully laid them around her neck. "These are my gift of love to you, Sharah," he said quietly.

She looked down at the pearls that fell over her breasts to reach to her knees, and within her proud soul another scar was carved. Darius had given her the extraordinary pearls to try to make her forget that even birds could fly free, but not she.

She raised her head, sending her hair rippling to her waist, a silken black cascade. "Am I free to do as I wish with these pearls?"

"Of course. They are yours."

She moved to one of the tall, arched tower windows. "Then I may throw them away?"

An expression of surprise crossed his face, but he nodded, wanting to humor her out of her sad mood. "Yes, although I wish you would not. It took a great deal of time and effort to collect pearls so perfectly matched."

"But may I throw them away?" she insisted.

Frowning, he said, "If you so desire."

She glanced out the window to the ground some hundreds of feet below. "And may I jump after them?"

"No!" Horrified, he raced across the room to pull her away from the window. "Sharah, what are you thinking of? If you jumped, you would be killed."

Gravely she stared up at him. "So I am free to do with the pearls what I will, but not myself."

"Sharah—"

"You gave me the pearls freely as a gift of your love. I, too, want to give you my love freely. But as long as I am kept against my will, I cannot."

"Sharah, how can I let you go?" His voice broke with his anguish. "You are my life."

She touched his face, so dear to her heart, and softly smiled. "No, Persia is your life. But you will have me, my dearest. Let me live as I was meant to be—free, like all those of my tribe, to shelter under the wide sky and ride with the winds. If you do this for me, I promise I will always come back to you."

"Sharah, I cannot . . ." He stopped as he saw her determined expression. "I have no choice, do

I? I must surrender you to the sky and the winds if I am to keep you at all."

She gathered his strong hand in both of hers and raised it to brush the palm with her lips. "You won't be sorry. I may not always be here when you want me, but I will always be here for you when you need me."

And so Darius had his goldsmith put on the gold backing of the pearl clasp a special mark. It was two intertwining circles, without beginning or end, and symbolized Darius's and Sharah's eternal love for each other.

And for the rest of Darius's life Sharah came and went from the palace at will. It was reported that at his death, Sharah, wearing her lover's pearls, was by his bedside. Then she and the pearls disappeared, never to be seen again at the court of the Persians. But the story of their love and the pearls was told far and wide until it grew into legend.

One

The old Gypsy woman deposited a long, gleaming rope of pearls into the hands of the dark-haired, dark-eyed young woman sitting across the small table. *"These pearls will bring you good luck. Soon a man with cinnamon-color hair will come into your life and magic will follow."*

Leah shivered, just as she always did when she heard one of Zarah's predictions. But she slowly shook her head. "You know I don't believe in magic."

"My child, you have been exposed to the mystic ways of the Gypsies since you were a small girl. You may not *think* you believe in magic, but deep down you know the truth—there are many things beyond the ordinary and that cannot be explained."

Since arguing with Zarah was fruitless, Leah simply smiled at the older woman, then bent her head to study the rope of pearls. Myriad candles illuminated the interior of Zarah's gold-colored tent, and in the subdued light the pearls gave off a breathtaking luminosity that seemed to spill onto Leah's hands, investing her skin with an almost unearthly radiance. Leah had a drawer full of beads and other trinkets that Zarah had given her over the years, but this necklace . . . "Are you sure you want to give this to me? It's so lovely."

"The pearls belong to no one and therefore are not mine to give. But I sense you are troubled. I want you to take the pearls, wear them."

She was troubled, but she was no longer amazed that Zarah could sense her moods. She had been five years old when she had wandered alone into the Gypsy camp and seen Zarah for the first time. The nineteen years since had not changed her opinion that Zarah was the most beautiful and the wisest woman she had ever known.

"You always seem to read my feelings," she murmured.

"What is it, my child?"

"The radio station where I work has been sold, and I'm worried about what the change will mean."

"But you are the station manager. Surely they won't make any changes without your consent."

Zarah had a beyond-the-normal understanding of many things, but business was not one of them, Leah reflected lovingly. "The organization that bought the station is known to be very tough," she explained. "They could fire me and bring in someone else. Or they could do away with the station altogether. We're very small, you know."

Zarah reached across the little table and ran an aged hand gently down Leah's sable-brown hair. "Oh, my child. In many ways you are as fragile as a butterfly, but you also have much strength you have yet to discover. Put the necklace on. Good things will happen to you, you will see." While Leah dutifully looped the necklace around her neck, Zarah eyed her with humor. "You haven't said anything about the cinnamon-haired man I predict you will meet."

"Zarah—"

The old Gypsy woman held up her hand. "Never mind. You have a Gypsy heart, good and true. Soon you will believe. But for now it is enough for you to know that I desire happiness for you as much as I desire it for Rafael, the son who was born of my body."

"I do know that." From outside came the sound of laughter and guitars, but Leah was reluctant to leave the tent. As a child, she had often taken naps on the daybed at the back of the tent as Zarah read palms and told fortunes. The tent had always been a place of safety and fascination to her, and the years had changed nothing. The rich fabrics seemed as worn as always, and the scarlet, gold, and green colors seemed as faded. The scent, too, was the same, flowery and vaguely mysterious. A cluck of Zarah's tongue brought her out of her reverie.

"How many other young women who had been

given such a necklace would wait this long to see how it looked on them?"

Leah grinned and got to her feet. "Sorry."

The cheval mirror in the corner cast back the expected image of a young woman who was slender and of average height, and who possessed large, velvety brown eyes and sable-brown hair that fell past her shoulders in soft, flowing, natural waves. She had worn the three-year-old skirt and blouse many times before—the blouse, a royal blue, off-the-shoulder peasant style; the skirt, full and tiered in colors of red, fuchsia, green, and royal blue. Leather sandals protected her bare feet.

But as familiar as the face, body, and clothes in the mirror were, there was also something different. Amazingly the pearls around her neck seemed to exude energy, and their lustrous beauty radiated outward to reflect onto her, making her skin luminous and . . .

"They make me look . . . almost beautiful."

Soft wonder tinted Leah's voice, and behind her, Zarah smiled. "Perhaps it is just that the necklace is making you see yourself as you were meant to be—shining and happy."

Leah went to the Gypsy woman, knelt down beside her, and laid her head in her lap. "I'm going to miss you so much, Zarah. Can't you stay a few more days?"

Zarah placed her hand gently on Leah's head like a loving benediction. "The stars have a time schedule all their own that we should not question. Haven't I taught you that? Now listen to me, my child. Tonight is the last night of the carnival. Tomorrow the men will start to prepare for our next journey. So go outside, have a good time, enjoy the night."

Leah stood and brushed her hand down her skirt. With her movement the unfamiliar weight of the pearls shifted across her breasts. "You're right. I'm taking up the time of paying customers. We can talk tomorrow."

Zarah caught Leah's wrist with a surprisingly strong grip. "You are more important to me than the money of the *gaje*. Never forget that."

To cover the fact that her eyes were misty with tears, she bent and pressed a kiss on Zarah's cheek. "I won't."

Outside the tent, Leah paused to blink against the sights of the carnival. Colored lights were strung in every available tree, around the booths, and on the rides.

Growing up, she had waited with impatience for early summer, when the Gypsies would come and stay for two glorious weeks. When she had turned eighteen, she had gone to live with the Gypsies, traveling with them for three years. The carnival crackled with color and vitality. She loved it and considered herself part of it.

But tonight the color dazzled, the lights seemed especially bright, and the sound struck her with a sense of unreality, because it was *too* real. She felt she had stepped out of Zarah's tent and into another dimension, and could not adjust to the warmth, gaiety, and energy of the night.

There was something different about this night, she realized, and she was a part of it.

Nothing seemed real. Not even she.

Everything seemed too real. Even she.

Could it really come from the magic of the pearls? Leah quickly answered her own question. Of course not; she didn't believe in magic.

She made her way through the carnival crowd, calling out greetings and stopping often to speak with one of the Gypsies. Slowly her cares drifted away. When she spotted Rafael, she headed toward him.

He was leaning back against a big elm tree, one hand holding a cigarette, one foot braced against the tree's trunk. He watched her approach from beneath permanently shadowed, heavy-lidded eyes. "Hello, pretty little girl," he said softly when she was near.

She grinned. He had said the same thing nineteen years before when he had found her wandering the camp, and over the years it had become his standard greeting to her. But no matter how often Rafael called her "pretty little girl," her mother had told her with more frequency that with her dark hair and eyes, she looked too much like the Gypsies to be pretty. As the years had gone by, she'd learned that it was really her father she favored—the father who had deserted her mother when Leah had been born, the father who had been killed in an airplane crash two years later. But knowing the cause of her mother's bitterness hadn't made her persecution any easier to bear.

Her mother had been dead for three years, but the power and the hurt of her words and actions remained with Leah.

"Taking a break?"

He nodded, brought the cigarette to his mouth, and drew heavily on it. "Mikalo is spelling me at the booth." Rafael was a skilled and gifted silversmith. During the winter months, when he and his tribe lived in Florida, he crafted exquisite jewelry and ornamental dishes.

"He won't have many customers," she said, singing her words with a teasing lilt, "because all the ladies will wait until you get back." Rafael was five years older than she and like a brother to her, but that didn't keep her from appreciating his darkly handsome looks.

His mouth twitched with amusement. "Don't start."

"Hey, it's not my fault women think you're sexy. It's that brooding, mysterious quality of yours—it creates all sorts of fantasies in the ladies' minds. I hear them talking."

"Leah—" He broke off, and his gaze lifted to a point behind her.

Curious, Leah glanced over her shoulder and saw Sheila Donaldson staring with meaningful intensity at Rafael. Sheila's blond fairy-tale beauty was emphasized by the pastel-flowered silk chiffon dress she wore, and the matching long, trailing scarf around her neck. Leah turned back, all teasing forgotten. "Rafael, you must be careful."

"The warning is not necessary."

"You don't understand. I live in this town, and I know things you don't. Sheila is married to a very prominent man. It's an unhappy marriage, and she's vulnerable."

He dropped his cigarette and ground it out with the toe of his boot. "I've heard all about her unhappy marriage and the husband who emotionally abuses her. You of all people should have a sympathy for her."

"And I do, but right now my concern is for you. Last summer . . . well, I noticed certain things between the two of you. I suspected you might be seeing her, but I thought—Rafael, don't do anything stupid."

He lightly flicked her cheek with a long brown finger. "Hey, you're not to worry about it. There won't be any trouble. My affair with Sheila ended last summer."

Leah's smile held relief and apology. "I'm sorry. It's none of my business. It's just that—"

"Where there is love, there is concern. I understand, and we can forget the matter." He touched one of the pearls at her neck. "I see Zarah gave you the necklace. She said she was going to."

She laughed. "These pearls look just like the real thing, don't they? Not that I've ever seen the real thing."

"What is real or not real is in the mind of the beholder. They are lovely and so are you." He paused. "Did Zarah tell you what she saw for you?"

"Magic." Her tone conveyed her opinion of magic.

"And your life has been filled with hurt, not magic, so you don't believe."

"Rafael, take the pity out of your voice. People live whole lives without believing in magic."

"Ah, but what kind of lives do they live?"

"Good lives, I'm sure. And," she added firmly, "my life is fine, thank you very much."

He gave a tug on her hair. "Not by Gypsy standards, and they are the only standards that matter."

Her brow furrowed with sudden curiosity. "Zarah has never told my future before. What are you two up to? Do you want me to go back on the road with you? Is that it?"

He smiled. "We've always wanted you with us, you know that. We stole you when you were six, didn't we? You would have been raised a Gypsy if that witch of a mother hadn't come to get you. But now Zarah has given you the pearls and . . ."

When he didn't continue, she prompted him. "Yes? And what?"

"And you have your job at the radio station."

"Is that really what you were going to say?"

He stared at her for a moment, his black eyes enigmatic, then he grinned. "No, I was really going to say that we *used* to want you on the road with us, but not anymore. When you were with us, you had this tedious habit of giving the customers the right amount of change. It ruined our reputation."

"You're one of the most honest men I know, Rafael. In fact, I'm probably the only thing you ever stole, so stop teasing me."

"But why, when pretty little girls are so much fun to tease?" He gave another yank on her hair. She lunged for him, but he was quick and ducked behind the tree. Laughing, she went after him.

Stephen Tanner docked his speedboat and started for the carnival. Restlessness had driven him from his house and onto the lake. He had skimmed over the water in his new, sleek, jet-engined boat, and for a while the speed had fed his need for action. But when he had seen the lights of the carnival, he had cut the engines, and for perhaps five minutes he had sat out on the lake watching the lights and listening to the music and the laughter. Then, in a spur-of-the-moment decision, he'd geared up the boat and wheeled toward shore.

He supposed he could chalk up his unexplained urge to investigate the carnival to the fact that he was having trouble relaxing in his new country home. The house had been completed only a few weeks before, and this was the first time he'd tried to stay the night.

The sight of the Gypsy woman standing beneath the tree, smiling up at the Gypsy man, interrupted his thoughts and brought him to a halt. He wasn't sure why she interested him. She wasn't doing anything extraordinary. Although she was quite lovely, she was no more lovely than any of a dozen women he knew.

He looked closer. Maybe it was just his restless

state, he thought, disturbed, but the colored lights behind her appeared alive, almost as if they were giving off a pulsing sensation. It seemed to him that she belonged with the lights, as if she were one with their vividness and their animation.

He squeezed his eyes shut, opened them again, and saw something different: a hauntingly still essence that intrigued and baffled him. How could she seem to be part of the pulsing vitality of the lights, and utterly tranquil at the same time? He had to be seeing things that weren't there.

Suddenly she moved, grabbing for the man, who feinted before taking off around the tree. Laughing, she went after him. They were playing like children, Stephen realized with surprise, and he wondered what it would be like to be able to abandon oneself to play. Or to anything besides work.

The thought passed, but his fascination for the Gypsy woman continued. When she slipped on a muddy patch of ground, his body tensed, instantly ready to help her, but the Gypsy man quickly grabbed her, preventing her from falling.

Amazed at his reaction to her, Stephen turned away, took a few steps, stopped, and turned back just in time to see the two embrace and each head in opposite directions—the man toward the carnival, the woman toward the pavilion.

Stephen followed her.

At the pavilion Leah kicked off her sandals, turned on the water spigot, knotted the hem of her skirt high up on her thigh, and stuck her muddy foot and calf into the cool stream of water.

Watching the mud melt away, she remembered how a few minutes in Zarah's tent had banished her heavy heart. It had always been that way. Except this time Zarah had given her the pearl necklace and a strange prediction. As if a necklace could make a difference . . . With one foot and calf clean, she stuck the other leg into the water.

"Hello."

Her head jerked up and her pulse lurched with alarm at the sight of the tall man standing in front of her. A man with *cinnamon*-color hair.

He'd been wrong, Stephen thought. She wasn't as lovely as any of a dozen women he knew. Her beauty was incomparable, and right now she was tensed with the hesitancy of a wild thing, trying to decide whether to bolt. He held out a hand. "Don't be afraid. I only want to talk to you."

Slowly she straightened and stared at his hair with large, wary eyes. The color *had* to be a coincidence. "Talk to me about what?"

"You speak English."

Her dark looks had led him to believe she was foreign, she realized. In fact, he probably thought she was a Gypsy. "I'm American."

"I'm sorry. I didn't mean to offend you."

"You didn't."

The town of Sunnyvale lit the pavilion with utilitarian fluorescent lights. The colored lights of the carnival were yards behind her, but the feeling remained with Leah that the reality of the night was too vivid, too loud, and therefore had blurred into an illusion of the mind. Was *he* an illusion?

His face was incredibly strong, and the cleft in his chin looked as if it had been put there with a hammer and chisel. Masculinity and sex appeal emanated from him in an amount almost guaranteed to unbraid a woman's equanimity. Under normal circumstances he was a man whom she would avoid, but the night seemed to be having a strange effect on her. Unsure about what to do, she unconsciously lifted her hand to the pearls. At their touch she felt her nerves of apprehension gradually dissolve. "What did you want to speak to me about?"

He shrugged as if what he was about to say were incomprehensible to him. "I saw you and followed you. I wanted to speak to you, but I'm not sure about what." He smiled.

She almost took a step backward. She imagined a charming shark would have a very similar smile.

"I guess you expect that," he murmured.

"Expect what?"

Her skin had a dark golden sheen to it, like honey in the sun. But there was no sun and he couldn't see the moon from where he stood. Still, the need to touch her was irresistible. He brushed his fingers along her bare shoulder. "Expect men to want to talk to you."

His touch was a revelation to Leah because of the warmth that surged then lingered on her skin; but emotional scar tissue protected, and the urge to run came naturally.

Somehow he sensed her intention and put his hand on her arm. "Don't."

She jerked away from him. "Do you usually command with just a word or a touch?"

His brows drew together. "Why would you say that?"

"Because you were so sure I would stay."

"You're wrong," he said gravely, aware that their conversation verged on the extraordinary. *She* verged on the extraordinary. "I wasn't sure at all."

Her emotions in turmoil, she bent to turn off the water, still tingling where his fingers had held her. When she straightened, she had unknotted her skirt and had her sandals dangling from her fingers by their straps. "Where are you from?"

"My business is headquartered in Dallas."

She made a motion with her head that sent her hair rippling over her shoulder. Now she understood. This man was a stranger who had no preconceived ideas about her. The notion was oddly stimulating. "I knew you weren't from around here."

"How?"

"Because I *am* from around here. I was born and raised in Sunnyvale."

He glanced toward the carnival, his confusion apparent. "But I thought you people traveled . . ."

"You people?"

"Gypsies."

"I'm not a Gypsy, although sometimes I feel like I am."

"But I saw you with the Gypsy man beneath the tree."

"That was Rafael, and he's a good friend."

"Really? That's interesting. I'd always heard that Gypsies never let non-Gypsies into their ranks."

"They don't." With a whirl of colored skirt and sable hair, she started back toward the carnival, her bare feet covering the uneven, sometimes rocky ground with ease.

"Wait a minute."

She heard him come after her and realized he was actually interested in her. All she had to do was let him catch her. *Magic*, Zarah had said, and Zarah had never told her anything that wasn't true. Maybe . . . just for tonight . . . it wouldn't hurt to believe. A heady excitement replaced her panic and made her feel strangely bold.

He caught up with her and fell into step beside her. "What's your name?"

"Leah," she said, glancing at him from the corner of her eyes. His body in motion was a study in measured power. In fact, everything about him was controlled. His chinos showed no wrinkles and fit over his hips and long legs with tailored perfection. His shirt was by a well-known designer and short-sleeved, but his arms, while appearing strong, showed no bulging muscles. Her instincts told her that he was deliberately restraining his strength and sex appeal and that she must be cautious.

But magic didn't always take instincts into account.

"I'm Stephen. Stephen Tanner."

At the spot where the illumination from the colored lights began, she stopped, looked up at him, and decided to be honest with him. "Did you know that you have cinnamon-color hair?"

He chuckled. "My mother calls it reddish-brown."

"I hope she doesn't say your eyes are just green."

"Why not?"

"Because green is not an accurate description. They're the color of a pine forest, cool, dark, and . . . they make me want to walk into them."

"What's your full name?" he asked softly.

"Leah Jayne Kellerman."

His glance dropped to her mouth, then returned to her eyes. "So, Leah Jayne Kellerman, where are we going?"

"We?"

"We," he said firmly, but with that charming smile she was sure could slice without warning into tender skin. "Letting you out of my sight would be impossible for me at this moment."

"Why?" She felt like a baby taking its first steps. The freedom was exhilarating, but she knew that a fall could be painful.

"Because you're fascinating, and you're beautiful, and I want to get to know you better."

She'd been fishing for a compliment, but in no way was she prepared for it.

He grinned. Her large brown eyes were very expressive, and her astonishment was genuine. When would she stop intriguing him, he wondered. "Besides," he added, "I've never been to a carnival before."

Her amazement was apparent. "You haven't? But that's awful."

He gestured toward the carnival. "Show me why."

She hesitated. Spending time with him would be risky; she wasn't used to taking risks. On the other hand, she was as familiar with the carnival as she was with her own heartbeat. Here she would be in command, her steps would be sure and on firm ground, there would be no danger of falling. And there was the necklace . . . and the night. She took his hand. "All right."

At the Shetland pony ride they watched while Toma, a teenager with black curly hair and infinite patience, coaxed a four-year-old boy out of his fear, then sat the child astride a pony. Toma looked up, saw her, and sent her a wink. She smiled, and with a toss of her head led Stephen on.

At the Ferris wheel, she asked, "Would you like to take a ride?"

"I don't think so." He gazed up at the top seat as it swayed, while at the bottom of the wheel, a couple was being let out. "Hanging in the sky in anything that doesn't have a jet engine doesn't appeal to me."

"I've ridden that wheel countless times, but I've never ridden in a plane before."

He looked at her oddly. "You've *never* ridden in a plane?"

"No. You see, it's unnatural to fly through the

sky with a casing of steel around you and artificial air piped in for you."

"Oh, the air isn't artificial. It's real, but it's just—"

"If you're going to fly, you should do it like the birds do it, free, unencumbered, and without someone else choosing your flight pattern."

"Flight pattern?"

"Besides, flying in planes is just too organized. Seats all in a row. Attendants in uniforms, serving everyone food with the same texture and design. You know, this Ferris wheel is perfectly safe. Kore is an excellent mechanic."

It took him a moment to catch up with her abrupt change of subject. "Kore?" He glanced at the elderly Gypsy man at whom she was smiling. "Do you know them all?"

"*Them?* They're not a species of insects. Gypsies are a proud, noble, and ancient race." Aware that her voice had risen sharply, she stopped and began again. "Yes, I know all of the Gypsies. Their carnival has been coming to this town for years."

He glanced around. "I didn't mean to be disparaging. It's just that I haven't noticed the Gypsies being friendly with any of the other townspeople."

"You won't."

He could count the minutes he'd known her, but he already realized she was the most complicated woman he'd ever met. He was convinced that if he smoothed his hands over her body, he'd actually be able to feel a network of finely tied-together nerves running beneath her skin.

She tossed her hair so that it fell behind her shoulders, and he caught a subtle, sensual scent of dark velvet flowers that made his imagination reel.

"Do you want to ride the Ferris wheel?" she asked once more.

"Maybe later."

She grinned. "You're making it very difficult for me to show you the carnival. You don't seem to want to do anything."

"That's because I'm not interested in the carnival. I'm interested in you."

Just then a man in his late twenties bumped into Leah's back. The man looked over his shoulder with a smile of apology, but the smile faded when he saw her. "Sorry," he said, and with a quick nod, walked away.

Stephen's gaze followed the man, a frown on his face. "Who was that?"

"Gary Mercer. He's a teacher at the high school."

She turned away, unwilling to explain about being raised by a mother who barely tolerated her. And how at a very early age, bewildered and lost, she had turned to the Gypsies for the love her mother couldn't give her. But the townspeople hadn't understood. They had seen a child who was allowed to run wild with the Gypsies, wearing colorful ragtag clothes Zarah made for her, and they had viewed her and her mother as strange and different. While accepting the entertainment the carnival provided as a break in their routine and appreciating the percentage of the take the

Gypsies paid to the town, the people had an inherent mistrust of the Gypsies and kept their distance. They kept their distance from her as well, and she had never gone out of her way to try to change their treatment. She accepted it just as she accepted that tomorrow the town would be buzzing about how she had been at the carnival with a stranger who wasn't a Gypsy, and about how she had actually been comfortable enough with him to hold his hand.

Her gaze suddenly dropped to their joined hands. His was a strong, capable hand, and she wondered what Zarah would make of his palm. "How would you like to have your fortune told? The woman who tells fortunes here, Madam Zarah, is very good."

"I don't believe in things like fortune-telling and astrology," he said firmly.

"No?"

He shook his head. "Do you?"

Rolling a pearl back and forth between her fingers, she gazed at his cinnamon-color hair. Like a drowning person reaching for a life preserver, she tried to grasp reality one more time before the night completely got away from her. His hair color had to be a coincidence, and her reaction to the night could be attributed to the fact that she was off balance because Zarah, Rafael, and the others would be leaving in a couple of days.

She told herself these things but in the end was unsure if she'd been successful in convincing herself.

"It's best not to discount something just because you don't understand it," she murmured.

He paused to wonder if she had answered his question, then concluded it didn't matter. The reflection from the colored lights blended their hues into her dark brown hair like shining ribbons. "What would you like to do?" he asked softly.

Something told her that he normally used that soft tone in only two situations: when he was seducing a woman and when he was threatening a man. But he hadn't been trying to seduce her. The softness had been meant to soothe, and so she decided to stay with him a while longer. "Let's just walk around."

"Leah," Bertole, a short man with a well-rounded body, shouted, as they passed his booth. "Bring the *gajo* over here."

"What's a *gajo*?" Stephen asked in a whisper.

She laughed. "That's you. A non-Gypsy. Come on." She pulled him over to the booth and explained the game. "One ticket will get you three balls. For every furred wooden cat you knock over, you win a prize. One cat gets you your choice of prizes on shelf one. Two cats gets you your choice of prizes on shelf two. The best prizes are on shelf three." She nodded toward the stuffed bears and dogs on the top shelf.

He gave Bertole two dollars, and the Gypsy set six balls in front of him. "I warn you, I never even played Little League."

"It's only a game," she said encouragingly. "What do you have to lose?"

"I'm not sure." He cast a dubious glance at Bertole, who smiled benignly back at him, then he turned to consider the prizes. "I think I'll win you that red teddy bear up there, Leah. Would you like that?"

Bertole rolled his eyes, his disdain plain. Leah thought of her enormous stuffed animal collection that the Gypsies had given her over the years. "You don't have to win me anything."

"But I want to."

In the next minute, six of the worst thrown balls Leah had ever seen sailed past the wooden cats without even ruffling their fur.

Bertole gave a hoot of derision. "Leah could knock down three cats in a row by the time she was eight."

Leah sent Bertole a dark look. "Stephen, let's try another game."

He slapped two more dollars down on the wooden counter. "I never give up."

Laughing, Bertole lay six more balls on the counter. The first two balls Stephen threw brushed the fur of two different cats. The third ball knocked down a cat. The rest of the balls missed altogether.

"Chose a prize from shelf one," Bertole said.

"Not on your life." Stephen produced another dollar. "I'm determined to win Leah that teddy bear."

"It seems I'm going to get very rich tonight," Bertole said cheerfully.

Stephen stared with concentration at the furred

cats, and Leah caught Bertole's eye and pulled at her ear. The Gypsy grinned and nodded.

Stephen suddenly cut his eyes to Bertole. "Don't you dare take them down for me."

Leah flushed guiltily, but a grudging hint of admiration edged into Bertole's eyes. Gypsies had no respect for people who were easily duped.

Stephen pointed a finger at her. "I don't need or want my ego stroked."

His sudden burst of anger directed at her took her by surprise and forcibly reminded her that he was a stranger whom she didn't know at all. Her chest tightened until it hurt for her to breathe. Her skin went clammy. She felt herself withdrawing, pulling in all the emotions she'd been so bravely exposing. It was a defense mechanism that stemmed from the times when her mother's diatribes against her would become particularly virulent and Leah's tender feelings could take no more. It was then that she'd search for the still peaceful place inside her to escape to.

But this time she was too angry with herself. She stayed and tried to face the situation. How could she have been so foolish as to let her guard down with this stranger? He would be driving back to Dallas tonight; tomorrow he wouldn't even remember her or this night. She didn't see Bertole's concerned look because her gaze was fixed on the back of Stephen's head.

He threw the first ball. A cat went down, as did two more cats with two more successive throws.

When he handed Leah the teddy bear, he was clearly satisfied with himself.

"Thank you," she whispered.

"You're welcome. Now what shall we do?"

She backed away from him, holding the teddy bear tightly to her chest, its softness acting as a buffer against the pain she felt trying to penetrate her. "I've shown you everything. You should leave now."

Completely bewildered by her reaction, he reached for her, but she flinched away. "What's wrong, Leah?"

It was beyond her to explain. "Nothing. You've just seen everything there is to see, that's all."

He closed the distance between them, this time taking care not to touch her. "I don't want to leave, Leah. I want to spend more time with you, and even if I have to get on that damned Ferris wheel, I will, if only you'll get that haunted look out of your eyes. Give me some help here. Are you angry with me for some reason?"

Her grip on the teddy bear tightened, pressing several of the pearls into her skin, and she remembered the necklace and Zarah's prediction. Little by little her confidence returned, and with it, reason. *If* he had been seriously angry with her—and she was no longer sure whether he had been or not—his anger certainly hadn't lasted, and it would seem he hadn't been rejecting her. He wanted to be with her to the point of being willing to do something he didn't want to do. Maybe if she kept reminding herself that tonight was special, illusory, and magical, everything would be all right.

She pointed to the ride closest to them. "How about the tilt-a-whirl?"

Stephen nodded his head. Damned if he knew what had just happened. For a minute there, Leah had looked at him with all the fear and vulnerability of a wild creature in great danger. What was going on?

"Maybe this whole carnival is enchanted," he said, "and you're a witch who has cast a spell over me. At this point the explanation makes as much sense as anything. Let's go."

She settled into the seat beside him, but kept her eyes averted. Rico, another teenage Gypsy boy, brought the bar down that would hold them in. She handed him the teddy bear and her sandals. "Will you put these somewhere for me? I'll get them later."

"Sure thing, Leah." Rico threw Stephen a suspicious glance, then went on to the next group of people.

"Could I put my arm around you?" Stephen asked.

"You're supposed to hold on to the bar."

"Leah, it's going to be very hard not to touch you on this ride."

"You're right, I suppose."

"Does that mean I can?"

He was amused and stymied. He'd known women who had been willing to hop into bed with him after a two-minute acquaintanceship, and Leah had to think about whether she'd let him put his arm around her.

"That means yes," she said.

The tilt-a-whirl began moving, and the car swiveled wildly while the whole ride turned and lifted.

Leah's torso slammed against Stephen's and centrifugal force kept their bodies fast to each other. The lights around them blurred together until Leah could see only colored streamers. The individual notes of music and squeals of laughter melded. A long, unmeasurable length of time passed. . . .

The ride slowly came to a stop. The world stilled. Colors and sound separated once more into their distinct identities.

Neither Leah nor Stephen moved.

"I have a boat at the dock," he whispered. "Let's go for a ride out on the lake."

The carnival was familiar territory to her. She had been taking baby steps there, but out on the lake . . . Her hand went to the necklace, and the feel of the pearls lent her courage.

Two

The boat skimmed over the midnight-black lake with Stephen at the wheel and Leah beside him. The speed, the night, and the man made her feel as though her blood had turned effervescent and was sparkling and bubbling through her veins. The wind whipped her laughter back to her, surprising her with the sound of her own joy.

She was feeling a freedom that she usually felt only with the Gypsies, a release from the constraints that normally bound her. Her baby steps were growing into giant steps, and she didn't want to hear the small voice in her brain that cautioned it was impossible to walk on water.

When they reached the middle of the lake, he cut the motor, and she pushed a handful of wind-blown hair from her eyes and looked questioningly at him.

"I thought it would be nice just to drift awhile." He held his hand out. "Come sit with me."

He was going to kiss her, she realized suddenly. The idea excited and frightened. She was twenty-four years old and had never been kissed passionately by a man before. What would it be like, she wondered. Would she be disappointed? Would he? Her heart was pounding so hard, she didn't hear him say, "Leah?" until he repeated himself.

She looked at him, startled. "What?"

His smile was gentle, and he brushed an errant wave from her face that she had missed. "Why do I get the impression that you're about to dive into the lake and swim back to shore?"

The breeze was cool, and wavelets lapped hypnotically against the boat's hull. In the distance the lights of the carnival were soft, and the music floating across the water was faint. "I guess because I was about to."

His expression was one of absolute fascination. "I don't think I've ever had that effect on a woman before. I'm not sure whether I should be flattered or insulted."

She bent her head, looking at nothing in particular. "It's not your fault. It's just that sometimes, I'm . . . shy. No, that's not right. Sometimes I'm . . . afraid." The necklace, whose length hung below her waist, caught her eyes with its iridescent glow. As she picked up one of the pearls, his chuckle sent a warmth skittering through her.

"I promise you I'll do nothing to make you want to jump overboard. In fact, if you'll look at me and smile, I'll even start the boat up and take you back to shore."

Slowly she raised her head, meeting his gaze, but she didn't smile. "Don't do that. I'd like to stay out here for a while. The breeze is cooler here, and it's quieter."

"Quieter?"

"Except for two weeks out of the year when the Gypsies bring the carnival to town, I lead a very quiet life."

"When I first saw you, there were colored lights behind you. They were pulsing. It seemed to me that you belonged with the lights. Then I noticed the stillness in you and decided I had been wrong."

"You were right both times," she said simply.

"You know," he said after a moment, "there was a time tonight when I wondered at what point you would cease to fascinate me. Now I know that such a point doesn't exist. Let's go sit at the back, and you can tell me all about the colored lights and the stillness in your life."

Her smile came slowly, and its loveliness made his knees weak. "I'm not sure I want to, because if I did, you'd be the one jumping overboard."

"Try me." He led her down the center aisle of the big boat to the stern, where he chose a wide-cushioned, sofalike lounge and brought her down beside him.

The moonlight rayed across the lake and high-lighted the compelling strength of his face. Who was he, she wondered, and why had he come to the carnival? A moment's thought brought her to the decision that it might be better not to question. After all, he was a stranger who would disappear at the end of the night. But before the night ended . . . "First, I'd like to ask a favor of you."

"What's that?" A sudden brief rush of wind lifted the ruffle of her peasant blouse and caused it to flutter about her throat. Without thinking, he smoothed it back into place and, in doing so, brushed his hand over her breast. The momentary contact was enough to make him go hard with need. Her next words left him aching.

"Would you kiss me?"

"That's the favor?"

She nodded.

Most women he knew initiated what they wanted. Most women offered no surprises. But then, he was quickly learning that Leah wasn't "most women." She constantly enchanted and astonished. "Why would you *ask* something like that?"

"Because the waiting is awful."

She had a way of addressing his questions from an angle that before tonight he hadn't known existed, and it was like being hit between the eyes with a stunning freshness.

"You certainly know how to get to a man," he said in a voice made husky by growing desire. Stroking a finger across her bottom lip, he felt her lip tremble. "Oh, yes, you certainly do." He lowered his head and lightly touched her lips with his. "There's no need to tremble," he whispered. "At least not yet." And then he moved his mouth back and forth in a sure, unhurried way that grazed the soft flesh with gentleness until he felt the trembling stop and her mouth grow silkily pliant.

He brought his hand to her neck so that it cradled her jaw and controlled the angle of her head, then he hardened the kiss by degrees until her lips parted and his tongue could delve into the depths that awaited.

Leah felt as though the universe had expanded. She'd never known such feelings existed. Fire that made her shiver, sweetness that made her melt. Without hesitation she reached for his shoulders, then wound her arms around his neck, wanting more, needing more.

How had he lived this long without kissing her, he wondered, deeply stirred. He'd never known a kiss like it. He felt caught in the middle of a kaleidoscope with changing patterns all around him that were made up of colors, light, and Leah. And each new pattern made him want her more, until he reached the point where he didn't think he'd be able to stand not taking her.

He pulled away, suffering physical pain as he tried to draw air into lungs that felt as if they'd never breathe again. "We'll go to my place."

"That was my first kiss," she whispered.

The shock he had felt at the fire of their kisses was nothing compared to what he felt now. "I don't believe it. You were incendiary."

"It was my first."

"But you seem so"—he searched for a word—

"worldly." The minute he said it, he knew he was wrong. She was *other*worldly.

All her defenses went up. "Just because I've never allowed a man to kiss me doesn't mean I'm not worldly. My mother never permitted me to date while I lived with her. When I was eighteen, I left home and went to live with the Gypsies. They were very protective of me when it came to men."

"Gypsies? Protective?"

She wasn't surprised at his conception of Gypsies, but nevertheless it made her sad. "It's not necessary to be worldly-wise to be experienced. My experience was gained by learning to survive—here in Sunnyvale and then when I traveled with the carnival. Sometimes I think I've had too much experience at surviving, because sometimes I think I'm too good." Her eyes held sadness and wisdom beyond her years as she looked at him. "Then other times I don't think I'm good enough."

He shook his head, feeling the need to clear it. "I don't understand."

"It doesn't matter," she said quietly.

"The hell it doesn't."

"Stephen, it doesn't matter. We met only two hours ago."

She had just said something logical, and he pounced on it. "*Exactly.* So why tonight for your first kiss? Why me?"

She shrugged. "It just seemed right."

"Right?" His voice rose and filled with incredulity. "Honey, if it had been any more right, we would have both gone up in flames."

Suddenly she laughed, at herself, at him, at their situation. "You're right. We kissed great."

He stared at her a long moment. "I'm not going to be able to figure you out, am I?"

"Why would you want to?"

"Oh, I don't know. How about to preserve my sanity?"

She grinned. "I'm not sure I know any sane people."

"Everyone I know is sane."

"Then we have nothing in common."

His hand closed around her throat, above the pearls. "We have the fire in common."

Her grin faded. "Yes, the fire. Perhaps we should leave well enough alone."

His thumb began to massage up and down the cord of her neck. "Can we?"

"Of course." The passion of the kiss rushed back full force to her, and she was vaguely aware that she put no trust in what she had just said.

"For someone so inexperienced, you're a very good liar," he said, and kissed her softly.

The care with which he kissed her made her feel scorched right down to her fingernails. "Lies are sometimes necessary for survival," she said when she could breathe again.

"So are kisses."

"Where do you live?"

He straightened away from her and rubbed at his brow. "Do you do it deliberately?"

She moistened her lips to ease the parting of his lips from hers. "What?"

"Do and say things that throw me. Never mind. I live right . . ." The boat had drifted, and he twisted around, sighted in the shore to get his bearings, then pointed. "There. Do you want to go over?"

Her gaze followed his finger to the newly built, modern, two-story cedar and stone house that sprawled on the shore. "So that's *your* house. Everyone was wondering who the owner was. You used Dallas contractors and labor, you know."

"Ah, yes. I was told they were the best."

"There were people around here who would have been equally as good and could have used the work. There was some resentment about the matter, and the Dallas people stayed to themselves, so no one gave anyone a chance to work out the problem."

"How do you know all of this?"

She shrugged. "It's a small town." The lake breeze was not cooling her heated flesh. She stood, took a few steps, then turned. "It's a nice house."

"Thank you," he said, amused. Somehow after all the money he had spent on the house, he'd rather expected something more than *nice*. "I built it because my friends, one of whom is my doctor, told me that having a country home would help me learn to relax and rest."

"And has it?"

"The first night's been a washout as far as relaxing goes." The way he looked at her made his meaning clear.

Her cheeks warmed. "I'm sure you'll get the

knack of it soon." She studied the house. "You left on several lights."

"I always do."

"That's something else we differ on. I never leave lights on. In fact, I prefer stars to lights."

"Most people don't have stars in their homes, so they have to settle for lights," he said, watching her. Her face was in profile to him. Sable-brown waves caressed her cheek and a moon-thrown shadow contoured her jawline. She was staring toward the shoreline, idly playing with the pearl necklace.

"There are times I can find peace only when I'm beneath the sky." It was something the Gypsies had taught her. Although they all had trailers, they spent as much time as possible beneath the velvet night sky.

"Do you often have trouble finding peace?"

She turned grave eyes on him. "Yes, but tonight there's been a different kind of peace that hasn't really been a peace at all, yet it's been every bit as nice. I really think it's the magic . . . and you."

He surged to his feet and took hold of her arms. "Let's go to my house and turn off the lights."

She knew that if they went to his house, they would make love. The heat between them was simply too strong for them not to make love. But in a few hours this night would be over, and when she woke up in the morning, she would be just plain Leah Jayne Kellerman again, Leah Jayne Kellerman accepted and loved only by the Gypsies.

"I think it's time I went back to the carnival."

"Stay, Leah. Stay with me."

She gazed solemnly into his eyes. "Tomorrow will be better if I don't."

A look of absolute frustration came over his face. "I can't even imagine what you mean by that."

She put her hand on his shoulder in a comforting fashion and wished she could comfort herself. "It's all right. It really is." Behind him she could see the lights from the carnival begin to go out. "Kiss me one more time before we leave."

He pulled her hard against him so that she could feel every line and bulge of his body. "If I kiss you, I won't stop, and that one kiss will last for the rest of the night. Is that what you want?"

"Yes . . . but I can't have it."

"Yes, you can. It would be the easiest thing you've ever done. All you'd have to do is say kiss me, Stephen."

She wanted to swallow, but she couldn't. Neither could she pull away from him. Her breasts were full and aching and crushed against his chest. Her lower body was throbbing.

"Kiss me, Stephen," she whispered. His hands tightened on her arms, his head began to lower, and she added in a louder voice, "But let me stop the kiss when I need to."

"Dammit, Leah."

He brought his mouth down on hers.

And the fiery contact almost split the night apart.

•   •   •

Stretched out under the sky in her backyard for the rest of the night, Leah longed for peace and sleep. They never came. When morning broke over the horizon, she found that the tomorrow she had said would be better if she didn't make love with Stephen was not better at all.

Tomorrow without Stephen hurt.

Lying on the quilt, gazing up at the gradually brightening sky, she remembered how hard it had been for her to end their kiss. And when she had, it had been as if something vital near her heart had been torn.

But as soon as she'd pushed against him, he had released her, started the boat, and taken her back to shore. Before he had handed her onto the landing, he had taken her in his arms and given her another kiss, this one soft and gentle. Then he had said, "I'm letting you go for now, but I'm not letting you get away from me."

She *had* gotten away from him, though, and it was for the best, she told herself. Firmly shoving him from her mind, she rose and went into the house to plan her day while getting ready for work. With any luck she could leave the radio station early and have that much more time with Zarah.

In her bedroom she tried to draw from the secure, warm environment she had created for herself. Ivory lace curtains fluttered at the open window. Cheerful rose striped wallpaper covered the walls. A wicker chaise lounge boasted plump velvet pillows that carried a small floral design. A fluffy sky-blue cotton comforter lay across the old wooden bed she had painted with white enamel. A rose and blue flannel quilt draped a round table that held a hammered silver mirror Rafael had made for her, along with a fringed lamp and an assortment of small pictures of her Gypsy friends. A pot of white tulips sat beside the bed. A straw hat that featured a band of red and pink cabbage roses decorated a corner.

She chose a white cotton two-piece dress to put on. Before heading out the door of her bedroom, she paused. The pearls lay on her dresser in lustrous splendor, the morning sun highlighting their soft pink blush. Zarah would be expecting to see them on her, she reflected. For Zarah she should wear them.

Deciding to use the necklace as a belt, she wound the pearls around her slim waist three times, then secured it by tucking both ends back into the pearls.

After a moment's hesitation she raised her eyes to the mirror. The pearls gleamed radiantly against the white cotton. As she had last night, she saw and felt their energy. And they made her look, well, very nice, she thought, immediately casting aside the superlative description that had been on the tip of her tongue. But her step was a bit lighter as she left her house.

Leah had been living and traveling with the Gypsies three years when her mother had died.

She came home with the idea of selling the house and returning to the Gypsies. But after she'd been in Sunnyvale a few weeks, she'd come to the startling realization that she didn't *have* to leave again. And there was also the feeling that she had relied on her friends, the Gypsies, long enough. Perhaps, she had thought, it was time for her to create a life within which she could function as a productive and independent individual.

And so, just as leaving home at the age of eighteen had been a step for her, so, too, was returning to stay.

Almost simultaneously with the drawing of these conclusions, she read in the paper that there was a position open at the local radio station, KSUN, for an assistant to the station manager. The more she thought about the idea, the better she liked it. She knew that KSUN programming was inconsistent and boring and that the community interest in the station was negligible. The challenge intrigued her. She got the job, learned the business, and succeeded to her boss's job when he resigned.

The station had come to mean a lot to her. Everything that was broadcast from six in the morning to nine in the evening had her stamp on it now. She supposed it was her way of reaching out and touching people without risk.

The radio station was housed in a rectangular brown cement building. There was nothing Leah had been able to do about the drab color on the outside. The owners had refused to sink any fresh money into the operation of the station, and they certainly hadn't been concerned with aesthetics. But with as much of her own money as she could spare, she had seen to it that splashes of color were everywhere on the inside of the building, from the blue of the curtains to the pink, green, and turquoise patterned slipcover she had sewn for the couch. Bright, vivid posters covered her office walls, and healthy green plants grew along the windowsill.

"Good morning, Leah," Margaret, the receptionist, said as Leah entered the building. "I have a message for you from a Mr. Roland, who called an hour and a half ago. He said to tell you he'll be driving from Dallas and should make the trip in about two hours, depending on the traffic in Dallas. Who is he anyway?"

Leah made a face. "He's TCIC's accountant."

At the mention of the new owners of the station, Margaret went pale. She was a widow in her late fifties who, because of her age, had had trouble finding employment. When she came to interview for the receptionist job at KSUN, Leah had seen the potential for a dependable, levelheaded, and loyal employee and had hired her on the spot. She had never regretted her decision. Now she tried to alleviate the older woman's distress.

"He only wants to look at the books. Everything's in order." Or will be, she thought, as soon as she had an opportunity to bring the books up-to-date. She usually did the bookkeeping in the evenings, but when Zarah, Rafael, and the Gypsies were in town, she spent that time with them. If she'd just had a chance to talk with this man before he'd started . . .

"I know he won't find anything out of line, Leah. I'm just worried that TCIC will feel our profit margin isn't great enough for them to keep us. If I lose this job . . ."

Margaret's anxiety tugged at Leah's heart. She understood what it was like to not be able to fit in anywhere or to be accepted. For her, Margaret, and most of the others who worked at the station, KSUN was a haven where they could function in a useful, hassle-free way and create something that was their very own.

She gave a brief smile to Margaret. "Try not to worry. I'm going to do my best to see that none of us loses our jobs." And if she only knew how she was going to do such a thing, she thought, then she could stop worrying too.

She bypassed her office and made her way down the hall. At the large broadcast-booth window she waved at Harry Morrison, who acknowledged her with a nod. "Everything okay?" she mouthed.

He nodded again.

A smile lingered on her face as she walked back down the hall to her office. Harry was a Vietnam veteran whose memories of that war had left him unable to hold down a full-time job until Leah had hired him. He didn't talk much and was happiest when he was in the control booth, surrounded by albums and tapes, and playing the mixed fare of pop hits and classic rock that he loved so much.

She took a seat behind her desk and wondered

how Pat Meredith, her advertising salesperson, was doing. Two days earlier, Leah had talked with Pat about a plan to bring in a substantial number of new accounts. She hoped to show TCIC officials that increased profit was a realistic possibility so that they wouldn't be quick to make changes. The plan meant double the amount of work Pat usually did, but she had quickly agreed. Pat was dedicated to Leah and the station because Leah and the job had given her acceptance at a time when she was desperate.

Pat was a twenty-one-year-old young woman who, two years earlier, had had a darling little boy named Bobby out of wedlock. The father had been a boy she had met at college. As soon as he had heard Pat was pregnant, he had left her high and dry. Pat's parents had disowned her. With no means of support and no one to care for Bobby while she worked, she had jumped at the chance to sell advertising for KSUN. For the first year of Bobby's life he had been carried papoose-style on his mother's back while she went from merchant to merchant selling advertising spots on the radio. And even though she was now making enough money to hire someone to care for Bobby, Pat still carried him with her a great deal of the time.

Leah sighed and stared down at the memo pad she had been doodling on. How had the name *Stephen* gotten there?

"You look very beautiful this morning," he said from the doorway.

She jumped. "How did you get in? How did you find me?"

He strolled casually into the office, stopping only when he came up against the front of her desk. "That's three questions, but I think I can handle them. A very nice lady out in the lobby directed me to your office is the answer to your first question."

"She usually notifies me of any visitors."

"I convinced her not to." His smile was the one that mixed charm with predatory sharpness. "Finding out where you worked was equally easy. As you said last night, this is a small town. And if you'll recall the last thing I said to you, you'll have the answer to your third question."

"You said you weren't letting me get away from you," she said slowly, "but I did get away. At least for a little while."

He bent over the desk so that their faces were level. "No, you didn't. You weren't free of me a minute. I was with you all night. Just like you were with me."

"That's not true."

"Really?" He straightened. "Tell me something. Where did you sleep?"

"Outside."

He nodded with satisfaction. "No peace, Leah. Just like I had no peace." With a quickness that did nothing for her emotional balance, he rounded the desk and hauled her out of the chair. "Do you know why we had no peace? Because we needed like hell to be together."

The kiss came as no surprise to her. Neither did the fact that desire flamed up in her so quickly she was left weak. Last night she'd experimented with his kisses and become an addict. He was right, she reflected hopelessly. Need for him was twisted all through her, a painful part of her that she felt each time she drew a breath.

He'd spent the night recalling her kisses, Stephen thought hazily, yet memory hadn't come close to the reality. He'd never known a woman with such instant, uncensored responses. It excited him as nothing ever had. The nerves that ran just beneath her skin were charged with currents of fire and emotion. And every time he came near her, kissed her, or touched her, she pulsed just like the colored lights. He was determined she would pulse for no one but him.

He slid his hand to the soft fullness of her breast.

"Stephen," she whispered on a sigh.

"Tell me you couldn't get away from me last night." He pressed kisses over her face while thumbing at the nipple through the cloth of her dress. "Tell me I was crawling through your bloodstream, just like you were through mine."

She gave a little cry. "Yes, oh, yes."

With a hard shudder he drew away and stared down at her with eyes as dark as a forest at night. "Okay, then, what are we going to do about it?"

"I—"

"You didn't need me to teach you how to kiss last night, Leah. You won't need me to teach you how to make love. After we come together, there may be nothing left but ashes. I think it's more than worth the risk. What do you think?"

She wasn't sure she *was* thinking, and she didn't care. "I agree," she whispered.

He yanked her back to him and kissed her fiercely.

At first she didn't hear the intercom.

"Tell her you're taking the rest of the day off," he muttered against her lips.

Her brain was filled with clouds and fire. "What?"

He raised his head. "Your receptionist is calling you on the intercom. Tell her we're leaving."

The clouds in her head parted. The fire remained. She turned in his arms and punched the intercom button. "Yes, Margaret?"

"That man is here," Margaret whispered.

Leah closed her eyes. Only one person would cause Margaret to lose her composure—the accountant from TCIC. "Give me five minutes, then bring him in." She released the button and looked up at Stephen. "I'm sorry, but I've got to see this man. It's important."

"I thought what we were planning was important."

"It is. I—I just have to see him."

"Then I'll wait."

"No." She pushed against him, but he didn't release her. "Stephen, you've got to leave. I'm going to be nervous enough without you being in the room."

He raised one reddish-brown brow. "Nervous? Then all the more reason for me to stay, I think." He stopped her next objection with a deep, thorough kiss. When he was done, he said, "I'll be sitting right over there in that corner, and when you're through, we'll go to my house." He kissed her again, more lightly this time. "Okay?"

She smiled her surrender. "I guess I don't have any choice, do I?"

"No." With an answering smile he retreated to the corner of her office and sat down.

Leah quickly straightened her dress and ran a hand through her hair. As she brought her hand down, she brushed the pearls at her waist. The contact with the necklace reminded her of Zarah's prediction. She had said a man with cinnamon-color hair would come into her life and magic would follow. By anyone's standards, that part of the prediction had certainly come true, Leah decided.

At first she hadn't believed in the magic. Then she'd chosen to think that the magic would disappear with the night. But irrefutable proof that she'd been wrong now sat in a corner of her office. And she had to admit that since she'd been wearing the pearls, she had felt and acted differently. Her appearance had even changed for the better.

The other part of the prediction had been that the pearls would bring her good luck. She was certainly going to need all the luck she could get if she was to save the station, she thought, unaware that she was running her fingers back and forth across the surface of the pearls.

The door opened, and Margaret ushered in a tall, slim man with a face that Leah decided looked rather like a ferret. She tried to remember. Weren't ferrets used to hunt down small animals?

"Miss Kellerman, I'm Mr. Roland with TCIC."

"Yes, I know. I've been expecting you. Won't you sit down?"

"Yes, thank you."

He took the chair she indicated, and Leah eyed him warily, having already forgotten Stephen. "I was notified by registered mail of the sale of KSUN some time ago, but you're the first person from that organization who's contacted me. What can I do for you?"

He folded his hands across his chest and stared hard at her. "I'd like to see your books, naturally."

Doing her best not to be intimidated, she graciously nodded her head. "Naturally." This was where the sticky part came in. "It's just that I wish I'd been here when you called. I could have saved you a trip today."

His head came up as if he had gotten a delightful sniff of something not quite right. "Oh, and why is that?"

"Because I need to make several entries before the books will be up-to-date."

"Why do *you* need to make these entries? Don't you have a bookkeeper?"

She gritted her teeth, not sure why she was letting this irritating man get to her. She'd certainly had to deal with more objectional people. "This is a very small station, Mr. Roland, and as I'm sure you can appreciate, I watch our expenditures very carefully to make sure that we show a profit. By my doing the books, I save an additional salary." And I can pay better salaries to Pat, Harry,

Margaret, and the others, she silently added to herself.

"Whether or not you are qualified to do the books is something I will, of course, look into. In the meantime, when will the books be ready for me to see?"

She did some quick calculations in her head. The men would be tearing the carnival down today. That meant the Gypsies would be leaving tomorrow or, at the latest, the next day. And then there was Stephen. "A week," she said quickly. "Maybe ten days."

"I'm afraid that's unacceptable."

She'd been told all her life in one way or the other that what she did was unacceptable. Sometimes it hurt; other times it made her angry. This time it made her angry, and she didn't bother to hide it. "And I'm afraid, Mr. Roland, that that's the best you're going to get."

He sat forward and jabbed a finger at her. "My dear young woman, you can't possibly understand who I am."

"I am not your dear young woman," she snapped, then could have bitten her tongue. She had to try to keep her feelings under control.

"*Who* and *what* you are may very well change after I see those books. TCIC has sent me here—"

"*That's enough,*" Stephen said suddenly, causing both Leah and the accountant to jump in surprise.

The accountant turned around, saw Stephen, and sprang quickly up. "Mr. Tanner, I had no idea you were here—"

"And I had no idea that anyone representing my company used such high-handed tactics." He came to his feet in a leisurely motion.

Leah was the only one in the room still seated. "In *your* company?" she said, stunned. She felt as if she had two separate pieces of information that belonged together but she couldn't quite make them hook together.

"I think it's time you left, Roland," Stephen said, his eyes on Leah's pale face. "I'll see you back in Dallas."

The accountant glanced between the two of them. "But—"

"Good-bye, Roland." As soon as the man was out of the office, he asked, "Are you all right, Leah?"

"Your name wasn't on that registered letter I got, was it?" she asked slowly.

"No. One of my executives sent the notification."

"And the TCIC. What does that stand for?"

He sighed and rubbed at his brow. "Leah, I can see where you're going with this, but there's really no reason—"

"*What* does the TCIC stand for, Stephen?"

"Tanner Communications and Investment Corporation."

She nodded. She was no longer stunned, nor was she confused. Anger and strength were growing in her by the second. "And just *when* were you going to tell me it was your company that had bought the radio station where I work?"

He slipped his hands in the pockets of his slacks

and eyed her steadily. "I don't know when it would have occurred to me. I had other, more important things on my mind."

"Of course you did. The same thing that's been on your mind right from the first—seducing the little Gypsy girl with the mud on her feet."

He brought his hands down on her desk and leaned close. "That's not the truth and you know it. You may be angry, Leah, but keep the game fair."

With an abrupt motion she pushed away from the desk and jerkily stood up. "Game, Stephen? Is that what this is to you?"

He closed his eyes for a moment and lightly massaged them with a finger and thumb. "Game was the wrong choice of word. I'm sorry. But the fact of whether or not I own this damn station has nothing to do with us. I just found out this morning that you worked here. If I hadn't, I wouldn't even have come here."

"You own it, and you wouldn't even have come to see it? Now I understand how you could employ someone who looks like a ferret."

He almost questioned her use of ferret, but he caught himself in time. "Let me try to explain this, Leah. Under my direction, TCIC recently took over Banner Industries. When we did, we automatically acquired all of Banner's holdings. KSUN wasn't my interest in the company, and it was a *very* small part of the acquisition." He made a gesture toward her. "Do you understand?"

"You may think I'm strange, but I hope you don't think I'm stupid."

His fist came down on the desk. "Dammit, Leah, stop twisting what I'm saying. Understand that I'm very probably falling in love with you. And understand that KSUN's profits for the year wouldn't buy a day's supply of paper clips for TCIC. And understand that those two facts have nothing in the world to do with each other."

His words hit her body with a different kind of force and impact. Her mind allowed her to absorb everything but his belief that he was very probably falling in love with her. To her it wasn't a fact, but an impossibility.

She'd found love and acceptance only with the Gypsies, and even a blind man could see that Stephen Tanner was as different from the Gypsies as night was from day. He had reached out and taken a handful of the world and it had not rejected him. In fact, the world embraced such men as Stephen Tanner, whereas it rejected people like her, Zarah, and Rafael.

For a little while she had thought magic might be possible. But now she understood that he wanted her only because she was different. His fascination for her wouldn't last.

"Leah, did you hear me?"

"You're going to sell KSUN, aren't you?"

Stephen felt like tearing something apart, piece by piece. He drove hard fingers through his hair. "For God's sake, Leah? *What* is going on inside you?"

"Aren't you?"

He sighed. "Probably. The station is not important in TCIC's overall business."

"It's almost the whole world to me and the people who work here."

He'd never seen anyone look so vulnerable and at the same time so well-guarded. He could deal with someone vulnerable, and he could deal with someone well-guarded, but how in the hell did he deal with both at the same time? "We'll work it out," he said quietly.

She wrapped her arms around herself. "Not between you and me, we won't. We are just too different. We have nothing in common."

"We have the fire."

She stared at him, emotion-laden silence and space separating them.

When the office door burst open, it was all Leah could do to wrench her gaze from his. Then she saw the anxious face of the nine-year-old Gypsy boy. "What's wrong, Bandi?"

"Zarah sent me to get you, Leah. Rafael is in jail."

"*Jail?* My God, what happened?"

"The *gaji* woman, Sheila Donaldson, was found dead this morning, and they're saying that Rafael murdered her."

Three

Leah's first sight of Rafael behind bars nearly stopped her heart. He was sitting on a bare-mattressed cot, his back against the wall, his arm resting on his raised knee, a cigarette in his hand. Enclosed in the small cell, locked away from the sun and the wind, his spirit had already begun to shrivel; she could sense it without him saying a word.

"Let me in," she said to Tim McCafferty, the young deputy sheriff who had guided her back to the cell area.

" 'Fraid I can't do that, Leah. Rules. He's been arrested for murder. That means he's considered dangerous and not allowed any visitors except for a lawyer, which he's refused."

Leah turned her head and looked at Tim. "Rafael won't hurt me and you know it. Now, do you want to search me for weapons?"

Tim's gaze dropped from hers. "Uh, no. I know you wouldn't bring in anything you shouldn't."

Leah's grin was involuntary. "No, you don't. You just don't want me to tell Pat that you searched me." Tim and KSUN's advertising salesperson had become quite an item as of late.

"Aw, Leah—"

"Are you going to unlock the door, or do you want to give me the key and let me do it?"

"I'll do it." Tim placed the key in the large lock, turned it, then slid open the heavy door. "I can give you only ten minutes."

"Alone, I hope."

He nodded.

She entered the cell. When she heard the door clang shut behind her, she knew immediately how Rafael must feel. She had the sensation of walls closing in on her and air being sucked from her lungs. Steeling herself against succumbing to panic, she sat down on the cot so that she faced Rafael. When he didn't say anything, she touched his hand. "Rafael? How are you?"

He took a hard pull on his cigarette. "Great."

"I don't understand why they think you killed Sheila, but they've made an awful mistake."

"They didn't make a mistake," he said tonelessly. "In fact, they followed procedure perfectly. Late last night, then again early this morning, they received an anonymous call. The first call told them they would find her body at her husband's fishing cabin, the second call said I had been there last night and told them the two of us had had an affair. They searched my trailer and found the rings and gold necklace she had been wearing. They couldn't do anything else but arrest me."

"But you *didn't* kill her."

The corners of his mouth lifted slightly. "No, I didn't." Reaching out, he gently caressed her cheek. "Pretty little girl," he added softly. Then he leaned his head back against the wall and closed his eyes.

"Rafael, talk to me. Tell me something that will help me get you out of here. You said someone placed you at the cabin last night. Were you there?"

"Yes. Sheila had asked me to meet her there, but I was late . . . too late." He fell silent.

"Rafael?"

"It will be all right," he whispered without opening his eyes. "Go now."

Deeply troubled, she went to the cell door and called for Tim.

Sheriff Johnson was a big, robust man with whom few dared to argue. Although Leah knew him by sight, she had never had occasion to talk with him. The fact that Rafael was in jail pushed all these considerations aside. "Rafael didn't kill Sheila," she said as soon as she entered his office.

He looked up from the form he was filling out. "Evidence says otherwise."

"Can't you see a frame when it stares you in the face?"

He leaned back in his big leather chair and

propped his booted feet on the desk. "So you think he was framed, do you?"

"I know he was. It's obvious."

"If it's so obvious, then tell me who you think framed him. Tell me who you think killed Sheila."

She thought fast. "Her husband. It had to be."

"Husbands are always the most likely suspects. Can't you do better than that?"

"But everyone knew they had a bad marriage."

"Bad marriages can be fixed real easy with divorce, Leah."

Frustrated, she clenched her hands at her side. "Didn't you even question Robert Donaldson?"

He grinned. "Don't you think after all these years I know my job? Of course we questioned him, and Robert has an ironclad alibi. He was at his office in his appliance store, doing his books, just like he does every Wednesday night. The security guard saw him."

"Well, then someone else murdered Sheila, because Rafael didn't."

He sat forward, folded his hands on the top of his desk, and fixed her with a hard, level gaze. "Look, Leah. Maybe you're right. Maybe your friend didn't do it. But all the evidence points to him, and until I find out for sure that someone else murdered Sheila Donaldson, I'm keeping him in jail." He held up a firm hand when she prepared to argue. "As soon as it gets out that Sheila's been killed and that Rafael is a suspect, you know what's going to happen. Jail is the safest place for him."

He was right, she thought angrily. Dammit, he

was right. Tears sprang to her eyes. "But he can't breathe in there."

"I'm sorry, honey, he's got to stay." He paused. "But I'll tell you what I'll do. The law says I've got to charge a suspect or release him within seventy-two hours. I've already told you why I can't release him, and there's no doubt in my mind, at any rate, that I'm going to charge him. But I'll stretch the law and hold off officially charging him for a while, not long, mind you, but I can give you a few extra days to prove that he didn't kill her. Don't ask me to do any more than that."

The first thing she saw when she stepped outside the jail was Stephen, leaning against the hood of his car, waiting for her.

"I told you not to wait," she said, striking out along the sidewalk.

He caught her arm and gently guided her into the plush interior of his Mercedes. "And I told you that I would."

"Stephen, this isn't that big a town. Everyone walks."

He shut the passenger door, and she was left to impatiently finger the pearls at her waist while he walked around the car and got in. He inserted the key into the ignition but didn't turn it. "We need to talk, Leah. Do you want to go to your house or mine?"

"I don't have time to do either. I've got to get Rafael out of jail."

"You can't," he said flatly. "He killed a woman, and he's going to have to pay." Incredibly she laughed, but her laughter held a weariness and a sadness that ripped at his insides and made him fervently wish he could take his words back.

"I thought I might have to explain to you what it's like to be a Gypsy, but now I see I don't. You already know the world is hostile and suspicious toward them. And you already know they're outcasts. And the reason you know is that you're one of those people who have made them outcasts."

"Leah, I'm sorry I upset you. I know he's your friend—"

"Yes, he is. But even if he weren't, I would help him, because I understand what it's like to be an outsider. And, just so you'll know, you didn't upset me. In fact, I would have been surprised if you had reacted any other way." It was true that she would have been surprised, but it was a lie that he hadn't upset her.

"Listen to me, Leah. I've admitted right from the first that I don't always understand you, but that doesn't mean I don't want to. You say you feel as if you're an outsider. Tell me why."

For a split second she had the urge to go into his arms, rest her head against his chest, and pour out her pain and fears to him. Instead, she reached for the door handle. "I have to help Rafael."

His hand covered hers before she could open the door. "That's what the police are for."

"Sheriff Johnson is going to come up for reelection this fall. One more term, and he'll be eligible to retire with a nice fat pension. Do you really think he's going to jeopardize that and go against public opinion to help an outsider?" She shook her head. "No. Until I can prove to him that someone else killed Sheila and give him the name of that person, he'll keep Rafael right where he is. I'm Rafael's only hope."

"Then I'm going to help you."

"*You?*"

He rested his left forearm on the steering wheel and leaned toward her. "Leah," he said quite gently, "I run a multimillion-dollar corporation. I'm really very competent."

"A multimillion-dollar corporation is entirely different from a small East Texas town. Sunnyvale has got nothing to do with profit or loss. It's people. And, I think, sitting day in and day out in your big office in Dallas, buying and selling companies that you never even see, you've lost touch with people."

He eyed her consideringly. "Tell me, Leah, do you touch people?"

"What?"

"I have the feeling that you don't *touch* a lot of people yourself."

"Okay." She acknowledged his point and waited for the uneasiness she was sure would come at his perception. None came. "But I know the people of this town. I've watched, and I've learned a lot from life. I know—"

"So teach me what you know. I want to be able to see the world through your eyes."

"It won't work."

"Let me tell you something about myself, Leah. Up until last night everything I've ever done has had reason and logic behind it. But last night happened. I didn't see a lot of reason and logic then, and I haven't since. And I'm still here. I told you that I never give up. I also told you that I'm falling in love with you."

"You said *probably*."

"Did I say probably? I was wrong. I'm *definitely* falling in love with you."

The hammering of her heart was almost louder than the softness of his voice. "You're not falling in love with me. No one but the Gypsies has ever loved me. You'll eventually grow tired or angry or impatient with me, maybe all three, and then you'll go away."

He smiled, suppressing his longing to pull her to him and kiss her until she believed him. "If I go away, Leah, I'll take you with me. But in the meantime, if you want to try to talk me out of loving you, go right ahead. It may be the quickest way for me to learn what I want to know about you."

"I'm right, you know."

"No, you're not." He placed his hand on the key, ready to turn it. "Where are we going? My house or yours?"

She blinked. "Neither. I want to go see Robert Donaldson."

"Donaldson? The husband? Okay, then that's where we'll go." He turned the key, and the big car's motor purred to life. "Tell me how to get there."

Robert Donaldson was a handsome man, Leah thought, trying to be as objective as possible as she watched him pour himself a drink with slow, uncertain movements.

His holding up the crystal decanter of whiskey to her and Stephen was an afterthought of a man obviously numbed by the shock of his wife's violent death. "I'm sorry. Would either of you like a drink?"

"No, thank you," Stephen said.

Leah shook her head.

Robert replaced the decanter on the leather and walnut bar, started to sit down, then changed his mind. "I'm sorry," he said again. "You have to understand, this has been such a shock. I'm having a hard time dealing with Sheila's brutal murder."

"We understand," Leah said softly, "and I apologize for our intrusion, but I'd just like to ask you if you can think of any reason why she might have been killed."

He took a sip of the whiskey. "I know you're a friend of the Gypsies, Leah, but what I don't understand is why you're here. You probably knew about Rafael and Sheila before I did. The police told me this morning that my wife and your friend had been having an affair since last summer. That was the first I knew of it. Seems just about everybody knew but me." His fingers tightened around the glass until they were white.

Leah felt a sinking sensation in the pit of her stomach because there was no doubt in her mind that he was telling the truth. "I doubt very seriously if anyone knew, Robert, and besides, Rafael told me that their affair had ended last summer."

"Really? If that's the truth, and I'm not sure that I believe it is, then maybe that's why the filthy bastard killed her. Maybe he wanted it to continue."

Beside him, Stephen felt Leah stiffen. He reached over and covered her hand with his, hoping the physical contact would help.

"Rafael didn't kill Sheila," she said firmly.

"Then who did?"

"I don't know, but I'm going to find out. And that's why I'm asking you, can you think of anyone who might have had reason to want Sheila dead?"

As he gazed down at the dark amber liquid, the conflicting emotions that ranged over his face signaled that he was fighting for control. When he raised his head, it was clear he had lost the battle, and he turned his anger loose on Leah. "When I found out this morning that Sheila and that damned Gypsy had been having an affair and that they'd been meeting in *my* cabin, my stomach turned six ways to Sunday. So you listen to me, young lady. No one else in town had any reason to do it other than your friend, who, for my money, is exactly where he should be. Frankly, I hope they fry him."

Stephen stood and pulled Leah to her feet. "Thank you for your time, Mr. Donaldson."

He quickly helped her out of the house. As soon as they got into the car he asked, "What do you think?"

"I'm disappointed," she said frankly. "It's as clear as crystal that Robert Donaldson's in shock over his wife's murder. He's also angry because he's just found out about the affair. But he's not grieving. Not really. Given the fact that he and Sheila had a bad marriage, he's reacting exactly as I would have expected."

"That's what I thought too." He paused. "It was unpleasant for you. I hated seeing you go through it."

Surprise came and went in her eyes. "I'm used to it. I grew up in this town."

"That sort of thing may happen quite often, but you're not used to it in any way, shape, or form." He reached out and ran his fingers down her arm. "Your skin is too sensitive; there are too many nerves beneath it."

She looked at him oddly. "It was nice of you to be there with me."

His fingers tightened on her arm. "When will you get it through your head? What I'm doing is not nice. It's compulsory."

She was left without words. It was daylight. There were no colored lights. She was worried about Rafael. Yet Stephen was getting to her, pricking away at her lonely soul. She wasn't sure how to act, and just for a moment she panicked. Then her hand sought out the pearls. Something about them made her feel better.

He smiled at her. "Where would you like me to take you now?"

"I'm not sure," she said, pondering his question. "I guess it would be best if I go home. I've got to decide how to proceed and what I should do next. I've never done anything like this."

His fingers glided with a velvet touch up and down her arm, trying to lessen the intensity of her distress. "I have an idea. We missed lunch. It's nearly time for dinner. Let's go to my place. I'll make us something to eat, and we can put our heads together over the problem."

"Eat?" She hadn't realized until he mentioned dinner how hungry she was.

"Yes, you know, food."

"And you're going to cook?"

"I, uh, am going to try my best to serve you, my guest, something that will be edible."

She grinned. "That might be interesting."

"Then you think it's a good idea?"

"Actually I think it's a great idea."

He started the car, inwardly marveling. One minute Leah would be quiet, withdrawn into herself. The next, she would be the Gypsy girl beneath the tree, backed by the colored lights, laughing and carefree. She was a mercurial delight who baffled and entranced him.

• • •

Stephen watched as Leah gazed around the living room of his lake house and wondered at the cause of the wariness he saw in her eyes. "The architect followed my instructions to the letter," he said. "I wanted big open rooms with lots of windows. I figured if I was going to live in the country on a lake, I wanted a view from every room in the house."

She nodded but made no comment. Her eyes were on the magnificent linen drapes that covered the front wall of the room. The pattern of the fabric was in shades of blue and turquoise.

"Here, let me open the curtains," he said, matching his actions to his words, eager for her to like his house, "and you can see the great view of the lake. It gives the feeling of being outside."

"But we're not outside."

"No," he agreed. "That's true."

She nodded her head and turned her attention to the pale blue sofa. It had been custom made to curve around the large room in such a way as to form ingenious conversation areas. All along it, pillows in the same pattern as the drapes had been thrown to create artful comfort. Beautiful blue and turquoise silk cloths covered the side tables.

"My interior designer wanted to pick up the colors of the lake," he said, eyeing her intently.

"The lake isn't blue."

"But one always *thinks* of lakes as blue," he pointed out with determination.

She nodded. "Is the kitchen close by?"

Feeling defeat near at hand, he exhaled and gestured. "Past the staircase and right down that hallway. I'll show you."

The kitchen was bright and filled with the late afternoon sun. An array of copper pots hung suspended over a long wooden table of a highly polished bleached cedar. The cabinets were also made of bleached cedar. "My interior designer assured me that the countertop is the latest high-tech material. It won't burn, scratch, dent, or break, and it blends well with the cabinets." He looked at her expectantly.

She nodded, her eyes still holding the same wary expression. "Maybe we could cook outside. Do you have a grill?"

"A grill?"

"We could go to my house. I have a grill."

"I have a grill, Leah. What's wrong?"

"Nothing. Oh, look at the beautiful deck."

Before he could reach for her, she was out the back door. He caught up with her at the railing.

She drew in a deep breath as if she'd been starved for fresh air. "You didn't mention that you have a pine woods at the edge of your backyard."

He slanted his body so he could rest his arm on the top of the railing and see her face. "Now, why did I fail to tell you that, Leah? Why does there always seem to be something else to talk about?"

Hearing the humor in his voice, she looked into his eyes, whose color exactly matched the pines. "You have beautiful eyes, Stephen."

"Yours aren't so bad either." He wrapped a thick

strand of glossy sable hair around his hand, then released it. "What can I do to make you more comfortable?"

"I don't know what you mean," she said, her tone cautious.

"Uh-uh. I'm not going to let you get away with that this time. You're uncomfortable in my house, and I want to know why."

Her hands tightened on the railing and she gazed down at them. "You've spent a lot of money on this place."

"Forget the money."

"And the decorator must have . . . worked very hard."

"And you can forget the decorator too. Come on, Leah. Out with it."

"Well, it's just that everything"—she swallowed hard—"matches."

He wasn't sure he had heard her correctly. "Matches?"

She glanced quickly at him, then looked back down at her hands. "You know. Everything fits too perfectly."

"And that's bad?"

She took a deep breath. "Many people like it that way, but I never have."

Because *she'd* never fit or blended, he thought with sudden insight. He took her hand. "Come with me."

"Where are we going?" she asked, surprised.

He didn't answer but led her back through the kitchen, down the hallway, and into the living room. Once there, he dropped her hand and marched with purpose to the bank of windows. Because he had already opened the drapes, they were grouped at either end of the wall. He took a firm grip on the linen material and pulled.

"Stephen, what on earth are you doing?"

"Getting rid of these curtains. They're ugly." Half of the drapes fell to the floor to form a big mound of blue and turquoise.

"They're not ugly," she protested. "They just—"

"Match," he said, now at the other end of the glass wall. In moments the remainder of the drapes lay on the floor, and he turned his attention to the rest of the room. "The table covers, right? They're really awful."

"Stephen—"

Four table covers joined the drapes on the floor. He studied his handiwork, then took half the sofa pillows and threw them on top of the two mounds. "That looks better. The sofa will have to stay for now, but I think as soon as possible I'll get . . ." He trailed off and turned to her. "What would you do with this room?"

She hesitated. "I like arrangements that feature different styles, textures, and patterns. Nothing organized."

"That's just what I was thinking."

Suddenly she started laughing. "I can't believe what you've just done. Your interior decorator is going to have a fit."

"What interior decorator? As of ten minutes ago I don't have one."

Still laughing, she shook her head. "Are you aware that you did something that doesn't make sense?"

"Well, then maybe, for the sake of my mental well-being, I'd better do something that makes sense before I go into withdrawal."

"What?" she asked, suddenly breathless at the heat in the depths of his cool green eyes.

He went to her, and drew her to him. "Kiss you," he said. "It makes all the sense in the world to me. What about you?"

"No," she said softly.

His gaze dropped to her mouth. "Why not?"

"Because I want you to kiss me too badly, and it doesn't make sense."

"It's all right. All you have to do is say, kiss me, Stephen. And then hold on."

Her gaze locked with his. "Kiss me, Stephen."

Kissing him was like entering a brand-new world. Lights, colors, and feelings were strange and bright. It made her want to open up, to absorb his strength and his heat into her. He was so utterly male, he surrounded her, and she abandoned herself to the sensations of the kiss.

"For God's sake, don't do that," he muttered, his lips still against her mouth.

"What?"

"Respond like that." He cradled her face, his hands firm but with the slightest of tremors, and looked down at her. "You're not ready to go where a response like that could lead. But I most definitely am."

"You're talking about making love," she whispered.

"Ashes, baby. That's what may be left. Are you ready? Because let me tell you something, I sure as hell am. And if you keep responding to me like that, your choice may be taken away from you."

Her throat moved convulsively. "I want you to know something."

He moved the fingers of one hand caressingly over her cheek. "I'm listening."

"I want you, Stephen. I don't want you to be in any doubt. I've never felt this way before. You look at me sometimes, and it feels like those green eyes of yours have removed my skin and left only need. And when you touch me—"

His thumb came up and covered her lips. "Stop it," he said, his voice low, hoarse, and raw. "You're going to have to stop it, because I'm not going to be able to take the *but* coming after."

"But—"

His chuckle was a mixture of hurt and longing, plus a cutting kind of humor directed at himself. "See? This just isn't going to work, not right now, at any rate."

"I'm sorry."

"No," he said emphatically. "You've got nothing to be sorry about. You're wonderful. In fact, you're magic."

"It's not me," she said, "it's the pearl necklace I'm wearing."

He looked at her for a moment. "And I thought I was the only one who had anything to learn." He pressed a short kiss to her lips. "Let's go find my grill, then search my freezer for something appropriate to cook on it."

Out on the deck Leah watched the sun setting by infinitesimal degrees over the roof of Stephen's house. He was in the kitchen, cleaning up after their dinner, but he had the window open so that she could hear the stereo, which she had tuned to KSUN. Borodin's symphonic poem "In the Steppes of Central Asia" was playing, and she closed her eyes and let the music take her away to the windswept land about which Borodin had written so stirringly.

During the day Randolph Moore taught music at the high school, and this time every night he took command of the broadcast booth and chose from records that ranged from classical to easy listening. He had his own criteria for what he played, and she never interfered. People didn't particularly like him because he was sternly intellectual, but they enjoyed his choice of music, and homes all over town tuned in to his show.

The music ended, and "Somewhere in Time," the sound track from the movie of the same title, began. The beautiful, haunting melody fit with the peace of the pine woods, the lake, and the time of day, she decided.

When she opened her eyes and saw Stephen sitting across from her, watching her, she was surprised. "I didn't hear you come back out."

"That's all right. I didn't want to disturb you. You seemed caught up with the music."

"Music has always moved me."

"What else moves you?" he asked, curious.

"Pine woods." She tossed her head, letting the evening breeze play through her hair. Then she smiled as she remembered. "When I was a little girl, Rafael used to take me along with him on his walks through the woods around here. Sometimes I'd get tired, and we'd stop. We'd lie down on a bed of pine needles and stare up through the boughs at the sky and listen to the gentle whisper of the wind." Her smile slowly disappeared. "I wish he were here. He'd love the peace and beauty."

"I'm glad you like it."

"I'm going to get him out of there, Stephen. I have to. He'll die if I don't. He needs to be free to travel winding back roads that lead to places he knows and places he's never been. He needs to lie beneath a wide night sky."

"From what little I've come to know of you, he sounds a lot like you."

"Zarah says I have a Gypsy heart. I think maybe she's right. There's really only one thing I know for sure: I have to find out who murdered Sheila so that I can get Rafael out of jail. And I'm going to start first thing in the morning." A sudden look of guilt crossed her face. "I won't be able to be at the station full-time. And the books—"

He uttered an oath. "Don't worry about the station. I'm sure your people are competent. As for the books, you can burn them for all I care."

"But Mr. Roland—"

"Is back in Dallas, and KSUN's books are the last thing on his mind, believe me."

"When are you going back to Dallas?"

"I don't know."

"Before last night, when were you going back?"

He slowly shook his head and grinned. "You constantly surprise me. You used a straight line to get from A to B on that one, didn't you?" She smiled, and he shrugged. "Before last night I would have probably returned to Dallas today. Now I may never leave."

"You'll leave."

"I'm not going to argue with you about it. But one of these days, years from now, you'll look around and notice that I'm still here. And then maybe you'll accept the fact that you were wrong."

She fell silent, and not until the stars began to appear in the sky above them did she whisper what she was thinking. "You can't be right. But if you are, it has to be because of the pearls. What other explanation could there be?"

Four

Leah swung her feet over the edge of the bed, surveyed the floor of her bedroom, and let out a groan. The clothing she had worn the day before was scattered about. And the pearl necklace lay in one corner, gleaming with beauty and mystery.

The previous day's events, following her sleepless night after meeting Stephen, had taken their toll on her. Once Stephen had dropped her off at her house last night, she'd barely managed to undress before she collapsed onto the bed and fell sound asleep.

She slid off the bed, and as she went around the room picking up her clothes and the necklace, she thought of Stephen. Could it be possible that he would stay as he said he would? Could she really believe that in time he wouldn't reject and shun her, as most people did, because she was different and odd? More important, if she gave him her heart, would her heart remain safe?

Or was it too late to be asking any of these questions?

In the shower she pondered what her next investigatory move should be and quickly decided that she had to go see Rafael again. And this time he had to talk to her, because until he did, she had nothing to go on. She also wanted to see Zarah.

She dried off and donned a bright red sundress with tiny straps. In marked contrast to yesterday morning, there was no uncertainty about whether or not she would wear the necklace.

She scooped the pearls into her hands and stared down at them with wonder, no longer in doubt that they were genuine. Nothing fake could produce the mystique and the magic that this necklace did. Each pearl had been made, layer by lustrous layer, by a living creature deep in the dark depths of the ocean. And she was utterly amazed that for whatever reason, the necklace was in her possession.

Grasping the two ends of the pearl rope, she raised her hands. Midway to her neck with the necklace she froze. The string that attached the heart-shaped clasp to the necklace was frayed, leaving the clasp connected only by a few fragile threads.

Bands of iron began to contract around her chest. She felt as if she might suffocate. Oh, Lord, she must have somehow jerked the clasp last night when she had unwound the necklace from around her waist.

And now she couldn't wear the necklace until it was fixed.

She had to take the necklace to the jeweler. Immediately.

She quickly glanced at the clock. It was eight o'clock in the morning, and Mr. Ogilvy didn't open his shop until ten.

What was she going to do?

Calm down, she ordered herself. In her hands the pearls seemed to shimmer with strength and beauty; she clutched them tighter. Everything was going to be all right. Really. A wait of two hours wasn't going to make that much difference.

With a great force of will she relaxed her fingers and placed the pearls on the bed. Taking a step back, she wiped her damp palms down the sides of her skirt.

She jumped at the knock on the front door.

Stop acting foolish, Leah.

She made her way through the house to open the door.

"Good morning," Stephen said through the screen.

"Good morning."

"I like the blue color of your house. I couldn't really see it last night in the dark."

"It was gray all the while I was growing up. I hate gray. I painted it after I came back to town." She tried to draw a breath, couldn't, and turned to hurry back to the pearls.

He let himself in and followed. He found her in a back bedroom that was decorated with different textures, patterns, and colors, just as she had described last night. He liked it, he decided, then turned his attention to her. "Leah, what's wrong?"

"Nothing really," she said, digging in a bottom dresser drawer. "The clasp on the necklace is in danger of coming off, and I have to take it to the jeweler, that's all. What are you doing here?"

"I told you last night I'd be here first thing this morning to help you try to find out something that will help clear Rafael of killing Sheila."

She briefly glanced at him. "I thought you believed Rafael did it."

"Yes, well, I had forgotten about the law in America that says a man is innocent until he is proven guilty. You made me remember."

"He *is* innocent," she said, and tossed a bright blue scarf over her shoulder. Half of the contents of the drawer now lay on the floor.

"Leah, what are you looking for? Can I help?"

"I just found it." She held out a gold and red shawl to show him, then stood up and crossed to the bed.

He watched her carefully wrap the pearls in the shawl. "Have you mapped out a plan for today?"

"I'm going to go over to the jewelry shop. Then after the necklace is repaired, I plan to see Rafael again. Somehow I've got to get him to talk to me." She straightened, holding the red-and-gold-wrapped bundle to her chest.

"Maybe I could see him with you and—"

"Rafael wouldn't talk at all if you were there."

"Then I'll wait for you outside as I did yesterday. And there's no point in arguing," he added as he saw the expression of unease cross her face.

She fingered a piece of the fringe on the shawl. "I won't argue. It's just that I'm not used to having someone by my side when I have to face difficult things."

"Get used to it. I may not be able to help much in getting Rafael out of jail, because, as you say, I don't know this town. But at least I can give you moral support, and, in doing so, we can be together."

She tilted her head to one side and gazed up at him through dark lashes. "I don't know if I want to be with you."

He smiled. "Don't you, Leah?"

She did want to be with him, she thought. She just wasn't sure if she should or not. How could she trust a love that was being built on the strength of the magic exuded by a pearl necklace?

Leah peered into the window of Ogilvy's Jewelry Shop and spied Horace Ogilvy at the back. Horace was another citizen of Sunnyvale with whom she had never had much direct contact, but she knew him by reputation as a crotchety old man with a soft heart. She tapped on the window until she got his attention, then waved and gestured.

Horace Ogilvy squinted toward the window through his rimless glasses and saw her. His face settled back into its perpetual frown as he plodded down the aisle between the display cases to unbolt the door. "What is it, Leah? You know that I'm not open for business yet, don't you?"

"But it's five minutes until ten, Mr. Ogilvy. Can't you please help me out even though I'm five minutes early?"

He gave Stephen a suspicious glance. "Who's this?"

"This is Stephen Tanner. He's just built a new home on the eastern shore of the lake."

Mr. Ogilvy nodded his head. "You mean the house that was built by those Dallas people."

"That's right," she said. "Listen, I really need your help with my pearl necklace. The clasp is hanging by threads."

"Pearl necklace, you say?" He hesitated, but a glance at Leah's distraught face seemed to sway him. "Well, I guess I could give it a look. Come on in."

Once seated behind his workbench, he held out his hands. She unfolded the scarf and carefully laid the pearls before him.

His gray brows shot up. "I don't believe I've ever seen anything quite like this. It's remarkable. Yours, you say?"

She didn't know how to answer his question. Zarah had told her the necklace wasn't hers to give, but that Leah was to take the necklace and wear it. Did that mean that one day she would have to give up the necklace? The idea filled her with cold fear.

Mr. Ogilvy interpreted her silence in his own way, and his glance at Stephen proclaimed his conclusion. "Hmmph." He adjusted his glasses and turned to examine the gold backing of the clasp. "Strange mark. Interlocking circles. What does it mean?"

"I don't know," she admitted. "The mark was put there before I received the necklace."

"Hmmph. Well, I can fix this clasp for you, all right. No problem. Just have to reattach it to the necklace. Should be ready by tomorrow."

"Oh, no!" Panic rushed back to grip her. "I have to have it today. Right now, as a matter of fact."

He lowered his chin and stared at her over his glasses. "Right now?"

"Can we wait? Please? You said it wouldn't take long."

"I do have a few other things to repair, young lady."

"Please. Please?"

Stephen spoke for the first time. "If you'll do it now for her, I'll pay you triple what you would charge her if she picked it up tomorrow."

"Figures from someone who hired Dallas people," the old man muttered under his breath. "Leah, you can wait, and I'll have it for you in a few minutes. At my regular charge."

"Thank you, Mr. Ogilvy." She didn't even try to keep the relief from her voice.

"Hmmph." He bent his head to his task.

Stephen's lips twisted with amusement. "It's a good thing that I've already admitted that I don't know this town," he whispered, "because Mr. Ogilvy made your point in spades."

She took his hand without even realizing she was doing so. "It's all right. I don't know Dallas. Probably never will."

"You will if I have anything to do with it. Why don't we look around? We might find something you like."

He'd just made two disturbing suggestions: one, that they had a future together, and, two, that he would buy her an expensive gift. But she didn't have time to dwell on either of those disturbing remarks because he pulled her along with him to gaze into the display cases.

Graduation and birthstone rings filled one case. Charms, another. Diamond wedding ring sets, plus plain bands for both men and women crowded a third case. And the fourth case held men's rings.

"Too bad about Sheila," Mr. Ogilvy said casually, still working on the necklace.

Leah looked back at him, startled. "Yes, it was."

"Hard to believe. It's a real tragedy. She was in here just the other day too. Real happy, she was." He scowled absently and reached for another jeweler's tool. "Seemed most interested in one of those."

"Those?"

He pointed with the tool. "One of those men's signet rings."

She didn't need the pressure of Stephen's hand to prompt her. "Do you remember which ring she was looking at?"

"Of course I do." His words were almost growled.

"Do you think I'm senile? She was looking at that ring down there in the right-hand corner. The one with the M on it. Your necklace is ready. That'll be ten dollars."

Leah stared at the jeweler, riveted by what he had just said. *M?*

When she didn't move, Stephen went to pay him and gather up the pearl necklace in her shawl. "Thank you very much, Mr. Ogilvy."

"Hmmph. No trouble. And next time you build something out here, young man, you might consider using local workers."

"I'll do that."

"And, Leah? That young woman with the little boy that works over at the radio station . . . ?"

"Pat."

He nodded curtly. "Have her come by. I'm thinking of running a little sale. If the rates are right, I may advertise with KSUN."

"Thanks, Mr. Ogilvy."

Out in the car, Leah turned to Stephen, barely able to control her excitement. *"M.* We've got to find out whose name begins with M."

"Don't get your hopes too high. This may be nothing at all."

"No. It's something. I know it is." She touched his arm. "Listen, her husband's name is Robert Donaldson—no M there—and at any rate, she wouldn't be buying him a gift. Her father's dead. She has no brothers. Rafael's name begins with an R."

"What's his last name?"

"They go by their given names, Stephen. Anonymity is very important to the Gypsies. Most of them go through life without being registered anywhere. There are no birth or school records, draft or census—"

"What about a driver's license?"

She shook her head. "If they bother to get licenses, they usually register under false names."

He made a sound of disbelief.

"Intense secretiveness is the way they survive, Stephen," she said defensively. "When everyone is against you, it's best to have as few records as possible on yourself. And I'll tell you something else, if I don't know Rafael's last name, no other *gajo* does."

"Not even a woman with whom he went to bed and to whom he whispered words of love?"

"No," she said flatly.

"You're very loyal," he said, reaching out to brush a finger down the soft skin of her jaw. "Okay, then, you wanted to visit with Rafael. While you're doing that, I'll see if the sheriff managed to get a last name from him."

Leah's sensitive heart perceived changes in Rafael that would be barely perceptible to anyone else. The shadows beneath his eyes seemed darker, his brown skin paler, his lean, muscular frame thinner. And he was sitting in exactly the same position and place as he had been yesterday, as if when they put him in the cell, he had ceased to move . . . and to live.

"I'm trying to help you, Rafael, but you've got to help me."

He turned his head and exhaled a heavy stream of cigarette smoke. "You have all the help you need, Leah."

She was accustomed to the cryptic way the Gypsies often spoke, but she was lost now. "I don't know what you mean. I have so little to go on. I went to the jewelry shop today and discovered that a few days before she died Sheila had been looking at a man's signet ring with the initial M. Do you have any idea who she could have been thinking of buying the ring for?"

He shrugged. "No. Why did you go to the jewelry shop?"

She touched the pearl necklace that hung from her neck and fell over her breasts. "Because the clasp was in danger of falling off."

He nodded as if he understood, and drew on his cigarette.

"Rafael, you told me the night Sheila was murdered that your affair with her was over."

"It had ended last summer."

"Then why did she want to meet you at the cabin?"

"To say good-bye."

"You mean because you were leaving?"

"No. Because she was."

"She was going someplace? Where?"

"I arrived too late to find out." He drew hard on his cigarette. "She looked so pitiful. I couldn't stand the thought of her lying there all night by herself. I called myself all kinds of fool, but . . ."

"You phoned and told them where to find her, didn't you?" The nod he gave was a barely discernible movement of his head. "Then do you have any idea who the person was who called to say you were at the scene of the crime? And if he saw you, did you see him? Rafael?"

He leaned his head back against the wall and fixed his gaze on the small, barred window set high above him. "I can see a bit of blue during the day and a patch of black at night. But they won't open it so that I can get air."

He had told her all he was going to. She shifted along the cot and lay her head against his chest. "Somehow, some way, I'm going to find out who murdered Sheila, and then you'll be free. I promise."

His hand came up to tenderly hold her head and he placed a gentle kiss on her hair. Then he returned his gaze to the window.

Leah spied a large pebble nestled in the grass not too far from where she sat with Stephen beside the lake. They had walked from town to this shaded, grassy spot after she had convinced him to leave his car behind, and during their walk she had relayed her conversation with Rafael. She reached for the pebble. "Either he doesn't know anything or he does know something but he's keeping it to himself."

"Why would he do that?"

"I don't know. He said I have all the help I need, and I have to have faith that he's right. Rafael and

Zarah are very wise, and he will be king of his tribe one day." She threw the pebble into the water and watched as the ripples spread in ever-widening concentric circles until they disappeared. "I just wish I knew what he meant."

"Tim McCafferty showed me the first page of the crime report," he said, "and you were right. Rafael gave no last name and a check of his fingerprints turned up no previous criminal record and therefore no last name."

"Rafael wouldn't have a record because he's not a criminal. And, anyway, it doesn't matter that we don't know his last name. Sheila wasn't thinking of buying that ring for Rafael. There was someone else in her life. She had asked him to come to the cabin so she could say good-bye. She was going to run off with someone, someone whose last name begins with an M. If I could just figure out who that person is . . ." Something he had said struck her. "Why did Tim show you only the first page?"

"Evidently that's all they'll show without a court order, and the first page gives only the name of the victim, the victim's address, date of birth, and approximate time of the crime."

Stephen was beginning to get intrigued with the murder, although, he admitted to himself, he wouldn't have the slightest interest if it weren't for Leah. His lips curved at another thought. And he certainly wouldn't be sitting by a lake in the middle of a workday if it weren't for Leah. It seemed his life had become a circle where everything led back to Leah. And he liked it.

His eyes followed the progress of a sailboat as it glided over the silver-gray water, its sails tilted to catch the wind. There was no one around them, and the only noise he heard was the chirping of birds. He waited for Leah to speak again. When she didn't, he looked at her and found her watching the sailboat. "It's nice here. I'm glad you suggested this."

"Zarah says life needs time to happen."

He gave what she said some thought. "I guess that makes sense . . . in a strange way."

She turned to gaze at him. "Is it really true that everything you've ever done has had reason and logic behind it?"

He grinned at her obvious amazement. "My father owns a chain of hardware stores in Massachusetts, and growing up, I spent a lot of time in those stores." Her expression of puzzlement made him go on. "Nothing makes more sense than a hardware store. Everything is bright and shiny with its own place and fits together perfectly with something else."

"But you have to find the something that the something else fits with, right?"

"Yes."

"And what happens if you find the wrong something else?"

"Then you keep looking until you find the right something else."

"And you never give up."

He shook his head.

"That's the problem with most people," she said

thoughtfully. "They find a bad fit, and instead of looking for something that will make it work, they throw the whole thing away."

"Is that what happened with you, Leah?"

"Yes. More or less. My mother . . ."

"Tell me."

"No. Not now, at any rate. Tell me more about when you were a little boy."

"Well, I studied a lot. I shadowed my father around his stores. I broke my arm once when my bike crashed into a neighbor's fence. I got into the normal amount of trouble." He shrugged, at a loss to know what she wanted.

"Tell me about your mother."

"She's a very nice lady. She's going to love you."

Leah doubted that, but didn't say so. "When I was six, the Gypsies took me. The only reason my mother came to get me was that she was afraid she'd get in trouble if she didn't. Besides, with me gone, she didn't have anyone to blame things on."

"My mother's not like that."

The sympathy she heard in his voice grated her nerves. "What's your favorite color?" she asked abruptly.

Once he recovered from his surprise, he laughed. "Why all the questions?"

She was silent for so long, he wasn't sure she was going to answer him. But finally she said, "The night we met, I decided it wasn't necessary to know anything about you. Now I know differently."

"Then I'm getting through to you."

Her smile was wry. "Definitely. And you really shouldn't be. I haven't made up my mind yet how much is you and how much is the pearls."

It no longer bothered him when she said something he didn't understand. He reached over and took hold of the necklace. "Why are you so hung up on these pearls?"

"Zarah gave them to me the night we met. She said magic would follow. It has."

"That night *was* magic," he said, his voice soft. "Along with every minute I've spent with you since. But you make the magic, Leah, not the pearls. The magic is *in* you."

She shook her head, feeling suddenly defenseless. "You don't understand."

"You're wrong. This is one thing about you that I understand perfectly." Still holding the necklace, he let his hand rest lightly against her breast.

Her lips tightened even as her pulse raced. "What's your favorite color?" she repeated.

He recognized the question for the evasion it was. "I don't know. I guess I've never thought about it before."

"Think about it now."

"All right." He considered the matter, then smiled. "My favorite color is all the colors you make me see when we kiss."

"That's not fair," she said on an indrawn breath.

His hand moved over her breast, brushing down over the nipple, then skimming upward to her throat. "If I play fair with you all the time, I may never get what I want. And I want you."

It seemed as if his hand were touching every intimate part of her body, when in reality he'd merely grazed his hand over her sundress. But he had her craving more. "I'm beginning to believe you were absolutely right when you said we may be nothing but ashes by the time this is all over with."

"Damn, Leah."

He reached for her, but she drew away. "No, Stephen, I'm—I'm sorry, but I'm . . ."

His hand closed into a fist. "You're not ready. I know. It's been the problem all along. That and the fact that I'm too ready."

Backed by the blue sky, his eyes showed a clear, deep forest green. For a moment she felt she could read every emotion he was feeling, and amazingly she realized she wasn't frightened by what she saw. "I don't want to deceive you in any way, Stephen. I may never decide that I'm ready. My life, my past, your life . . . There are too many differences between us."

"None that matter."

"It's been my experience that people think differences are very important." She shrugged. "Anyway, right now I have to concentrate on helping Rafael."

He was barely able to stifle his impatience. "It doesn't sound like Rafael wants help."

"He wants help desperately. Every hour that he's locked up takes an hour off his life."

Stephen gave a deep, resigned sigh and gazed down at his still-clenched fist, resting on his upraised knee. Slowly he relaxed his hand. "Okay. Okay. What next?"

She studied him. He was a man clearly out of his element, yet it didn't seem to bother him. He was caught up in magic and didn't realize it. He was involved in a murder investigation and knew neither parties involved. He was trying to understand her, and she was trying *not* to understand him. He made her heart beat fast and her lower limbs heat, and he said he wanted her.

"You should go back to Dallas," she said quietly.

His head came up. "Dallas has lost all interest for me. It has no colored lights."

She bit her bottom lip. He really was smart. He said things in a way that resonated within her. Anytime now, it would cease to matter whether or not she thought she was ready.

"About what we should do next," she said slowly. "Sheila's best friend was a woman named Dorian Brown. I think we should talk to her."

He heard the *we* and was satisfied. "Let's go then."

Dorian and Sheila had been two years ahead of Leah in school, both of them pretty and popular and with no time for an insecure younger girl. Both of them had entered into loveless marriages. Dorian had become a hard, discontented woman, and Sheila had been murdered. It would seem her life had turned out the best, Leah mused. Still, she found it extremely difficult to question Dorian.

And to make matters worse, she had the feeling that if Stephen hadn't been with her, Dorian wouldn't have invited her into her home.

Firmly grasping the end of the pearl necklace, she swallowed the huge lump in her throat only to have it come right back up and interfere with her words. "I was . . . uh, wondering . . ."

"Yes?" Dorian was posed in front of the pink marble fireplace in her living room, unwilling to take her eyes off Stephen.

"First let me say that I know that you and Sheila were best friends, and I'm sure her death has been a terrible shock to you."

"Shock," Dorian agreed. "I've heard about your new home, Stephen. I'd love to see it sometime."

His answer was a pleasant smile, but he reached over and took Leah's hand.

His gesture had a calming effect on her. "Did she tell you she was preparing to leave town?" Leah asked.

The question jolted Dorian and switched her attention to Leah. "How did you find out about that?"

She instantly decided on an evasive answer. "You weren't the only person she told."

Dorian shook her head in disgust. "The little fool. First of all, I tried to tell her that after the grand passion faded, Gary wouldn't be able to make her happy. But do you think she listened?" Leah went still. Oblivious to Leah's reaction, Dorian rushed on. "Then I told her, for heaven's sake, keep your plans quiet. Maybe you can leave town with a few things, you know . . . by the time Robert misses them, you'll be long gone."

Dorian obviously believed she knew who she was talking about, Leah realized. Possible ways in which she could get Dorian to say the man's last name flew through her head, but she was unable to settle on one.

"Gary?" Stephen asked Dorian in the polite, puzzled tone of a newcomer to the town.

"Gary Mercer. Can you believe it? Sheila was willing to throw away her life for someone who draws a salary, and a *teacher's* salary at that. He couldn't offer her one third of what Robert could. I told her—"

Stephen pulled Leah to her feet. "Thank you very much, Dorian. It's been a pleasure meeting you."

Five

Honest, grief-stricken emotions were displayed on the handsome face of Gary Mercer as he sat talking with Leah and Stephen on the front porch of his small house. "I loved Sheila. I was willing to give up teaching, move to a strange city and start all over again. And now"—his voice broke—"it's all over. She's gone, and I can't . . . I can't believe it."

As Leah listened to Gary, she decided he couldn't have murdered Sheila. His pain was palpable. She'd felt an awful sinking sensation when she'd come to the conclusion that Robert Donaldson hadn't killed his wife, but for Gary Mercer, she experienced only sympathy.

And the question remained: Who had killed Sheila?

"Did anyone besides Dorian know of your plans?"

He swiped at his eyes. "No, of course not. Robert Donaldson is a prominent man in this town. Neither Sheila nor I wanted to be around when the scandal about us broke. We planned to leave separately, meet up in Dallas, and then decide where we'd go from there. We didn't care where we ended up as long as we were together and far away from here."

"When did you plan to leave?"

"The next day, that is, the day after she was . . ." He cleared his throat and now his expression turned accusing. "She planned to tell the Gypsy, Rafael, that very night. She asked him to meet her at Robert's fishing cabin—Robert was always too busy to use it—and that's where she and I met whenever we could. I didn't like the idea of her meeting with the Gypsy, but she insisted that he had been there for her during a particularly rough time last summer when the carnival was here." He hesitated, his expression hard to read. "She admitted to me that they'd had an affair."

Leah wasn't sure what to ask next. She threw Stephen a helpless glance.

He stepped in right on cue. "Are you absolutely sure that Sheila's husband didn't know about your affair with her?"

"Positive. As I said, he's a busy man, what with his business and his position in town and all. He largely ignored Sheila, except for those times when he'd verbally beat her black and blue." He shook his head. "I can't believe she's gone. We were so close to happiness . . . so close. . . ."

•   •   •

Stars blazed in the night sky above Leah's head, and the breeze whispered through the pines, scenting the air with a sweet freshness. The night had an innocent feel to it, she thought. A good feel. Yet Gary Mercer sat all alone in his small house, grief-stricken, Zarah waited in the Gypsy camp for her son to be released from jail, and somewhere a murderer felt satisfaction that he had gotten away with killing Sheila. Leah's hands tightened on the railing that edged Stephen's backyard deck.

Stephen had taken her to see Zarah after they'd left Gary's house and had stayed in his car while she visited with her. She hadn't been able to offer any comfort to Zarah regarding Rafael, but strangely she had been comforted simply by being with the woman who loved her like a daughter.

"Can I get you something more to eat or drink?" Stephen asked, coming up behind her.

She turned to him with a smile. "No, but thank you. I'm not accustomed to being waited on."

"It's entirely my pleasure." He pushed at the sides of her hair so that its lustrous brown length fell behind her shoulders. "I'm not sure who I have to thank for getting that grill for this house, but I'll have to find out. I'm getting pretty good at grilling."

"Are you telling me that last night was the first time you'd ever cooked on a grill?"

"That's right, but there's really nothing to it. In fact, the whole process is very logical. You get the briquettes hot, put on the steaks, pork chops, or whatever, watch them to make sure they don't burn, then take them off when they're done."

She snapped her mouth shut. "Is everything so easy for you?"

"Not everything," he said, gazing at her. "But most things."

"Then you're very blessed."

"In many ways," he agreed, "but I've also had to *make* a lot of those blessings."

She shook her head in disagreement. "I'm sure you leap over obstacles with a single bound."

"It's more like I use the hand-over-hand method of climbing to get over those obstacles. And along the way, some purchases I reach are easy, some aren't."

She regarded him thoughtfully. "I'm well aware that I haven't asked you a lot of questions about yourself," she said slowly. "And under the circumstances, I suppose my lack of questions has been a little unnatural. I don't know. I think perhaps it's been an unconscious act to protect myself."

"You don't need protection from me," he said softly. "I would never hurt you."

"Maybe not deliberately."

He curved his long fingers around the back of her neck and rubbed at the taut muscles he found there. "Not in any way, Leah. Besides, you know quite a bit about me. I think you instinctively *feel* a lot about me. And you understand that having you love me as I love you is my greatest ambition."

Tears welled in her eyes, and she blinked them

away. His words made a part of her feel warm and wonderful inside. So why did she have to fight those feelings, she wondered with despair. Why did there have to be a part of her that was constantly and terribly frightened to reach out for happiness? "What I understand is that up until two days ago, making a profit was your greatest ambition. But you'd conquered the mountain of business. Then you saw me and you saw a new challenge."

His eyes glinted with gentle admiration. "You really know how to go straight to the heart when you want to, don't you?"

Standing so close to him, her sundress provided no shield against the rising heat of his body. She wasn't sure why, but she was so attuned to him, she could measure his growing need inside her own body. She brought her hand between them and grasped the pearl necklace. "Am I right?"

"Yes, Leah, you're absolutely right. To a point. The night we met, I was restless. I'd discovered that trying to relax when I really wanted to work eighteen hours a day was very irritating. I was driving my boat fast to try to get the restlessness out of my system, when the carnival drew me. That's when I saw you and everything that is you—stillness, colored lights, fear and laughter, beauty and sadness. And I saw the most intriguing challenge of my life. It didn't make sense. It completely baffled me, but suddenly I was perfectly happy to be where I was. Suddenly I fell in love."

Scared and very fragile, she broke away from him and put the width of the deck between them. "That's not true."

He folded his arms across his chest, staying where he was. "Why don't you think so?"

"Because . . ."

"Ah, because."

"Because . . . it just isn't true."

He studied her for a moment. "You want to know what the real reason is? You won't *let* yourself believe, Leah, which I find rather amazing. You believe that your pearl necklace is magic when it's really just a piece of jewelry, very lovely and probably very valuable, but still just a piece of jewelry. You believe that your friend Rafael is innocent when all the evidence says otherwise. Yet you won't believe I love you. Why is that?"

"Because," she replied, angry and tormented, "it doesn't hurt anything to believe this necklace might carry magic. And it can only help Rafael for me to believe he's innocent. But if I let myself believe you love me, then I'd have to rearrange every thought I'd ever had."

He smiled. "But, Leah. You've already begun to rearrange your way of thinking. You're simply not ready to face the conclusions you're reaching."

His smile and his gentle persistence worked on her anger, diffusing it. "You're right," she said in a small voice. "And I don't want you to be right."

He slipped his hands into the pockets of his slacks and started toward her, keeping his pace slow and unthreatening. "All you have to do is accept, Leah. Accept that I love you."

Warily she followed his movements as he crossed the deck and stopped in front of her. "I can't do that," she said softly. "Because I'll hurt too much the day I realize you don't love me."

Stephen bowed his head, experiencing his own pain. No matter how hard he tried, there was still a part of her he couldn't reach, a self-contained, cautious, fearful part of her, and he didn't know what to do about it.

She sensed his suffering and was at a loss. The gentle breeze tangled in her hair, caressed her face, and whispered in her ear. She heard Zarah's voice speaking of the stars, wisdom, and peace. She heard Gary Mercer saying, "we were so close to happiness . . . so close."

Her gaze locked with his, and a portion of her resistance gave way. "I can do one thing," she said. "I can accept the fact that I love you."

His whole body jerked. "You love me?"

She nodded solemnly.

To his dying day he would remember this moment, he thought. But to him the next moments were equally important. The touch of his hands was light on her shoulders, even though the muscles of his body were burning from being held rigid with iron control. "And what's it going to take to prove to you that I love you and won't ever leave you?"

"Does it matter so much that I don't believe?"

"It matters one hell of a lot."

Her brow wrinkled. "Can't you just take what I can offer? It's a lot."

"Actually, Leah, to have you say that you love me means everything to me. But I want things perfect between us, and perfect means that you accept that I love you. Until you do, we can't plan a future."

She almost gritted her teeth with frustration. "Stephen, listen and try to understand. You may be used to having things perfect in your life, but I'm not. There are too many elements of my life that are flawed, too many people who are depending on me for their livelihood. But I've discovered and admitted my love for you, and that love is like a bright corner of my life. You're here with me now. You've been with me through interviews with people that would have been unbearable for me without you. You've stood beside me regardless of your feelings about Rafael's guilt or innocence. You've looked at me and made me feel as if I'm very precious to you. You've touched me and made me feel as if I'm the most beautiful, most desirable woman in the world. And you've made me love you and want you. For now, take what I can offer you. The future—well, the future is just too unpredictable. But there's tonight. Let's take it."

"Damn, Leah, you don't make things easy." His hands tightened on her shoulders. "And you make them too easy."

"I'm *trying* to make them easy. Did you hear Gary Mercer? He and Sheila were so close to happiness, and in one horrible moment it was all taken away from them. Tonight is being offered to us. We need to accept or we might not be given another chance. Kiss me, Stephen. Please kiss me."

He trembled as he brushed his lips across hers and felt his control evaporating into the pine-scented air around them. "If I start kissing you, I won't be able to stop this time," he muttered. "Are you sure that's what you want?"

"I want you."

"How I love you, Leah, and one of these days soon, you're going to know it too. But until then . . ."

His mouth pressed roughly against hers, but his arms around her were compellingly tender. To him, the kiss was a summation of all the feelings that had been growing between them and a portent of what was to come. He had the tremendous, almost unbearable urge to try to possess her. But a thread of sanity told him that possessing Leah would be impossible. Instead, he'd wrap her around him and become a part of her for a little while. He'd absorb her colors into him. And when it was over, he'd care for her and do everything in his power to make sure she had no pain. And then he'd make love to her again.

Her arms went around his neck and her fingers threaded into his hair. Desire came crashing down around her like a heavy, driving rain of fire. She reeled with its force and clung to him, savoring everything that was Stephen, and everything that together they made each other feel. Then the time to savor passed, because all too soon she found herself ablaze, dissatisfied, and yearning for what her body was telling her could be. She dragged her mouth from his and dipped her tongue into the dimple in his chin, then ran a line of kisses up his jawline until her lips were against his ear. "I don't know how much longer I can stand."

He shuddered. "Let's go into the house."

"No. I want our first time to be outside beneath the stars." Her words were breathless.

"But—"

"Don't you have a quilt or something?"

"Leah—"

"I want you *and* the stars."

"I'll be right back." He tore away from her and disappeared through the kitchen door.

She'd gotten her way, but without his physical support, she was left swaying like a delicate flower in a strong wind. The red skirt of her sundress pressed against the heated need of her thighs, and a strand of hair blew across her sensitized lips. She felt buffeted by need, aroused beyond reason.

Within a minute he returned with the comforter from his bed. "This doesn't match a thing," he said. With her hand in his he led her down the steps of the deck and onto the lawn. At the edge of the woods he spread out the quilt and brought her down onto it with him.

Their clothes soon were in a pile to one side; the pearl necklace was laid carefully on top of the clothes.

The grassy lawn and the comforter cushioned them. The moon and the stars provided their light.

The passion and sweat of their bodies and the needles of the pine trees made the perfume.

Poised above her, he looked down and said, "This will be the first time I've ever actually made love."

Then he entered her with exquisite tenderness, and made himself a part of her. Sweetness and primal cravings looped and swirled and knotted within them until they created new colors and redefined the height of the sky.

Pale light filtered through tall, undraped windows as Leah awoke in a huge bed wrapped in Stephen's arms. A sense of contentment and happiness to which she was unaccustomed filled her. She turned her head and studied the soft thick cinnamon-color lashes that rested over the hard cheekbones of his face. Such a man of contrasts, she thought. He could be so gentle with her, so patient, yet he had planned to sell the radio station without seeing it, taking jobs away from people without ever meeting them. And he probably still planned to sell it.

Why had he come into her life, she wondered. Could their meeting have been just a coincidence? Or had their love been directed by the magic of the pearl necklace? Did the necklace *really* have a special power? Or was its power held within her belief in its power?

She sighed. She supposed she should view the matter as she would a superstition. Maybe it wouldn't hurt anything to walk beneath a ladder. But why take the chance when there was an alternate route?

The lashes raised, and dark green eyes looked at her with a lazy seductiveness.

"You have beautiful eyes," she said, and lightly ran her hand over his night's growth of beard.

He smiled. "And you're beautiful all over."

She felt herself turn pink. "I feel marvelous. Rested. Tingling. Strange."

He chuckled and gathered her tightly against him. "All of that, huh?"

"All of that and more. It's shameful. I need to get up, but I don't want to."

"Then don't."

He rose on one elbow, curved his hand around her breast, and covered her mouth with a languid kiss. A fire kindled inside Leah and grew as the kiss intensified and his hands explored her body, searching for and finding the highly sensitive spots he had learned so well last night.

She began to move against him, and he responded with a hunger that took her breath away. He stroked and touched her until she was writhing beneath him, senseless with passion.

Then, incredibly, he paused and looked down at her. "You taste like morning and flowers. I love the way your body feels to my hands, and I love the way I fit into you."

Her eyes widened as she grasped the significance of his words. "We do fit, don't we?"

"We fit so perfectly that when I'm inside you, I

never want to leave. And when I'm not inside you, like now, I want to be."

Her throat clogged with desire, but slowly the glow in her eyes died. "It's utterly impossible."

"Convince me, Leah."

She uttered a sound that combined passion and anguish, wrapped her arms and legs around him, and drew him into her. "Not now."

Wearing the pearls and the red sundress she'd had on the day before, Leah walked around the lake, her head bent, her thoughts disturbed. When they had awakened after their morning's lovemaking, Stephen had told her he needed to make some phone calls.

For several days now she'd had him all to herself, and she felt jealous and threatened that he was communicating with what she'd come to consider his other life—even though she'd told herself a hundred times that their relationship had too many complications to survive. It was just that his almost constant presence beside her had been so easy for her to accept. But now it was brought home with full force that he was an important man with a demanding business and a whole different life back in Dallas, complete with friends and other relationships.

She hadn't been able to stay in the house while he made the calls, and despite Stephen's protests, she had insisted on taking a walk. Running a length of the pearls back and forth through her

fingers, she tried to convince herself that everything would be all right. She failed.

"Leah, my dear, what an extraordinary necklace."

It took a moment for the words and the voice to
jell in her mind. Then she looked up into the face
of Jane Scoggins, the woman who had recently
retired from a thirty-year career as Sunnyvale's
high school English teacher. "Miss Scoggins. What
are you doing here at the lake this morning?"

"Just out for a little constitutional, my dear.
Every year it gets harder and harder to convince
myself to exercise. The necklace is simply lovely."

"Th-thank you."

The tall, heavily built woman lifted the necklace
and studied it through her bifocals. "Not everyone
can wear pearls, you know. Some women have too
much acid in their skin. Ruins the luster. But
these pearls have a wonderful sheen. You must
agree with them." She dropped the necklace. "How
have you been, my dear? You're doing a bang-up
job at the radio station. Listen all the time. Of
course, there's not much else to do when you're
retired." She paused from her clipped, fact-filled,
instructorlike way of talking to draw a breath.

"Thank you," Leah quickly inserted.

"You were one of my brightest students. I wish I
were still teaching, but the school board has this
stupid rule about retirement. Getting old is the
very pits. Youth is everything. Enjoy it while you
can." Miss Scoggins sighed with regret. "I guess
I'd better turn around and head home. I can walk
only so far at a time. I envy Gary Mercer."

The name brought Leah's wandering mind to attention. "Gary Mercer?"

"He *jogs*. Routine as clockwork. Jogs past my house about ten most nights, then turns around at the end of the block and heads back up the street. I can't get to sleep before one or so in the morning, so I sit in my front room and sew and see him every night at ten. Of course, there was the other night when he was jogging at midnight." She shook her blue-haired head, baffled. "Where does he get his energy? And that night he just kept right on going toward the lake."

"He came this way? Do you remember which night that was?"

"I'm old, my dear. I can't sleep like I used to be able to. And I never could jog, but I can still remember." She gave a cluck of her tongue. "Besides, it was the night poor little Sheila Donaldson was killed. Terrible tragedy. Maybe I made a mistake in not jogging when I was younger. Of course, young ladies didn't run back then. Well, good-bye, my dear. It was nice seeing you. Keep up the good work at the radio station."

"Good-bye, Miss Scoggins."

The tires of Stephen's car kicked up gravel as they rolled to a stop in front of Gary Mercer's house. Gary was on his front porch, a beer in his hand.

"It's a bit early for him to be drinking," Stephen said as he switched off the car's engine. "And he doesn't look too pleased to see us."

"It can't be helped. On our last visit I let my sympathy for him cloud my judgment. All I was concerned with was whether or not he'd killed Sheila. When I decided he hadn't, I forgot to ask him one important question." She opened the door, but right before she stepped out, she glanced back at Stephen. "Do you think I could have been wrong about Gary? Do you think he could have killed Sheila after all?"

"All I know is that someone killed Sheila. If it wasn't Rafael, and we don't think it was Robert, then that man up there on the porch has got to be a suspect, and he could have had any one of a dozen motives. Maybe he and Sheila argued over Rafael. Maybe at the last minute she'd gotten cold feet about leaving town with him."

She nodded and got out of the car. "Good morning, Gary."

"What do you want?"

He'd had more than one beer judging by the belligerence in his tone, she reflected as she made her way across the small yard to the porch steps. She noted Stephen's presence behind her with gratitude. He hadn't blinked an eye when she had burst into his study and practically dragged him to the car. "I need to ask you a question, Gary."

"I won't talk about Sheila, if that's why you're here. It hurts too damned much."

"You want her murderer caught, don't you?"

His eyes and voice were dull. "He's already been caught, Leah. Everyone in town knows that but you."

Stephen's hands closed warmly around her arms to reassure her. Unconsciously she leaned against him. "Gary, I need to know if you were at the cabin the night Sheila was killed."

His face twisted and he took a deep guzzle of beer. "Yeah," he said softly. "I got there, saw that Gypsy leaving, went in, and found her lying on the floor. I didn't even have to touch her to know that she was dead." He held up a helpless hand. "I couldn't seem to take it in. I mean, I'd seen her at the carnival just a few hours earlier. She'd been so happy, so alive. Then she was lying there . . ." He looked away, his teeth clenched against his grief. "I just couldn't cope. I ran."

She eased away from Stephen and climbed the steps to the porch. Laying a hand on Gary's shoulder, she knelt beside his chair. "Why did you go there in the first place? Had she asked you to meet her there?"

"No, not really. Because of the carnival, I jogged later than usual, and I decided to run by her house to see if she was back from her meeting at the fishing cabin. The garage door was up and the garage was empty, so on impulse I jogged out there to see her."

"Have you told the sheriff any of this?"

He took another swig of beer. "I saw no reason to get involved and every reason to stay out of it. She was dead and so were our plans. No one knew about us. I figured I had to go on living and working in this town . . . somehow." His voice faltered. "I was too broken up that night to do much of anything except get home. But the next morning I made an anonymous call to the sheriff's office and told them Rafael had been there. I decided I should do that much." He glanced down at her, an angry expression on his face. "I also told the sheriff about Sheila's affair with Rafael. It's my guess that he went into a rage and killed her after she told him about us. It's the only thing that makes sense."

But it *doesn't*, Leah thought.

Six

Sitting on her bedroom floor with her legs crossed, Leah stared at the pearls she held in her hands. She'd come home to shower and change, and she now wore an off-the-shoulder cotton dress of deep turquoise.

"Leah," Stephen asked, "what are you doing?"

She glanced up. He sat relaxed in the big lounge chair she'd upholstered in a hot pink corduroy. He looked good there, she thought absently. "I'm fretting."

"Fretting?"

"It's the pearls. Ever since Zarah gave them to me, it's like they've been leading me."

"You're imagining things."

"No, just listen." She tossed the pearls onto the bed and scooted across the floor to him. "I'll skip the part about you and me, because . . . well, just because. What I'm talking about now is how the necklace seems to be drawing me through a maze of untruths and truths toward the killer."

He shook his head. "Leah—"

"*Think* about it, Stephen. I went to visit Robert because he seemed the most likely suspect and found a dead end. The next morning I really had no idea what I should do. But then I discovered the clasp on the necklace was in danger of falling off, and I had to take it to the jeweler. It was there we were offered the fact that Sheila had been looking at signet rings, and that fact eventually led us, through Dorian, to Gary. He also seemed like a dead end, until this morning, when Miss Scoggins stopped me to admire the necklace and she let drop a remark that sent us back to Gary."

"But we didn't learn anything. Well," he amended, "we did learn that Gary made the second phone call to the sheriff. That could've been an attempt on his part to cast guilt on Rafael, but that's certainly not anything we can take and run with."

She chewed on her bottom lip. "I don't know. It seems to me that the pearls keep pointing to him. I feel there's something significant buried in what he said that I'm just not grasping."

"Honey, do you have any idea how strange that all sounds?"

Her brown eyes were very grave as she looked up at him. "To you I'm sure it does. But even with your logic and need to make sense of things, you must admit that life holds many mysteries."

"I admit it, but—"

"The night we met, Zarah reminded me that I had been exposed to the mystic ways of the Gypsies for many years. I guess that's why I can believe."

He reached down and pulled her up so that she knelt on her knees between his legs. "If only you would believe in you and me."

She smiled softly. "Ah, well, you and me. We're certainly something that seems to *be* at the moment, aren't we?"

"That's right," he said eagerly, "and what we feel for each other cannot be disputed."

Her smile slowly faded. "Remember the tilt-a-whirl we rode?"

"Of course I do."

"I feel I've been on it ever since, spinning and going up and down. Everything's blurred, yet at times things are so clear it hurts to look at them."

He groaned. "Leah, you're a fabulous creature. If I put the stars, moon, sun, rivers, and sky together, maybe I would have your mind."

Not knowing what to say, she put her arms around his neck and hugged him fiercely.

When at last she drew away, he threaded his fingers through one side of her hair and lifted the mass away from her face. "I've got something that I've been putting off telling you."

All the softness in her body disappeared as she tensed.

"Hey, it's not that bad," he chided gently. "It's just that I've got to drive back to Dallas today. In fact, I should have been on the road an hour ago."

The old feelings of fear and anxiety threatened. She got to her feet, went to the center of the room, and gazed blindly around her.

He was immediately beside her. "It's not even noon yet. It'll take me two hours to drive there. I'll spend a few hours in the office, and I'll be back this evening."

"It's all right. Really." She wrapped her arms around herself, warding away the cold and the withdrawal. "I know you have responsibilities. I've known all along. It was only a matter of time."

He took her in his arms and cradled her close. "I said I'll be back this evening, and I will. I'm not leaving you. I'm simply going to Dallas to see to some things." With a tender smile on his face he spoke softly and rubbed her back with caressing, soothing circles. "You haven't told me a lot, but I've been able to figure out certain things for myself. And one thing is very clear to me—you've had so much rejection in your life, you're afraid to let yourself see how much I love you. But I do love you, Leah. And I will always come back to you."

She listened carefully and discovered that she wanted with all her heart to believe him. And perhaps, she thought, *wanting* to believe was the first step toward actually believing. Warmer now, she pulled back and looked up at him. "I'll miss you."

"Come with me."

She shook her head. "I can't. I need to talk to Zarah."

He hesitated. "Will you be all right?"

"Why wouldn't I be?"

"I don't like the idea of you pursuing this investigation all alone. It could be dangerous."

"If you think that, then you believe the murderer is still walking around free, while Rafael sits in jail for something he didn't do."

He grinned. "You have a very persuasive way about you."

She wasn't satisfied. "*Do* you think Rafael is innocent?"

He sighed. "I haven't seen any hard, cold facts to support his innocence, but yes, I guess I do think he didn't murder Sheila."

A glow of happiness settled over her face. "That's good. And I *am* going to miss you."

"You'd better," he said, and ground a kiss onto her lips.

As always, being with Zarah in her tent gave Leah a sense of well-being. No candles had been lit yet today, but the sun filtered through the gold-colored fabric of the tent, gilding everything including the two women who sat side by side on the daybed and the dress that lay across Leah's lap.

She gazed down at the creation with amazement and delight. The strapless bodice was a haze of spangly magenta stars. The skirt was drifting silk panels of magenta, pink, and fuchsia. "You've never made me such a beautiful dress before."

"I wanted you to have something special."

"This is more than special, much more. I love it. I can't imagine anything more gorgeous."

"And there are high-heel shoes that match." Zarah's tone implied she was well satisfied with Leah's pleasure.

Leah chuckled. "And you're the one who taught me the joys of going barefoot."

Zarah lifted her shoulders and let them fall. "Sometimes there are events . . ."

"I don't know what it would be. I never go anywhere where I could wear something like this."

"That is not a matter over which you should be perturbed. An occasion will present itself, I am sure."

"But, Zarah, you shouldn't spend your money on me like this."

"*Bah.* You are my child. I shall make you clothes if I choose. Now let us speak of why you are here today." Zarah smiled. "You have come to ask me about the pearls, have you not?"

Leah felt no surprise at Zarah's precognition. "I don't think you've told me everything you know about the necklace."

"You are right."

"But why, Zarah? Why have you kept it from me?"

"Because we were waiting for the pearls to do their work."

"We?"

"We, the Gypsies, are descendants of a nomadic tribespeople. Who's to say where we first started? Who's to say who we really are? It is not important that we know."

"What is important?"

"The pearls. They have been with us for over twenty-five hundred years. But not continuously. They disappear for long periods of time, yet when there is trouble for our people, the pearls always appear. So when the pearls showed up this time, we knew to prepare for trouble."

She knew better than to discount what she was hearing, but still . . . "You mean you just turned around one day and the pearls were there?"

"Yes. And one day they will disappear again."

"And you knew the necklace was here to help you?"

"It is our history."

"That's incredible." She gazed down at her lap, where the bottom loop of the necklace lay pooled on top of the magenta stars. The pearls and the stars appeared to gift each other, the stars receiving a glowing iridescence from the pearls, and the pearls drawing a slightly deeper color of pink from the stars. A sudden thought occurred to her. "But why did you give the necklace to me?"

"Because, my child, you have a pure heart, and we consider you one of our own. We knew that you would help us if we couldn't help ourselves. When Rafael was put into jail, we knew we had been right. We were outsiders in this town. No one would tell us anything. Besides, a Gypsy has no chance in a white man's court. You were the only one who could help us."

"I don't know how much help I've been, Zarah. I've discovered certain things, but I'm not sure

I'm any closer to finding out who killed Sheila than I was the day I started."

She patted Leah's hand. "You should not be concerned. I am not. Neither is Rafael. The pearls will do their work."

"I worry about him. He is losing his spirit in that place."

"But he knows that soon he will be free."

"I wish I had your faith."

"You have all you need. You are attuned to the mysticism of the universe even if you are not aware."

Leah grimaced. "Stephen would tell you that I'm too attuned. Poor man, I drive him crazy."

"Stephen? Ah, the cinnamon-haired man of whom you've spoken."

Uncertainty entered her dark eyes. "Zarah, about Stephen . . . You made a prediction for me when you gave me the pearls, and it seemed to come true. The night I met him I felt different. Since then my life has changed both in little ways and in big ways. And there's the unalterably and amazing fact that I've fallen in love with Stephen. But I have to know how much the pearls have to do with all of this."

"It is up to you to decide."

"*Zarah.*"

The old woman held up a hand. "No, I have said all I can."

"All you can or all you will?"

Zarah smiled slowly. "Again, my child, that is up to you to decide."

• • •

"It's working," Pat reported gleefully. "Our revenues are up. The new management has got to be impressed now."

"You've been doing a great job, that's for sure," Leah said, studying the reports on the accounts Pat had acquired over the last few days. "I'm glad I decided to stop by the station."

"Margaret told me about that awful man. The accountant," she added when Leah looked at her in query. "She said he wasn't in here long at all, and we couldn't decide if that was good or bad."

"That makes three of us," Leah said wryly, then went on in a more serious tone. "I don't really know what to tell you on that subject. As you know, I've been very preoccupied with trying to find something to help clear Rafael of Sheila's murder. But as soon as Rafael is free, I plan to present these new figures to . . . to the management. I just hope he, I mean, the management, thinks they're as impressive as I do. And in the meantime, I've been given the impression that TCIC won't take any negative action."

"Well, that's something, at any rate. You know, I've been pleasantly surprised by the response I've gotten. The people of this town have heard about the TCIC buy, and they don't want to lose the station any more than we do."

"It's gratifying to know that people are enjoying what we're doing here."

Pat wiggled in her seat, then sat forward. "I can't stand it any longer. I just have to ask."

Leah chuckled at the avidly curious expression on the younger woman's face. "I can tell you right now, I don't have any answers."

"You'll be able to tell me this, because it's about that necklace. I've been hard pressed to keep my eyes off it, much less my hands. It's gorgeous. Where did you get it? Did you buy it somewhere, or did someone give it to you? If you bought it, how much was it? I mean, could I afford one? And if someone gave it to you, for goodness' sake, tell me who." Suddenly Pat grinned and drew in a deep breath. "Will you listen to me? I sound like I'm filling out a crime report. You can sure tell I'm dating a deputy sheriff, can't you?"

Leah stared at Pat. "That's *it*. Good heavens, why haven't I thought of it before?" She shoved the phone across the desk so that it was within easy reach of the younger woman. "I need you to do me a big favor."

The hinges creaked as Leah pressed her foot against the porch and propelled the swing back and forth. She didn't know how long she had been sitting there, her gaze fixed firmly on the road that ran in front of her house, but she did know that it had been dusk when she'd come out on the porch and now it was night.

Stephen will be here, she told herself. He said he would return tonight, and he will.

Headlights brightened the horizon. Leah's pulse leapt, but the headlights flashed quickly by and disappeared down the road. He'll come, she thought, and had no idea why she felt such confidence.

Absently she picked up one of the pearls and rubbed it between her fingers. If only Rafael weren't in jail. But she was close to the truth. She could feel it. Hopefully if everything went well tomorrow, she would have her answer.

Another pair of headlights appeared. The necklace dropped from her fingers and settled against the turquoise bodice of her dress. Forcing herself to remain calm, she watched the car decrease its speed and turn into her driveway. The Mercedes pulled to a stop in front of her house, the engine cut off, the door opened, and Stephen stepped out.

Leah leapt from the swing and launched herself off the porch toward him.

Laughing, he caught her to him. "I said I'd be back."

"I've been waiting for you."

"Have you?" He pressed a kiss to her lips. "I would have been here sooner, but there was a traffic tie-up on the interstate coming out of Dallas. On the way to Sunnyvale I decided I should buy a helicopter."

She drew back in horror. "Oh, no—"

"It sure would be convenient. It would cut my commuting time to—"

"But you'd be *flying*!"

He smiled down at her. "Bad idea, right? Okay, I'll forget it, for now, at any rate." He glanced up at the house. "No lights?"

Bewildered, she followed his gaze. "What?"

"You didn't turn on any lights."

"It never even crossed my mind." She took his hand and led him up the stairs and onto the porch. Pulling him down beside her on the swing, she asked, "Do you have to go back to Dallas tomorrow?"

"No. I'm set for a few days." He paused, afraid that what he was about to say was going to bother her. By the dim light of the moon he could make out her features, but he wanted to be able to see every nuance of her expression. "Why don't we turn on a few lights?"

"Why? It's so peaceful."

"Peace is inside you, Leah. Not around you."

She thought about it. "That's not always true."

He got up and flipped on the porch light, then sat back down. "I've gone an awful long time today without seeing that lovely face of yours. Do you mind?"

She grinned. "How could I when you put it that way?"

He placed his hand along her jaw and tilted her mouth up to his. He tried to hold back his passion and fill the kiss with a pure love that would bolster her in the next few minutes. His stratagem worked only to a point, and then desire began to take over, pulsing through his veins and reminding him of how very much he wanted her. He broke off the kiss and gently stroked her face. "I have some good news."

"What's that?" Her dark brown eyes softly gleamed with trust and love.

"I talked to several of my friends this afternoon, and they reminded me that I had planned to throw a housewarming party as soon as the house was complete." He felt her stiffen and deliberately gave a light chuckle. "They actually threatened me. They said they'll be down Friday night, with or without an invitation. So I guess we're throwing a party night after next. It'll be fun, don't you think?"

Leah couldn't answer. The familiar fear and anxiety closed in on her and left her paralyzed.

Stephen skimmed his fingers from her face to her bare shoulder, feeling the clamminess of her skin. "I know you're worried about Rafael and probably don't feel like a party, but you won't have to do anything other than show up and have a good time. My secretary is contacting everyone, and I'll hire a catering service to handle all the work." He infused humor into his tone. "And, naturally, I'll use a *Sunnyvale* caterer. I've learned my lesson."

Leah willed normalcy back to her body. Didn't Stephen understand? She truly believed that the only reason she'd allowed herself to fall in love with him was because he hadn't known her and hadn't had any preconceived ideas of her. That and the pearls . . .

But now his friends would be coming, and he wanted her to meet them. She'd spent years being an outsider in a town populated by people probably just like his friends. What if these people he obviously admired and felt affection for saw that she was different? What if they treated her as an outsider? Would he think less of her then?

Her chest was tight, breathing was difficult. Her hand urgently clenched around the pearls.

"Leah? I'm touching you, but I'm not reaching you. You're withdrawing and I refuse to let you. Talk to me. Tell me what's wrong."

She took several deep, shaky breaths until her lungs once again had life-giving air going in and out of them. "Your friends are all sane," she finally managed. He looked at her oddly, and she went on. "The night we met, you said that everyone you know is sane."

"They're very nice people."

"I'm sure they are," she said with grave doubt.

He took her arms and swiveled her body in the swing so that she faced him. "I'm not going to lie to you. I could have stopped them from coming. In fact, I almost did. But then I realized that it would be good for you to meet my friends. You have it so firmly fixed in your mind that there's this huge chasm of experiences and life-styles between us. And I can't deny that we're bringing diverse elements into this relationship. But that just makes it all the more interesting, and it's wrong to look at these things as something to overcome. Because of the different things we know, we can learn from each other and create a rich, full life together."

"You really believe that, don't you?"

"Yes. And I won't stop until I can make you believe it too."

She stood, walked to the edge of the porch, and leaned her shoulder against one of the supports.

Her heart still beat erratically, but at least she was breathing more easily. "I guess the least I can do is try."

He came up behind her and rested his hands on her shoulders. "You're wonderful," he said. Having gotten her to agree to what he wanted, he decided it best not to dwell on the upcoming party. "I'm hungry."

"You're always hungry," she murmured dryly.

"Just at mealtimes, which you tend to forget. Would you like to go get something to eat? Or we could drive to my place, and I could throw something on the grill."

"I'd rather stay here."

"Okay then, I could run to the store and—"

"No." She turned her head and looked at him over her shoulder. "I want to sleep alone tonight."

His brow creased into a frown. "You're not withdrawing from me again, are you?"

"No. I just need to be alone tonight."

"Leah—"

"Please, Stephen. Try to understand, this has nothing to do with you."

He wanted to argue. He wanted to stay and hold her close all night long, to reassure himself that she had not withdrawn from him. But her set expression convinced him he wouldn't be able to change her mind. Reluctantly he gave in and left.

And Leah spread her quilt beneath the midnight-black sky, pulled around her every particle of peace she could grasp, and slept.

Seven

Tim McCafferty opened the back door to the jail at Leah's knock and nervously checked the alley behind her to make sure no one was about.

"For goodness' sake, Tim, let me in."

He cracked the door only wide enough to let her slip in, then closed it with a sigh of relief. "No one can know that you're here."

"I understand, and I really appreciate this."

"The only reason you're going to get a look at that crime report is because Pat asked me. I could lose my job. Do you know how many laws I'm breaking?"

"Not really, but as I said, I really do appreciate it. And do you suppose you could get me a cup of coffee? At six A.M., my body demands caffeine."

"Leah, for heaven's sake, just read the report and *leave*."

"Okay, okay. Where is it?"

He motioned for her to follow him into a small, unused office and pointed to the desk which was bare except for a brown folder. "Stay in here and keep the door closed. I'll come get you in ten minutes."

She sat down behind the desk, pulled the file toward her, and began reading a detailed description of what the police had found when they'd arrived at the cabin. The description noted the position and condition of Sheila's body, and the state of the room in which she had been discovered. Apparently the room was in order. The report also listed the spilled contents of Sheila's open purse that was found beside her: a compact, comb, lipstick, car keys, cleaner's receipt, checkbook, and a small package of tissues. Nothing unusual, Leah concluded. A dust for fingerprints had turned up four sets: Sheila's, Robert Donaldson's, Rafael's, and one set that was unidentified. Gary Mercer's, Leah thought, and turned to the statement that indicated a search of the area around the cabin had turned up nothing. Lastly there was the coroner's report and a set of photographs of the body.

She closed the file, sickened by the clinical account and the gruesome pictures, just as Tim came back into the room. "I brought you a cup of coffee," he said, handing her a paper cup of dark, steaming liquid. I hope you take it black."

"That's fine."

"Did you find anything that you can use to help your friend?"

She shook her head. "I don't know. It all seems so cut and dried, but I can't help thinking that there's something obvious I'm missing."

"It seems a pretty open-and-shut case to me, Leah. Maybe you should save yourself a lot of grief and accept the fact that Rafael killed her."

She pushed back from the desk and stood up. "Thanks for the coffee, Tim. And thanks again for bending the rules."

"*Bending?* Leah, I broke them clean in two." All at once a shy grin broke out over his face. "But I'd do anything for Pat. She's terrific, don't you think?"

Leah smiled. "I sure do."

Outside in the alley again Leah automatically headed around the side of the building. Sipping her coffee, she went back over what she had just read, putting it together with what she had learned previously.

At the front of the building she turned the corner and headed toward the lake. What *was* it that was nagging at her, she wondered. There was something that was staying just beyond the reach of her mind, something that if she could only get hold of it . . . she completely lost her train of thought as she collided with Robert Donaldson.

"Watch out! *Dammit,* look what you've done."

She gazed in horror at the coffee stain spreading over the front of his white shirt and gray suit. Her hand flew protectively to the pearls around her neck, but no coffee had splashed on either them or the blue dress she wore. "I'm terribly sorry. I wasn't watching where I was going."

"That was obvious. Now I'll have to go home and change."

She straightened with composure. "I said I was sorry. And if you'll send me the cleaning bill, I'll be glad to pay for it."

"You can bet you will. What are you doing here so early anyway? Visiting your Gypsy friend?"

She eyed him coolly. "I was just out taking a morning walk."

He glanced toward the building and back to her. "Well, I'm here for a purpose. I want to make sure that there are no hitches in getting that bastard convicted. The sheriff has been dragging his feet on charging him, and I want to know why."

"Have a nice day, Robert." She turned on her heel and headed for the Gypsy encampment.

She spent the morning visiting with Zarah and talking out the information she had gathered while Zarah offered tea and reassurance. But Leah was able to garner no new insights, and beneath Zarah's confidence, Leah detected an increased anxiety over Rafael.

Leah made her way to the radio station with a heavy heart. When she entered the station, she found Margaret beaming. "That nice Mr. Tanner is in your office."

An alarm bell went off in her head. "What's he doing in there?"

"He asked to see the books, and after he explained who he was, I gave them to him." The sight of Leah's pale face made her add, "I hope that was all right. I mean, he owns the station, and he does seem so nice. Lots nicer than that other person who came from Dallas."

"Don't worry about it, Margaret. You did fine. I'll go see if he needs anything else."

She walked toward her office, a cold feeling in the pit of her stomach. When she opened the door, he looked up from the accounting books spread over her desk and smiled. "There you are. I've been waiting for you."

"So I see." She closed the door behind her.

He rose, skirted around the desk, and met her in the center of the room. "Where were you this morning? I went by your house, and when I found you gone, I decided to come here."

"I just came from Zarah's. Earlier I was at the jail."

"Visiting Rafael?"

She shook her head. "No, reading the crime report."

"Really?" His eyes narrowed. "Should I ask how you got to see it?"

"You definitely shouldn't."

"Okay, then. Did you find out anything from the report that can help Rafael?"

"Unfortunately, no."

"I'm sorry."

"I am too." She walked around him and eyed her desk. "Stephen, I wish you'd told me you were going to do this. I was under the impression we had a tacit agreement." She turned to look at him. "I mean, I thought we were going to put this aside for the time being until I could get Rafael out of jail."

"It's all right, Leah."

"*No*, it's not. These books don't tell the story. For one thing, they're not up-to-date. For another, we have new accounts—"

"I'm not selling the station."

"What?"

"I'm not selling the station. That possibility completely vanished as soon as I saw how much KSUN meant to you."

She waved her hand toward the desk in silent bewilderment.

"Since I had the time, I thought I'd look into my newest acquisition. I think my interest was natural, don't you? To tell you the truth, I didn't care what I found. If there was more red than black, TCIC would have simply used KSUN as a writeoff, and you could have continued on as you had been. But I discovered that you've been doing a great job. I also talked with Margaret and the fellow in the booth, Harry Morrison."

"Harry talked to you?"

Stephen nodded. "He told me how much this job means to him, and how grateful he is to you for giving it to him."

"Really? He's never said anything like that to me."

He regarded her thoughtfully. "You've really done

a remarkable thing here, Leah. You've employed people who for various reasons were unable to fit in anywhere else, and in the process you've given them a sense of self-worth and usefulness. I admire that."

On some barely conscious level she'd wanted desperately to do just what he'd described, but she hadn't been aware of exactly what she'd accomplished until she'd heard it from him. His words meant everything to her. She blinked away the tears that stung at her eyes. "I have to ask you something."

"Anything, you should know that."

"Are you keeping the station only because of our relationship?"

He took his time in answering. "Yes."

She clasped her hands tightly together and looked down at them.

With a knuckle beneath her chin, he raised her face. "You want me to be honest with you, don't you? If it hadn't been for my caring so damned much for you, I would never have even seen this place, much less talked with Harry and Margaret. Those are simply the hard, cold facts of my business."

"Then let me ask you another question."

"All right."

"When . . . if our relationship ends, what will you do about the station?"

"Always expecting the worst, aren't you?" he asked softly. "Well, then let me put your mind at ease. I have seen the station. I've even listened to it. And I've talked with Harry and Margaret. There's no way I'll sell the station as long as I know it's operating the way it is now."

The relief she'd been suppressing surged forward. "Thank you, Stephen. You're a remarkably nice man."

His eyes held laughter, but his handsome face expressed indignation. "You're just now figuring that out?"

She angled her head and regarded him thoughtfully. "I recognize that you've been very gentle with me. I suspect you saw you had to be. But I also recognize that you have another side. You have a smile that reminds me of a shark. Granted, I haven't seen it since that first night, but I'm sure you can flash it in an instant."

"One way or the other, Leah, you keep me constantly amazed. That's quite an analysis. And very accurate. Regarding the station, there's one more thing you should know. Sometimes my business decisions are hard as hell to make, but this one was a cinch. It made perfect sense. And regarding you, I love you very much, and while gentleness and patience don't come easily to me, with you it's a cakewalk."

A lovely smile melted away her serious expression. "And there's something you should know. I wouldn't have fallen in love with you if I hadn't seen your basic niceness. Just don't use that shark smile on me, okay?"

"Okay." He brought her to him and held her

close for a minute. "Why don't we go have some lunch?"

"There you go again with the food."

"It's time for another meal. My bet is you skipped breakfast."

"Yes, well . . . There's a little café we can go to that serves a really great steak sandwich. On the way there I'd like to tell you what the report said and get your opinion. Maybe you'll be able to see something I'm missing."

"That's a good idea. My car's out front."

"Why don't we walk?"

He rolled his eyes at the suggestion of walking. "I'm hungry. Let's take the car."

On the way to the café Leah related in detail to Stephen the contents of the crime report. She explained about the condition of the room, the fingerprints they'd found, and the position of Sheila's body. She mentioned Sheila's purse with its spilled contents. She even went into the coroner's report with him.

He threw her a glance as he pulled into the parking lot of the café. "That must have been hard for you to read. I wish you'd told me you were going there this morning so that I could have gone with you."

She leaned against the door and shrugged. "Tim would have been doubly nervous with both of us there. *Oh*—I ran into Robert Donaldson outside the station. Literally." She grinned. "Spilled coffee all over him."

"Was he awful to you?"

"He was angry, but then, I'd just ruined his shirt and suit. And he's still angry at Rafael. He said he wanted to make sure nothing went wrong. He doesn't want him to get away on a technicality, and I'm sure he intends to try to press the sheriff into charging Rafael."

"Let's go in and toss what we know back and forth. Maybe it'll help."

"I hope so. I feel like there's something staring me right in the face." She shifted so that she could grasp the door handle, and somehow the rope of pearls hooked on the handle. She automatically tried to pull them free, but at the same time she straightened, causing the tension on the pearls to tighten.

"Oh, damn."

"What's wrong?"

"It's the pearls. They're caught on the door handle."

He chuckled. "Relax. The car doesn't want your pearls. Just lean forward—"

She went still. "The car . . ."

"What?"

"I told you the pearls kept pointing to Gary— that I felt he was saying something significant I wasn't grasping." As quickly and as carefully as she could, she freed the pearls, then, excitement gleaming in her eyes, she turned to him. "It's the *car.*"

"The car?"

"Gary told us that he jogged by Sheila's home, he didn't see the car, and decided to go to the lake. Now, though he didn't say it outright, it seems to me his actions imply that he believed she *drove* to the cabin. But the crime report said that they found nothing around the cabin—surely they would have mentioned her car—and her car keys were in her purse. Don't you see?"

He nodded slowly. "If her car wasn't in the garage, and it wasn't at the cabin, where was it?"

"Exactly."

"Could Robert have driven it to work?"

"They have a two-car garage. Gary said the garage was empty. That means both cars were gone."

"Okay, then we'll assume she drove to the cabin."

"Then someone had to drive the car away from the cabin after she was murdered."

"Why afterward?"

"I can't imagine anyone stealing a car in Sunnyvale, but even if someone did, Sheila would have heard the car start up and gone out to see what was going on. Then she would have been killed outside."

He regarded her levelly. "You're sure about that?"

She looked doubtful for a moment. "I haven't heard anything about Robert filing a stolen-car report."

"Would you have heard?"

"Well, under normal circumstances, yes, I would. KSUN has a local news report. But I have to admit that I've been out of touch."

"So maybe he has filed a report."

"Let's go ask him."

He stared at her. "Now?"

"Now. He'll be at his office. I'll show you which way to go."

"Sheila's car is sitting at home in the garage," Robert Donaldson said implacably. "Where did you ever get the idea that it had been stolen?"

"Because it seems to be unaccounted for the night Sheila was murdered."

"You're mistaken. The car was in the garage the whole night."

Stephen spoke up. "How do you know that? You were here."

Robert's eyes were hard and cold. "Sheila often walked to the lake. Besides, the car was in the garage when I got home. If you think that it was someplace else during the murder, then I suggest you talk to the bastard who's sitting in jail."

Leah sat forward in her chair and leaned her arm on the desk. "Robert, your wife has been killed. It's all been horrible for you. But if there's the slightest doubt that Rafael killed her, that means that the real murderer could be walking around free. You don't want him to go free, do you? Don't you want to make sure that the right man is tried and convicted?"

"But I'm already sure that's going to happen." His fist came down hard on his desk. "Leah, for God's sake, if you hadn't been practically raised as one of those filthy Gypsies, you'd see that Rafael killed Sheila. He has been placed at the scene of the crime and the jewelry that Sheila was wearing that night was found in his trailer. What the hell more do you want?"

She stood her ground, pale but steady. "I want to find the person who murdered your wife. And I'm going to do exactly that, with or without your help."

Robert pushed back his chair and jerked to his feet, his face red with anger. "Then it's going to be without my help, because let me tell you something—I've cooperated with the sheriff, and I've spoken with you twice now, answering every one of your stupid questions, but this is where it ends. I'm fully aware that people around here considered that Sheila and I had a bad marriage, but I never did. Now she's gone, and I have to deal with that fact as well as the brutal way she was murdered. The sooner I pull my life together and go on, the better."

"I understand—"

"You can't even begin to understand. And if you bother me again, I'll turn you in to the sheriff for harassment. Now get out of my sight."

The file drawer shut with a metallic clunk, and Sheriff Johnson turned back to Leah and Stephen. "You've been mighty busy, Leah."

She'd told the sheriff about Gary and Sheila's affair after deciding it was important that he know.

"No one else in this town believes that Rafael is innocent. I've had to be busy." She hesitated, but received no response. "Gary said the garage was empty. Robert said the car was there. I think it's significant to know exactly where it was."

He eyed her thoughtfully. "What made you latch onto the idea of the car?"

Unwilling to jeopardize Tim's job and tell the chief that she had seen the report, she hedged. "It just struck me as odd. Doesn't it make you wonder?"

Stephen spoke up. "One of the men is obviously lying. The trouble is, their outrage over Sheila's death seems very real, and then there's the problem of motive. Do you think Robert might have known about his wife's affair with Gary Mercer? If he did, that would sure give him a motive."

The sheriff shook his head. "I've known him a long time. Why, he was one of the best quarterbacks Sunnyvale High ever had. He played cards with me and a few of the boys the night before Sheila was killed. Trust me. He never had a clue. He didn't know about Rafael until I told him the next morning, and he sure as hell didn't know about Gary. Hell, *I* didn't even know, and I generally know everything." He settled his large frame into the chair behind his desk with a disgruntled expression on his face.

Leah squirmed with impatience. "But will you question Robert and Gary?"

"Robert became very angry with Leah," Stephen

explained, "and said he didn't want to see her again."

"Can't say as I blame the man. After all, his wife has been murdered, and to top everything off, he's found out she'd been having an affair with a Gypsy." He shook his head regretfully. "Now I'll have to tell him about Gary."

"Sheriff, we all feel bad for Robert," Leah said. "And for Sheila. And *I* feel bad about Rafael, if no one else does, because he's innocent. Now I've asked you to do something that's nothing more than your job. Will you?"

The sheriff sighed heavily. "All right, Leah. You've made your point. I'll check into the now-you-see-it-now-you-don't car, but I'll tell you this much, I don't think it'll amount to a hill of beans. When I went to tell Robert about Sheila that morning, both cars were in the garage. And I will let you in on one fact. Her car was not at the cabin. My money is that Gary made a mistake."

"But he seemed so sure. As a matter of fact, that wasn't even something I asked him. He just let it drop very casually."

"I'm not saying he was lying. In these sorts of circumstances, you've got to remember the setup. It was dark, he was running down a street that's not that well lit, and he glanced up at the house and *thought* he saw an empty garage. The door could have been down, and from his position on the street he just misinterpreted what he was seeing." The sheriff spread out his hands. "An honest mistake."

Leah's hopes that she had discovered something that would free Rafael took a dive. Nevertheless, she persisted. "You said you'd check—"

"Like a dog with a bone, aren't you? Don't worry, Leah. I'll talk to both men and let you know what I find out."

"Thank you."

Rafael's black eyes had grown dull, and his brown skin held an unhealthy pallor. Leah ran her hand down his cheek with a loving caress. "It hurts me to see you locked up like this."

"I need to leave this place," he said simply.

It was the closest he'd come—or would come—to breaking down in front of her, and she felt helpless to comfort him. "Trying to find out who really killed Sheila has been the hardest and most important thing I've ever done, and I'm not sure I've made any progress at all. Every time I think I've discovered something, it turns out to be a dead end."

"Perhaps one of those dead ends will open up soon and show you the way."

"Is there anything else you can tell me, Rafael?"

"Just this one thing. You have great strength, and you have the pearls. You will succeed. I trust you."

"About those pearls," she began.

He drew her to him, and cradled her against him with arms and hands still powerful no matter the state of his spirit. "Zarah has told you all you need to know. Now I want to hear about the man with the cinnamon hair."

"He's wonderful. I love him. And he says he loves me, but . . ."

"Pretty little girl," Rafael murmured softly, threading his long fingers through her hair, "you've known so much hurt in your life, you can't bring yourself to believe that lasting happiness might finally be yours."

"Rafael is a tough man," Leah told Stephen later on that night as they sat out on his deck. "But keeping him locked away as they are is a crime against his soul. He tells me not to worry. Zarah tells me not to worry. But they and all the Gypsies are worried. There has been only melancholy music being played in the Gypsy camp the last few days, and there has been no dancing."

"Let me get Rafael a lawyer. I'll bring in the best I can find."

"Rafael wouldn't allow it."

"Then let me hire a team of investigators. They'll scour this town until they find something."

"They'd find nothing because this town would close up tighter than a nuclear submarine."

He grinned wryly. "So what's new? Sunnyvale hasn't struck me as open up to now."

"But we've learned things, and I think when we find out who moved the car, we'll know who murdered Sheila."

"I hate to say this, Leah, but what the sheriff said made sense."

"Maybe that's why I don't believe it."

"Okay, let's say you're right, and the car was moved. Let's come at it from another angle. Instead of *who* moved the car, let's ask *how* the car was moved."

She looked at him with interest. "That's a good question."

"Thank you."

"Sheila's keys were found beside her body, so whoever moved it didn't use her keys. Therefore, he or she would have had to use another set or hot-wire it."

"We've discussed the possibility of a car thief and dismissed the idea," he said thoughtfully. "But Robert would have had a set of keys to her car."

"That's right," she said, sitting forward, then had a thought that made her excitement drain away. "Or Gary could have hot-wired it."

"And as we've noted before, both of those men seemed to have been hit hard by Sheila's death."

She toyed with the pearl necklace. "I don't know. At the time I didn't think either of them was acting."

"I had the same impression, but guilt is a great incentive to act well."

"I realize that now, and one of them had to have killed her."

Stephen reached across the table and took her

hand. "Well, we've made progress. We've decided that the killer has to be one of two people."

She looked at him and said very quietly, "Have I told you lately how having you by my side has made everything infinitely easier." In one easy, natural motion, she rose from her chair and transferred to his, curling onto his lap and wrapping her arms around his neck. "Thank you, Stephen, for being with me through all of this."

"This was exactly where I wanted to be. All I had to do was talk you into letting me stay."

She smiled. "You were very convincing."

"Have I convinced you that I love you?"

She rested her forehead against his. Her silence lasted so long, Stephen began to worry, but he remained quiet and waited.

"I think I do believe," she said at last. "I'm just not sure *why* I do."

"Does it matter?" he asked, his voice rough and uneven as he tried to contain his happiness lest it frighten her.

She lifted her head away from his and looked down at the necklace she wore. In ancient times pearls were worshiped as moon symbols and harbingers of good fishing and safety on the water. No other gem seemed to hold such a powerful mystique. These particular pearls possessed a beauty that was magical. But were *they* magical? And if they were, what would happen if they were ever to disappear from her life . . . their life? She had no answer for either herself or for him.

"Will you stay with me tonight?" Stephen asked softly.

She nodded. "Out here."

Stephen placed quilts over a mound of pine needles for their bed, and together they lay down. Overhead, a soft wind whispered through the scented pine boughs. And they made sweet gentle love beneath the stars.

Eight

"I hate wearing the same clothes I wore the day before," Leah observed, wrinkling her nose at the dress she had had to put back on. She and Stephen were eating breakfast in the glassed-in sun-filled morning room that looked out over the lake. The water sparkled with light.

"There's an easy cure," he said with a smile. "Move all your things over here."

Her fork halted midway to her mouth.

He groaned. "I'm sorry, that was clumsy of me. But it can't come as a surprise to you that I want very much for us to be married."

Slowly she lowered her fork to her plate. "Let's don't talk about this right now."

He made an abrupt gesture. "Look, I'm making a mess of this, so I want to make sure you understand. A live-in relationship was not what I had in mind when I suggested that you move your things over here. It would be only a temporary measure so that we can be together while we decide what kind of wedding we want. Or, rather, what kind you want. I couldn't care less. All I want is you, and for the rest of my life."

"Stephen, I'm not ready."

"I don't understand," he said, momentarily thrown off balance. "Am I missing something? Last night you said that you finally believed that I love you."

She rubbed fretfully at her brow. "I do."

"And you've said that you love me. So what's keeping you from completely committing to us?"

"I told you. I'm just not ready."

He sat back in his chair and threw his napkin onto the table. "That doesn't make sense."

"I know."

The sadness in her voice made him all the more frustrated. But he had come to know her better than she thought, and he understood that at this point, pushing her would do no good. She had to come to things in her own way. The level of the coffee in his cup had lowered by half before he spoke again. "You're right. Now is not the time to talk about this. Rafael is still in jail. And there's the party this evening. I need to stay here at least part of the day. I have some work to do, and Mrs. Beacon and her people will have to be shown around."

Leah's eyes widened. "You asked Loretta Beacon to cater your party?"

"Well, yes. I inquired and was told she was the best. Why?"

She chuckled, feeling better now that the subject of their future had been dropped. "She's the *only* caterer in town."

"Is there something I should know? She seemed very enthusiastic when we talked yesterday, and she assured me that she'd create something really special for the party, but, now that I think about it, I have to admit that there was something about her that bothered me."

Leah nodded. "She's flaky."

"Oh, good, Leah, *now* you tell me."

"I don't recall you asking. But don't worry. She'll come through for you in the end. Loretta is a wonderful cook. It's just that she has this sort of inner catering muse that she listens to, and sometimes that catering muse leads her astray."

A look of foreboding came over his face. "Inner catering muse?"

"I think it's a very good idea for you to stay here and make sure things run smoothly. The last wedding she catered, she made six different three-tiered cakes before she was satisfied. They were all quite beautiful, I understand, but the wedding guests saw and ate only one."

"What happened to the other five?"

"We had a lot of fat, happy little birds around town that winter."

"Ah."

"Also the bride and her family had planned a sit-down dinner after the wedding. When they arrived after the wedding, they were confronted by an hors d'oeuvre buffet. When they asked her why, she replied that the crab hadn't spoken to her as a main course; rather, it had insisted on being an hors d'oeuvre."

"I'll stay here."

She laughed and got to her feet.

"Why don't you stay here too?"

Even though his tone was entirely casual, she didn't miss his concern. "Don't worry. For the moment, at least, I've run out of ideas. As much as I hate to, I've got to wait and see what the sheriff's investigation turns up. So I'll visit Zarah and then spend the rest of the day at the station."

He rose and took her into his arms. "Good. What time shall I pick you up this evening?"

She gave a groan of dread and buried her face against his chest.

He pressed a kiss on top of her head. "You're going to be surprised how easy this party will be for you."

"I'll bet."

"You're going to have fun, you'll see, because I won't give up until you do."

With a smile she tilted her head back and looked up at him. "And you never give up."

"Not about something I care about. Now, about that time . . . Everyone should start arriving by around seven, seven-thirty, somewhere in there."

"And you'll need to be here. Why don't I just make my way over by myself?"

"Oh, no. Not on your life."

"Do I detect a distinct lack of trust?"

"You detect a distinct and definite love."

She sighed. In the face of such sincerity she had no argument. "Then come over whenever you like."

Leah spent the day just as she'd told Stephen she would. But she couldn't keep her mind on any one subject or project for long. At four she gave up the effort and went home.

But once there, she couldn't relax. The coming ordeal of the party loomed large in her mind. She took a long hot bath and then gave herself a manicure. Finally, when she couldn't think of anything else to do, she got out the beautiful dress that Zarah had made for her and put it on.

Looking at herself in the mirror, she thought once again that she'd never seen such an incredible dress. The strapless bodice of star-shaped magenta-colored spangles glinted with reflective brightness. The magenta, pink, and fuchsia silk paneled skirt clung seductively to the curves of her hips, then floated in uneven lengths to around her knees.

She brushed her hair until it hung in dark glossy waves around her face and halfway down her back. Then she wrapped the pearl necklace once around her neck and let the rest of it fall down over the magenta stars to the silk skirt.

When she ventured a look into the mirror, she saw that the pearls had added their special magic to both her and the dress. *I'm beautiful*, she thought, and tentatively reached out to touch her image.

A great sense of relief flooded over her. Maybe for once in her life she would fit in.

It was Stephen's knock on the front door that brought her out of her reverie. And the stunned expression on his face when he saw her confirmed her expectations.

Delighted by his reaction, she laughed and circled the living room with a series of barefooted pirouettes. The silk-paneled skirt and the pearls swung outward, free of her. When she stopped, they wrapped around her body, embracing her, then slid back into place. "Zarah made the dress for me. Isn't it wonderful?"

"You're what's wonderful. You look like some earthbound angel encircled with colored lights. Come here."

She ran eagerly into his arms. He was wearing a dark brown suit, pale beige shirt, and brown, gold, and mahogany tie. He smelled vaguely woodsy, she thought, and very masculine. And suddenly she wanted him.

At the first touch of their lips the fire began.

He groaned. "It's been a hell of a long day without you."

"I should have stayed with you," she agreed, and parted her lips for his kiss. A quick, hot response flooded her veins when their tongues met and tangled. The need was piercing and its intensity almost swept her away. Her arms wrapped around the back of his neck as she held on to him and centered herself in him and the feelings they were making.

Without asking, he unzipped her dress and took a step backward, relieving the pressure of their bodies to allow the dress to slide to the floor. Then he scooped her into his arms and turned in the direction of the doorway.

"What about the party?" she murmured, and glided her tongue along his jaw.

"We have time. Hell, we'll *make* time." He tightened his grip on her so that her breasts were pressed into his chest.

Suddenly she stiffened. "Wait, I don't want the pearls to get broken."

Stephen started for the bedroom. "To hell with the pearls."

She managed to get the necklace off and toss it onto a chair right before he strode out of the living room and into the bedroom. With her mind at ease regarding the necklace, she wrapped her arms around his neck. And when he lowered her to the bed, she didn't release him.

"I have to get these clothes off," he muttered, tortured by even the thought of the seconds he'd have to be physically parted from her.

"No," she whispered, agonized by the same thought as he. "Don't leave me." She kissed every part of his face she could reach, needing the taste, touch, and sensation of him.

"Leah—" Her lips came in contact with his mouth, and he gave up. He lowered himself to the bed beside her and kissed her with a hot, savage pressure. The heat that licked through him was scorching. He wanted more than anything to give her pleasure, but he wasn't sure he'd be able to. All he could think of was taking her as hard and as fast as he could, but she deserved such care. He tore his mouth from hers and closed his lips over the peak of her breast. "You taste like sugar and fire," he whispered hoarsely, and took a hard draw on her nipple.

It felt as if flames were eating their way down the center of her body to her thighs. Urgently she pushed at his jacket and without taking his mouth from her, he lifted slightly and slid out of the burdensome garment. Hungering for contact with his skin, she tore at his shirt and managed to separate it from the waistband of his pants. With a moan she spread her fingers across his back.

Her touch was almost too much for him. He slid his hand down her body to beneath her panties and found the wetness and the heat. His breath came raggedly as he stroked her.

She arched against him, and he pressed her back down with the heel of his hand. Her spasms of release began; he felt them and brought his lips down hard on hers. Soon she was cresting again, and her untamed response drove him to near madness. He thrust his tongue deep into her mouth time after time, but the act offered no satisfaction, and he knew he had endured all he could.

He unzipped his pants and entered her.

She cried out as exquisite pleasure bolted through

her with a violence that left her weak. He gave her his power, pushing it into her body until she twisted and bucked beneath him. And then they both went out of control.

She stirred and felt his arms around her. He breathed in and smelled the dark velvet-flowered scent of her and the fragrance of their mingled passion. Their lids fluttered up at the same time, and they stared into each other's eyes.

"I love you," he whispered, and stroked her face tenderly.

"I love you," she murmured, and kissed his fingertips.

"Whatever's bothering you, Leah, I'll wait for you to work it out. We have no differences that cannot be overcome. Do you believe that?"

"I want to, it's just that . . ."

Their eyes widened simultaneously, as they exclaimed, "The *party*." They rolled off separate sides of the bed and hit the floor running.

"Everyone's probably already there," he said, shoving his shirt into his pants and zipping them. "Run a comb through your hair, and I'll bring your dress to you."

Leah rushed to the bathroom to freshen up. Then, back in her room, she grabbed up the brush and pulled it through her tangled sable-brown hair.

Stephen dashed back into the bedroom carrying the dress. One look at her standing in front of her dressing table, naked except for a fresh pair of panties, and he groaned. "You need to put this dress on right away or we'll never get to the party."

She took the dress from him and slipped it on, knots tying and untying in her stomach. "The way I feel right now, that wouldn't be such a bad idea."

"I know you must be nervous," he said, helping her zip her dress, "but I'm going to be right there with you. They can't wait to meet you."

"You *told* them about me?"

"I love you, Leah. Naturally I wanted to tell my friends."

"Naturally," she said, her voice faint and carrying notes of doom. She turned back to the dressing table and hastily refreshed her light makeup.

Behind her, he finished straightening his clothes and retrieved his jacket. "Where are your shoes?"

She pointed toward the closet. "In there—the high-heel magenta ones."

He grabbed the shoes in one hand, her hand in the other, and pulled her out of the room. "Let's go."

It didn't take them long to reach the lake. Leah sat quietly beside Stephen, still slightly dizzy and disoriented from the incredible passion they had just shared. The party was going strong when he pulled his car into the driveway. A few of his friends were standing out on the front porch, and they waved and called to him. He opened his door, and Leah slipped out on his side.

Before starting up to the house, he bent and pressed a reassuring kiss to her lips, still slightly swollen from his lovemaking. "You look beautiful, Leah. In fact, I don't think I've ever seen anyone look more magical."

"Magical?" She went cold with horror, and her hand flew to her neck. *It was bare.* "Oh, no, Stephen! I've got to go back to my house! I left the pearl necklace there!"

He hesitated. "I know that necklace means a lot to you, but you don't need it. You look beautiful without it. I told you—"

She clutched at his arm, close to hysteria. "Please, just give me your car keys. I'll drive myself."

"Stephen," one of his friends called. "Come on up. We're all waiting to meet your Leah."

Watching her closely, he put his arm around her shoulder and drew her firmly to his side. "They've seen us. You can't leave now. Come on," he said, leading her up the path. "Everything will be fine. I promise."

Unreasoning and overmastering fear came crashing down on her and took her in its grip. Her chest went tight until she couldn't draw a breath. Her heart beat painfully and erratically. She searched frantically, but she couldn't find that still-peaceful place within her. She was totally helpless to escape the disaster that awaited.

On the porch, faceless people surrounded them. Stephen introduced her, but she heard no names. They said things to her, but she couldn't hear. And then they were inside the house. She blinked against the lights, but she couldn't see anything or anyone.

She needed the pearls.

Without the pearls she had no confidence or beauty.

Without them she had no magic.

"Leah, this is Jed and Sarah Kosta, two very good friends of mine."

Her hand was taken in a firm handshake. "It's a pleasure to meet the lady who did what every woman in Dallas has been trying to do for years—make Stephen Tanner fall in love," a deep male voice said.

A soft, lovely voice chimed in. "And you're just as beautiful as Stephen told us you were. We're delighted for both of you."

Leah's gaze slowly focused on a petite blond-haired woman who was smiling at her.

Stephen spoke again. "And this is Mary and Carl Harris. Carl cheats at poker, but otherwise I like him."

Carl Harris, a tall, brown-haired man, threw back his head and laughed heartily. "I absolutely do not cheat, Leah, but there are times I'd like to take the chair and break it over Stephen's head. He's too damned good."

Mary Harris, an attractive woman of about forty, grinned. "Carl and Stephen are both very competitive, but I'm sure you already know that about Stephen. I hope you don't mind us coming down like this, but once we heard about you, we couldn't resist. Please say you'll come into Dallas soon. I'd love to show you around."

"For heaven's sake, Mary, quit talking so I can ask her where she got that incredible dress." Leah's gaze switched to a cheerful raven-haired woman of about thirty-five. "Hi, I'm Jessica Blakemore, and if you tell me you can buy clothes like that in Sunnyvale, I'm moving here immediately."

"A friend of Leah's made it for her," Stephen said, "and none of you can move here. This place is my retreat, and I'm guarding it with my life."

"That's very selfish of you, Stephen," Sarah Kosta said. "Sunnyvale even seems to have a first-class caterer. The food and drinks are wonderful."

"Loretta and I decided on foods from the Southwest," Stephen said to Leah. "Nachos, fajitas, and the like, and I made her stick to the menu."

"Good food," Carl Harris echoed in his booming voice, "but I have to ask you about that ice sculpture over there. It looks sort of like a shrimp standing on its tail and wearing a sombrero."

Leah heard Stephen laugh. "That's what it is. Loretta is just learning to do ice sculpture. I figured if her inner catering muse was busy concentrating on the ice sculpture, she wouldn't have time to get creative with the food."

"Did you say inner catering muse?" Sarah Kosta asked.

"Tell me about your friend who sews such wonderful creations, Leah," Jessica Blakemore said.

Leah couldn't speak. Her throat burned with an awful dryness. Out of the corner of her eye she spied a waiter with a tray of drinks. With a stiff jerky movement she reached out, and her hand hit the edge of the tray, causing the tray to tip. The waiter took a step backward, trying to regain the tray's perfect balance, but to no avail. The drinks slid off and smashed to the floor, shattering the crystal glasses and sending various types of liquid flying.

"Are you all right, Leah?" Stephen asked urgently.

"I'm sorry," she managed to say.

"Don't be silly. There's nothing to be sorry for. Everything's fine. Let's just move away from this area so it can be cleaned."

As they walked to another part of the living room, with the six other people following them, Leah became aware that Stephen's arm had never left her shoulders since they'd entered the house. He'd told her he would stay by her side, and he was doing just that. But didn't he understand? She had to have the pearls. Tonight was going to be a disaster unless she went home to get them. She'd already managed to destroy a tray of drinks.

"Let me get you something to drink, Leah," Jed Kosta said. "What would you like?"

"Uh . . . ice water, please."

"Are you sure? Those boys over there at the bar are turning out some great margaritas."

"Ice water."

Leah jumped in surprise when the petite blond woman briefly squeezed her arm in sympathy. "Don't be nervous," she said softly. "Stephen loves you. That means we like you already."

Leah wet her lips. "Thank you. You're . . . uh . . . ?"

"Sarah. Sarah Kosta. And don't worry that you can't remember anyone's name. You'll be meeting a lot of new people tonight. We're only meeting one person."

"You're very kind." She turned to take the glass of water from Jed Kosta, bumped her hand against its side. Water sloshed onto his suit. "Oh!"

He laughed. "Now, now, it's only water, and it dries without a trace. Wish I'd invented it. Here, there's plenty left in the glass for you."

She took the offered glass and drank deeply of the cool water. Her throat immediately felt better. She cast a shy look around the group and felt Stephen give her shoulders a hug.

"I think I told you all that Leah is the manager of the local radio station here," he said proudly.

A chorus of yesses followed.

"I envy you, Leah," Jessica Blakemore said. "It sounds like a really interesting job. Oh, here's my husband. Darling, where have you been?"

"Just looking around." The slight, fair man held out his hand to Leah with a smile. "Hi, I'm Kirby. You have a remarkable face. I'd love to paint you."

Everyone laughed. His wife playfully punched his arm. "Kirby, you must learn to wait at least five minutes after meeting someone before you say something like that." Jessica turned to Leah. "I guess you've gathered by now that my husband is an artist."

"Of course," Leah murmured, "Kirby Blakemore. I've never been lucky enough to see one of your works except in photographs, but I think they're wonderful."

His eyes lit up with pleasure. "Then you will let me paint you?"

His wife punched him again. "It hasn't been five minutes yet. Stephen, I really like this bare look. No curtains. I think if I lived in a place like this, I'd do the same thing. We could tell as we drove up that you have a fantastic view."

Stephen answered Jessica, and Leah began to feel herself relax. It was true that she'd made some really awkward blunders, but these people still seemed to like her. She'd never once caught them looking at her as if she were strange. In fact, they were going out of their way to make her feel comfortable. Her hand went automatically to her bare neck. Maybe . . .

Her attention was suddenly caught by a man standing at the buffet table holding his throat, gasping for breath. Quickly she broke away from Stephen and moved toward the man. His eyes fixed on her, panic-stricken. Without saying a word, she moved behind him, placed her arms around him just below his rib cage, grasped her left wrist with her right hand, and exerted sudden strong pressure inward and upward. The man coughed, and a tortilla chip flew from his mouth.

"Are you all right?" she asked anxiously, moving back around him.

"Lord, how can I thank you?" he said, rubbing his throat. "I was scared to death. I thought I'd had it for sure. I couldn't get anyone's attention."

"I'm thankful I saw you. How do you feel now?"

The man nodded. "Fine, I think. I'll sit down though."

Stephen had come up behind her and he signaled to one of the waiters. "Get Mr. Dowell something to drink. Roy, do you think we should take you to the hospital?"

"No, and thanks to your lovely lady here, you won't have to take me to the morgue either. She was wonderful."

"You were," Stephen said softly, and kissed her cheek.

Several of the men went with Roy to sit with him. The women gathered around Leah.

"How did you know how to do that?" one asked.

She shrugged, amazed and pleased with herself. "I had read about the procedure, but I never knew if I'd be able to do it or not in a real emergency until I saw that man in distress."

The party continued. Stephen had hired several high school students who had their own band to play mariachi music, but they soon segued into soft rock, which was fine with everyone. Stephen's constant presence, plus the genuine warmth and friendliness of his friends, gradually put Leah at ease. So much so that late in the evening she'd relaxed enough to contemplate leaving Stephen's side, and she decided to go outside for some air.

"I'll be back in a minute," she whispered to him, and slipped from the circle of his arms.

Nine

A full moon was holding court over an absolutely clear night, Leah discovered as she made her way out back to the deck. Alone for the moment, she inhaled her fill of the pine-scented air, then smiled as she saw the small colored lights that had been strung around the railing.

She leaned her elbows on the railing and gazed back toward the house. The band was taking a break. Through the uncurtained windows she could see Stephen and his friends talking, laughing. They were a congenial group who seemed genuinely to like one another . . . and her.

Without the pearls.

True, she'd made some blunders, but anyone as nervous as she might have done the same stupid things.

"Leah."

A frown marred her smooth forehead. She turned to look toward the woods. Had someone just called her?

"Leah."

She peered through the moon-cast light to a tall, slim man standing at the edge of the woods. "Robert?"

He gestured for her to come to him. "I have some information that will help your friend."

She threw a hesitant glance at Stephen through the window.

"Come alone," he said. "I don't know any of those people, and I don't want to. Dammit, are you going to come out here, or am I going to leave?"

Her foot paused on the first step that led off the deck. "What kind of information do you have?"

"I know who killed my wife."

She wasn't blind to the danger of the situation. There was a fifty-fifty chance that *Robert* was the murderer. But for Rafael's sake she had to go to him and hear what he had to say. She would just need to be very careful. And it was reassuring to know that Stephen was just yards away, and if need be, she could run like the wind.

Robert was standing in front of a tall pine tree, and she stopped a distance that was halfway between him and the deck so that she was still visible from the house.

"Closer, Leah."

"I'm close enough. I can hear just fine." She saw his body change position, as if he might be thinking of leaving, and she quickly tried to distract him. "How did you know I was here?"

"Are you kidding? Loretta started broadcasting the news of the party as soon as she got the job."

"I see." Leah clasped her hands in front of her. "Okay, tell me. Who killed Sheila, because I know it wasn't Rafael."

"You're right," he said, his voice pitched low so that she had to take a couple of steps forward to hear him clearly. "But I sure as hell wish you weren't."

"Robert, you really didn't know about Sheila and Rafael, did you?"

He shook his head. "I told you, I considered our marriage good. When I saw her driving by my office that night, I had no idea where she was going."

"You *saw* her driving?" An excitement began to burn in the pit of her stomach. She'd been *right* about the car.

"I'd taken a little break from work and walked outside. I called to her, but she didn't hear me. So I got curious and jogged after her." He shook his head in disgust. "She'd told me she was going to stay home and do some needlework, and I'd believed her. I gave her everything she wanted. Everything."

Except love, approval, and respect, Leah thought, but didn't say it.

"When I realized where she was going, I got even more curious. I arrived at the cabin just a short time after she did, and I went in and confronted her."

He gave a low, harsh laugh that sent chills down Leah's spine and had her looking toward the house. A glimpse of Stephen bolstered her courage.

"Sheila was really upset to see me, and then she turned defiant. Said it was just as well that we have it out, and she told me about her and Gary Mercer. I couldn't believe it. I mean, I really couldn't *believe* that she'd been having an affair, and I hadn't even known it. God, I was furious. I told her she wasn't going to make a fool of me."

"It was *you*," she whispered, but he didn't hear.

"I took the two ends of that scarf and started pulling. I only meant to make her say she'd forget Mercer, but next thing I knew she was dead." He smiled crookedly. "You were so close to figuring it out, I knew it was only a matter of time before you did. Can you imagine, Leah, how shocked I was? My wife was dead, and I had *killed* her! To this day I have a hard time dealing with that."

He *hadn't* been acting, Leah realized, feeling as though her intuition had been vindicated. He had been stunned by the manner in which Sheila had died. And he hadn't known about Gary prior to that night. But only two things were important now. She needed to find out the rest of the story, and she had to lure him out of the woods. There was no doubt that the happenings of that night were a nightmare that constantly haunted him. He seemed obsessed with telling her the story. Maybe . . .

"If Sheila drove the car to the cabin, how did it get back to your house?" She took a step backward.

"Why did you have to figure out about the damned car?" he asked, almost snarling and taking a step out of the woods toward her. "It wouldn't even have occurred to most people to think of the car. I didn't for a while. You see, as soon as I realized Sheila was dead, I knew I had to leave fast. It seemed natural to take her car."

"But you didn't drive straight home, did you?" she asked, backing slowly.

His smile appeared eerily off balance in the white moonlight as unconsciously he drew closer to her. "You're very smart. But then, so was I. I decided to sneak the jewelry she was wearing into one of the Gypsy trailers. Everyone knows what dirty, lying thieves they are, and they were about to leave town. No one would have trouble believing that one of them killed Sheila for the jewelry."

The band had started to play again, making her aware that the music cut her chances of being heard if she screamed. She was also forced to raise her voice so that Robert could hear her. "How did you know which trailer was Rafael's?"

His lips drew back from his teeth in a laugh she could barely hear. "I didn't. Isn't it ironic? And so damned right. He deserves everything he's going to get."

Just a few more feet to the deck, Leah thought, taking two steps backward. He was following beautifully. "So then you drove home?"

He nodded. "And then I remembered that my

car was back at the office. So I jogged over there, taking the back way, of course, and got into the building without anyone seeing me." He was close enough now that she heard the laugh he gave this time, and it frightened her. "And right after I got there, I made sure the security guard saw me coming out of my office to get some coffee."

"You have to give yourself up, Robert."

"Why? You think confession is good for the soul?"

"You confessed to me."

"That's because you'll never tell anyone. Don't you understand? That's why I'm here. To kill you."

She wheeled for the deck, but she forgot to allow for her high heels, and one of the heels struck the forward edge of the step. Losing her balance, she fell forward. Robert grabbed her by the hair and yanked her upright. A sharp pain lanced through her head, and tears sprang to her eyes. She gave herself mere seconds to recover, then brought the spike of her high-heel shoe down hard on his instep. Robert let out a yelp, and his hold on her loosened. But when she tried to run, he snatched her back, wrapped her neck in an armlock, and began dragging her toward the woods.

Stephen was showing Jessica and Sarah the upstairs of the house and happened to glance out the window. His blood turned to ice at the sight of Robert Donaldson dragging Leah toward the woods.

Dear God, how was he ever going to get to her in time?

"Call the sheriff," he shouted to the two women, then sprinted for the stairway.

It had been a big mistake for her to think that if she stayed within sight of the house, she would be safe, Leah thought, engaged in the biggest fight of her life against panic and terror. But she couldn't die. She wouldn't. Not now, when the love and happiness for which she'd yearned all her life was about to be hers.

"Stop your damned squirming," Robert said, just short of the woods. He held her away from him, then brought a backhanded blow across her face. Stunned, she fell to the ground.

"You've got to die," Robert said, jerking her roughly upright and back to him. "Then everything will be all right. The sheriff will forget all about Sheila's death because he's got the Gypsy, and he'll never connect me with you."

Desperation gave her a surge of energy. Using all her strength, Leah jammed the heel of her hand upward into his nose. Both of his hands flew to his face. Blood gushed from his nose, and he dropped to his knees, crying out in agony.

Stephen rushed out the back door, down the stairs, and across the yard to Leah's side. "Dear Lord, are you hurt? What happened?"

She leaned against him, half sobbing. "Robert killed Sheila. He just told me everything."

He pulled her to him in a protective hold. All of the party had poured outside. "Take him out front and keep him there until the sheriff comes," he said over her head to two of the men. "Tell him Leah will be in tomorrow to make a statement."

She lifted her head. "Tonight," she said softly. "I don't want Rafael to have to spend one more minute than he has to in that awful place."

Stephen took her face in his hands, being careful of the mark already discoloring her cheek. "Are you sure you're up to it?"

"I'm sure."

Leah gave her statement, and in another room Robert broke down and confessed. When Rafael walked out of his cell, she was there waiting for him.

"Hello, pretty little girl."

She ran to him and his arms closed around her. For a long minute they were content in the happiness of the moment, then she drew back and smiled up at him. "I'm not so pretty. Did you see this bruise I've got on my face?"

A muscle moved in his jaw. "You have always been and will always be beautiful, Leah. It just makes me sick that you have so much as a mark of pain on you, and I grieve that you received the bruise helping me."

"I would have gone through much worse to help you."

He gently stroked a finger over the bruise. "What

you did was remarkable. You've finally realized the strength inside you. Now we must go tell Zarah everything that has happened."

Leah glanced over her shoulder at Stephen. "You go on. Stephen and I will be there shortly."

Rafael looked up at Stephen and slowly smiled. "That is a good idea."

In front of Leah's house Stephen turned the ignition key. He automatically reached for his door handle, but she stopped him with a hand on his arm.

"Let's just sit here for a few minutes. I need to catch my breath."

"All right." He studied her carefully. Other than occasionally touching her face, she didn't seem as if she felt bad. He wished she'd allowed him to take her to the doctor, but he decided to let the subject drop unless he noticed some sign that she felt worse. "I'm glad you wanted to be alone for a little while."

"So much has happened since we were last alone. I find it all amazing."

"I find you amazing," he said, and reached across the seat to draw her to his side. "You were wonderful tonight, but let me tell you something, if you ever put yourself in danger like that again, I'll . . ." Words failed him.

She smiled. "But everything worked out all right, didn't it?"

"Yes, thank heaven."

"Rafael is finally free as he was meant to be."

"Thanks to you and your persistence."

"You helped too."

"Not that much."

"More than you know," she murmured. "I was going to people for information, people who under normal circumstances I would never have had the courage to approach. And I was able to fight my way out of fear and anxiety attacks that only a few weeks ago would have sent me into full-scale withdrawal."

"You would have done the very same things alone. Look what you did tonight. You were clearly terrified, but you went into a party of strangers and completely won them over."

"They were nice."

"Granted. But their being nice or my being present didn't stop you from saving Roy Dowell's life."

She shrugged it off, even though she felt a glow of pride. "That was something I did without thinking."

"Exactly. And then you went out and confronted a murderer. He was going to kill you, but you put him out for the count."

"Not out for the count."

"You incapacitated him. Besides being in an incredible amount of pain, he couldn't see, and he couldn't breathe out of his nose. You did it all, and you did it without the pearls."

She stared at him. "You understood, didn't you?"

He nodded. "I knew you were confused about the pearls and Zarah's prediction and how they affected us. You'll never know the agony I went through when you asked me to take you back home. My heart told me to take you; my head told me to let you learn how wonderful you were on your own without the pearls. But I had faith in you. All I had to do was wait for you to learn to have faith in yourself."

"You were taking an awful gamble."

"Not really. I told you all along. The magic is in you."

"In us," she said softly. "In us."

He kissed her long and deeply, and despite the gentleness, the fire came. Leah relished the feeling. Yes, they would always have the fire, but now they also had their love, and the fire was stronger for it. It was with great reluctance that she ended the kiss. "The Gypsies will be leaving, and I want to say good-bye."

He smiled tenderly at her. "That's fine. We have the rest of our lives to kiss and to share the magic."

She leaned forward and briefly brushed her lips across his, silently agreeing with him. "Let's go inside for a minute. I want to see if I can cover up this bruise with some makeup. I don't want Zarah to be upset."

He nodded.

Inside, she passed through the living room on her way to the bedroom. But at the door to the hall she paused and looked back at the big easy chair. "That was the chair I threw the pearls onto before you carried me to bed."

He grinned. "Really? I didn't notice."

"But they're not there." She bent over the chair and ran her hands down the sides of the cushion. Then she lifted the cushion. "Where are they, Stephen?"

"Maybe they fell underneath it." Stephen shifted the chair out of the way.

She straightened, realization of what had happened dawning. "Stephen, the pearls have *disappeared*."

"I'll call the sheriff."

"No, wait." Staring down at the chair, she chewed on her bottom lip. "It's all right. Zarah told me that one day they would disappear again."

"Disappear? They've obviously been *stolen*, Leah."

"Have they?" she asked.

"What else could possibly have happened to them?"

She went to him and put her arms loosely around his neck. "Stop trying to make sense out of this, Stephen, and just accept that they're gone."

"But—"

"I'll miss wearing them. What woman wouldn't? They were incredible. But I don't *need* them anymore. Neither do the Gypsies. And hopefully it will be a long, long time before the pearls come to them again."

He slowly shook his head. "You're as mystical

and as mysterious as the pearls, Leah, and I love you with all my heart. Marry me, live with me, never stop loving me."

"Yes, Stephen, oh, yes."

The Gypsies danced and sang around their big campfire, their celebration lasting all night. At dawn Leah and Stephen waved good-bye to them.

"I'll miss them," she murmured, "but they'll be back."

"And we'll be here waiting for them."

"Yes, we will."

"One of the hottest and most prolific writers in romance today."
— *USA Today*

MISTRESS

Available in paperback by the *New York Times* bestselling author

AMANDA QUICK

With stories rife with wicked humor, daring intrigue, and heart-stopping passion, Amanda Quick has become a writer unmatched in the field of romantic fiction. Now the author of seventeen New York Times bestselling novels offers another unforgettable tale as a proper spinster embarks on a delicious masquerade and a handsome earl finds himself tangling with the most exotic and captivating mistress London has ever known.

DANGEROUS
TO KISS
by Elizabeth Thornton

"A major, major talent . . . a genre superstar."
—*Rave Reviews*

Handsome, kind, and unassuming, Mr. Gray seemed the answer to Deborah Weyman's prayers. For once she accepted the position he offered, she would finally be safe from the notorious Lord Kendal, a man she had good reason to believe had murdered her former employer—and was now after her. But there were certain things about Mr. Gray that Deborah should have noticed: the breadth of his shoulders, the steel in his voice, the gleam in his uncommonly blue eyes—things that might have warned her that Mr. Gray was no savior but a very dangerous man.

LONG NIGHT MOON

by the spectacular

Theresa Weir

"Theresa Weir's writing is poignant, passionate and powerful . . . will capture the hearts of readers."
—*New York Times* bestselling author Jayne Ann Krentz

With her rare insight into the human heart, Theresa Weir creates tender, emotionally compelling, powerfully satisfying love stories. Now the author whom Romantic Times praises as "a fresh and electrifying voice in romantic fiction," offers LONG NIGHT MOON, a novel that touches on the nationally important issue of domestic violence and affirms the power of love to heal the deepest sorrows.

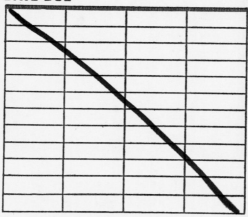

International Aspects
of Civil Strife

Gabriel A. Almond, *The Appeals of Communism*

Gabriel A. Almond and James S. Coleman, editors, *The Politics of the Developing Areas*

Gabriel A. Almond and Sidney Verba, *The Civic Culture: Political Attitudes and Democracy in Five Nations*

Cyril E. Black and Thomas P. Thornton, editors, *Communism and Revolution: The Strategic Uses of Political Violence*

Robert J. C. Butow, *Tojo and the Coming of the War*

Bernard C. Cohen, *The Political Process and Foreign Policy: The Making of the Japanese Peace Settlement*

Bernard C. Cohen, *The Press and Foreign Policy*

Percy E. Corbett, *Law in Diplomacy*

Charles De Visscher, *Theory and Reality in Public International Law*, translated by P. E. Corbett

Frederick S. Dunn, *Peace-making and the Settlement with Japan*

Herman Kahn, *On Thermonuclear War*

W. W. Kaufmann, editor, *Military Policy and National Security*

Klaus Knorr, *The War Potential of Nations*

Klaus Knorr, editor, *NATO and American Security*

Klaus Knorr and Sidney Verba, editors, *The International System: Theoretical Essays*

Lucian W. Pye, *Guerrilla Communism in Malaya*

James N. Rosenau, *National Leadership and Foreign Policy: A Case Study in the Mobilization of Public Support*

Rolf Sannwald and Jacques Stohler, *Economic Integration: Theoretical Assumptions and Consequences of European Unification*, translated by Herman F. Karreman

Richard L. Sklar, *Nigerian Political Parties: Power in an Emergent African Nation*

Glenn H. Snyder, *Deterrence and Defense*

Sidney Verba, *Small Groups and Political Behavior: A Study of Leadership*

Myron Weiner, *Party Politics in India*

International Aspects
of Civil Strife

EDITED BY

JAMES N. ROSENAU

PRINCETON, NEW JERSEY

PRINCETON UNIVERSITY PRESS

1964

Acknowledgments

SEVERAL of the papers in this symposium were revised subsequent to having been discussed at staff meetings of the Center of International Studies of Princeton University. We are thus pleased to record our appreciation of the helpful criticisms offered by Gil C. AlRoy, Davis B. Bobrow, Harry Eckstein, Andrew C. Janos, Peter Paret, Charles Tilly, Sidney Verba, and Karl Von Vorys. A special word of thanks is due Klaus Knorr, the director of the Center, whose support facilitated completion of the symposium and whose substantive comments on the various chapters were particularly useful. The editor also wishes to express gratitude to his wife, Norah, for her help on Chapters 1 and 3 and Appendix A.

None of the foregoing persons nor the Center itself is responsible for the final form of any of the chapters. The editor and the authors should be held to account for any flaws that may yet remain in their respective contributions.

Chapter 9 originally appeared as a publication of The Council on Religion and International Affairs and we are grateful to the Council for permission to reprint it here.

JAMES N. ROSENAU

New Brunswick, New Jersey
July 29, 1963

v

Contents

vii

International Aspects
of Civil Strife

CHAPTER 1

Introduction

☆

BY JAMES N. ROSENAU

LIKE most symposia, this one lacks formal coherence. Indeed, the varying levels and styles of analysis reflected in the eight essays are one of its distinguishing features.

Often, however, good and justifiable reasons underlie the incoherence of symposia. In this case the diverseness of the essays springs from the nature of the undertaking. The subject is so broad and unexplored that seven authors can hardly be expected to converge upon the same set of problems and to cast their approaches at the same level of analysis.

The breadth of the subject results from the fact that both international and domestic affairs fall within our scope. A focus upon the international aspects of internal war requires us to concern ourselves with the convergence of two sets of phenomena that are ordinarily treated separately. Most students of foreign affairs hold domestic variables constant. They have enough to study without probing deeply the national sources of international behavior. Likewise, most students of domestic matters attempt to achieve a modicum of simplicity by ignoring international variables or controlling for their effects. No such delineation was possible here, however. The international aspects of internal wars cannot be analyzed apart from the conflicts that foster them. For, as several of the essays emphasize, what happens abroad is inescapably a function of what happens within strife-ridden societies and, conversely, the dynamics of internal wars are conditioned, perhaps even sustained, by external events. The interplay between the two sets of variables is continuous and complex, leaving the analyst no alternative but to examine a broad range of political and social processes, from subnational to national to international.

Nor can we say that violence serves to delimit our focus. To

1

be sure, phenomena involving the use or threat of domestic violence are the first to attract our attention, but this does not permit us to circumscribe our interests and ignore nonviolent phenomena. The international aspects of civil strife cannot be meaningfully analyzed unless one seeks comparisons with the external ramifications of civil tranquillity. Further, since the process by which civil tranquillity collapses into civil strife is itself linked to international variables, nonviolent phenomena may compel attention long before the scene is marred by violence. In short, the international aspects of internal war are all-encompassing. The editor thus finds himself more impressed with the few overlaps that link the essays than with the many gaps that separate them.

The enormity of the subject would be less awesome if more of its various dimensions had been previously subjected to research. Aside from topical and historical discussions of particular internal wars, however, the interrelationship of civil strife and international affairs has never been the subject of systematic inquiry outside the Communist literature. Quite apart from their international aspects, in fact, it is only recently that internal wars themselves have been seriously studied.[1] For reasons that are obscure and elusive, political and social scientists have tended to treat social disorder as an aberration of social order and therefore have not directly examined, either theoretically or empirically, the subject of internal war. Revolution, for example, is not ignored by social theorists; but, as Harry Eckstein points out, neither is it located at the center of their theoretical foundations.[2] Eckstein contends that a primary reason for this relative neglect of the phenomena of internal war lies in "the intellectual world of the social scientist." Stated briefly, he argues that the subject of internal war has not

---

[1] See Harry Eckstein (ed.), *Internal War: Problems and Approaches* (New York: Free Press of Glencoe, 1964).

[2] Harry Eckstein, "Toward the Theoretical Study of Internal War," *ibid.*, pp. 2–3.

been processed for theoretical examination and rigorous quantitative treatment: "In consequence, social theorists confronted by the subject are understandably at sea—like shoemakers working not on leather but an ox." [3]

If the domestic aspects of internal war have yet to be processed for theoretical and empirical analysis, research on its international aspects can hardly be expected to be more advanced. On the contrary, since the various fields of international study lag far behind their domestic counterparts, students of foreign affairs have been perhaps even more neglectful, if that is possible, of internal war as an analytic focus. As noted above, writers on foreign affairs tend to hold domestic variables constant. This tendency is especially pronounced in the case of those variables pertaining to more profound social processes. Governmental decision-making personnel and processes do receive some recognition as central determinants of international action, but conceptualizations of international life that accord a prominent place to socio-economic processes which generate, initiate, and maintain internal wars are virtually nonexistent.

In part, of course, neglect of the international aspects of internal war can be attributed to the absence of well-developed theories and well-processed data pertaining to internal war itself. Perhaps students of foreign affairs would be more inclined to probe such matters if their colleagues on the domestic side had made theoretical and empirical materials available and had thereby raised questions which could be resolved only through an exploration of external variables.

The concept of national sovereignty is perhaps another reason for the lack of research into the subject. Students of foreign affairs have long treated sovereign states as the primary, if not the only, international actors and thus they adhered, explicitly or otherwise, to the view that international relations are essentially relations among governments. Consequently, it has been traditional to assume that events within a society only

[3] *ibid.*, p. 5.

3

become relevant international phenomena if and when officials of that society are affected by them and adjust their foreign policies accordingly. Similarly, in the field of international law both practitioners and jurists have for centuries asserted that the domestic life of nations is national business outside the jurisdiction of either international agencies or international law. This idea is clearly enunciated in Article 2, Paragraph 7, of the United Nations Charter: "Nothing contained in the present Charter shall authorize the United Nations to intervene in matters which are essentially within the domestic jurisdiction of any state or shall require the Members to submit such matters to settlement under the present Charter. . . ."

Nor have the newer, more theoretical formulations of international politics stimulated attention to the external aspects of internal wars. While the recasting of international phenomena in terms of "systems" has had a salutary effect on research in the field, it has at the same time tended to close off certain lines of inquiry. A systems approach focuses on equilibrium and order, thereby drawing attention away from phenomena which, like internal wars, move international systems in disorderly directions. Like sovereignty, moreover, the systems concept necessitates the assumption that all international actors have similar characteristics and motives. Wars internal to a member of an international system serve to upset the rules by which the system is sustained. Hence it is only natural that students of systemic processes are inclined to view every international actor as speaking with a united voice—that of its government—rather than being represented by two or more domestic factions, each claiming authority to engage in international action.

Whatever the reasons that explain this lack of attention to the international aspects of internal war (and there are no doubt many more than we have mentioned), the situation deserves remedy. Violence within societies is too widespread a phenomenon not to become a major focus for both basic and ap-

4

plied research. In recent years internal wars would appear to be widening in scope and mounting in frequency. Hence the more theoretically inclined analyst cannot help but feel challenged by the need to account for the increasing role of internal wars in international affairs, and the more practically oriented observer can only experience a great sense of urgency over the new policy questions which are presented. Modern technology has rendered the globe smaller and smaller, and, as the world shrinks, events in one country become increasingly relevant for every other nation. What were once strictly "domestic matters" are now quickly transformed into global issues. Consider the restless, sometimes violent movement of American society toward equal rights for its Negro citizens: not only is each event in this dramatic episode a landmark in the nation's history; it is also a major occurrence in the cold war. And much the same is true of the fight for independence in Angola, the explosive strife in South Africa, the struggle for coherence in the Congo, the clash of Castro and anti-Castro forces in South America—to mention only a few current situations that illustrate the international importance of domestic conflict. The technological revolution, moreover, has hastened the pace of social change in many nations that do not yet have institutions which enable a peaceful adjustment. Consequently, the more rapid the rate of social change becomes, the greater the likelihood of intrasocietal violence. The insufficiency of historical data makes it impossible to demonstrate that internal wars are more frequent today than in any earlier period; but, if the frequency of such conflicts is primarily a function of the pace of social change, such a conclusion would certainly appear to be highly plausible.

Even if the frequency of internal wars remained constant, however, there would still be a compelling reason to probe their international aspects. The vast revolution in military technology has profoundly altered the way in which great powers relate to one another. The advent of thermonuclear weapons has reduced the probability of major nations launching direct and all-out attacks on each other. Instead, the new weapons technology has forced the great powers to test each other's strength and contest each other's influence through involvement in the internal wars of small neutral nations. Thus internal wars always pose the potential danger of breeding larger conflicts. The Spanish Civil War and the more recent contests in Korea, Laos, and Vietnam amply demonstrate the emerging geopolitical and strategic significance of internal wars. Indeed, if the world is to avoid an all-out nuclear holocaust, it may require agreements among the great powers limiting the conduct and scope of internal wars.

Given the importance, the breadth, and the unexplored character of the subject, it seemed inappropriate and arbitrary to attempt to organize a symposium within a tightly knit framework and to require contributors to adopt a particular approach. Rather it seemed likely that the international aspects of internal war would emerge more clearly if the authors were left free to apply their distinct modes of analysis to whatever aspects of the topic they preferred. No initial effort was made to specify what kinds of phenomena consitute international aspects of internal wars. We did not even start with a precise definition of internal wars. Brief *coups d'état* in Latin America were considered as much grist for the mill as were full-fledged and lengthy struggles in Southeast Asia. Nineteenth-century rural uprisings were regarded as no less relevant than modern urban riots.

Nor were all the authors ever convened at the same time for a discussion of their papers. Seven of the papers were written as part of a larger inquiry into internal war undertaken by the Center of International Studies at Princeton, but only three of them were formally considered and criticized at the Center's weekly staff meetings. Indeed, most of the chapters were written at different times over a period of four years. This lack of coordination stems from the fact that the symposium was an afterthought. Initially the Internal War Project at the Center was designed to examine internal war as a self-contained and self-generating phenomenon. No special focus on its international aspects was planned, since these were viewed as being of secondary importance. Early in the deliberations of the Project, however, it was argued—mainly by George Modelski, whose written expression of the argument constitutes Chapter 2—that external variables were primary determinants of the onset, course, and termination of internal wars, that to study such phenomena in isolation from international politics is to engage in oversimplification, perhaps even distortion. While the main direction of the Internal War Project was not deterred by this view and has resulted in several publications in which the international aspects are held constant, it was recognized that the argument was not without merit and ought to receive more extensive consideration. An initial survey of the subject was then undertaken (see Appendix A) and yielded the clear-cut finding that the international aspects of internal war were numerous indeed. Consequently, this symposium was conceived.

The result of this unpremeditated genesis is, as was noted at the outset, considerable diversity. Some of the essays are abstract and deductive. Others are empirical and inductive. One of the authors attempts to develop a new model to cope with the subject; three undertake to derive relevant hypotheses from previously existing models; and the other four identify and assess changing historical patterns. While two of the essays are passionate and emphasize certain values, the other six authors seek to maintain an analytic distance between themselves and their materials. Only one chapter contains quantified data. Three deal with policy aspects of the subject, whereas the remainder are more encompassing in their coverage.

This variability, however, need not hinder what the reader derives from the symposium. Symposia cannot and are not intended to have the coherence of a work written by a single author. Rather, the test of coherence ought to be applied to each essay in a symposium and a collection of eight essays thus ought to be treated as if, in a sense, it were eight books, each independent and self-contained, with its own objectives, methods, and conclusions. Unlike eight books chosen at random, however, symposia have a common focus and offer an opportunity for comparison. The essays can be read both for what they contain as separate efforts and for the light they shed on each other. They enable the reader to identify both the settled and the controversial dimensions of the material. Viewed in this way, the contradictions of style and emphasis no longer seem hindering, but instead provide an opportunity to clarify one's own conception of the subject. It is possible, in short, to look beyond the variability of symposia and take advantage of the wider coverage and expertise which they afford.

Furthermore, and far more important, in the editor's view this symposium does succeed in fulfilling its main objective— that of starting to bridge the gap between international studies and the phenomenon of internal war. Despite the variability —and in some ways because of it—we have managed to show the relevance of internal war to some of the more important approaches to the field. At the very least we have identified, in one or another of the essays, sociological, systemic, legal, political, strategic, and moral links between internal wars and international processes. Several authors went even further and found ways of integrating the linkages into a broader analytic framework. Perhaps the most all-embracing and integrative essay is George Modelski's analysis of "The International Relations of Internal War." Parsonian in its orientation, this essay is the only one to develop a formalized model and, in so doing, it identifies and interrelates a wide variety of social and political processes whereby internal wars are internationalized. Modelski incisively contends that such processes are built into the structure of the international system and that therefore the outcome of internal wars is "always dependent" upon external

8

factors. Irrespective of whether one accepts or rejects this hypothesis—and, as noted, there is plenty of room for argument —Modelski's formulation has the additional virtue of giving fresh meaning to such standard international practices as intervention, subversion, foreign aid, mediation, and diplomatic recognition. Placed in an internal war context, these phenomena are seen not only as forms of foreign policy, but also as mechanisms by which international systems absorb and adjust to internal wars.

Although less sweeping in its coverage, the editor's essay on "Internal War as an International Event" supplements Modelski's analysis and develops additional socio-political linkages between internal war and international phenomena. Where Modelski tends to treat internal war as a constant rather than a variable factor, this essay distinguishes three basic types of internal wars and attempts to trace how the process of internationalization varies from one type to another. In this chapter, moreover, an affirmative answer is found to a crucial question which Modelski does not raise: whether the external consequences of internal violence are substantively different from those that accompany nonviolent events which transpire within nations.

Still another set of systemic linkages is identified by Morton A. Kaplan in Chapter 4. Focusing on the incentives to intervene in internal wars, he manages to overcome the equilibrium bias inherent in systemic analysis and to compare the different ways in which balance-of-power and loose bipolar systems adjust to internal wars. His analysis cogently demonstrates that interventionary propensities are much more likely to be heightened in the latter type of system than in the former type. Indeed, Kaplan concludes that intervention in internal wars is "to be expected" in a loose bipolar system.

It is precisely the norms which sanction and legitimate intervention in modern internal wars that have evoked the stimulating, occasionally passionate, chapters by Richard A. Falk and Manfred Halpern. Falk, concerned that the traditional system of international law is inadequate to cope with prevailing interventionary practice, persuasively indicates several ways in which international legal precepts can and need to be reformulated if the law is to restrain foreign participation in internal wars. Even as he does so, however, Falk emphasizes that the rhetoric and doctrine of traditional international law still remain viable in some respects and that it is no less important for nations to take advantage of these viabilities than it is to construct new international norms which will strengthen tendencies toward world order. Thus, among other things, Falk's analysis serves as a thorough review of the points at which internal war and international law have been, are, and may yet be linked to each other. In a similarly vigorous fashion Halpern's essay identifies and probes a wide range of moral issues raised by the ever-mounting tendency for nations to intervene in each other's affairs. His immediate focus is the interventionary practices of the United States in a variety of situations, but his trenchant analysis contains much that is relevant to internal wars. Indeed, Halpern's essay, especially his useful scheme for distinguishing among several kinds of intervention, serves as a clear reminder that the international aspects of internal war cannot be viewed in isolation, that for policy-makers they are but one part of a larger and more complex set of concerns. Halpern does not condemn intervention *per se*, but, like Falk, he concludes that the norms associated with intervention have to be reformulated if a more stable world order is to emerge. The reader may find it instructive to consider the specific moral problems associated with internal wars in the context of Halpern's belief that "more constructive forms of intervention" can be developed.

The other three contributions to the symposium deal with more selective political and strategic aspects of the subject. Their narrower foci, however, do not prevent the authors from tying still other important international phenomena to the study of internal war. In Chapter 5 George Modelski touches upon some of the delicate aspects of diplomacy inherent in internal wars. He is concerned with the processes which terminate internal wars, especially that process whereby other nations help bring about a cessation of hostilities through negotiated settlement. Modelski presents a convincing case for the proposition that, while most internal wars end with the "outright win" of either the incumbents or the insurgents, international society is more capable of bringing about negotiated conclusions to such conflicts than is generally realized. This point coincides nicely with the suggestions of Falk and Halpern for improving international stability and, taken together, these analyses indicate that the prospects for greater stability are not inversely related to the frequency of internal wars—that, indeed, the chances of international order are not as bleak as our concentration on national disorder might suggest.

Andrew M. Scott's paper links internal war with another approach to the international field. His analysis considers the subject from a foreign policy perspective and demonstrates that the fomenting of internal war can, under certain circumstances, serve as an instrument of policy. Scott's point that this instrument is especially attractive to underdeveloped nations because it is much less costly than the more conventional techniques of foreign policy also links up the study of internal war to that important area of the international field known as capability (or power) analysis. Obviously the attractiveness of internal war as a policy technique also has considerable bearing upon the discussion, in the Falk, Halpern, and Modelski papers, of the relationship between international stability and intrastate violence.

While capability analysis is also central to the chapter on which Karl W. Deutsch and Morton A. Kaplan have collaborated, they place it in the larger strategic context of inter-bloc politics and, consequently, their paper serves to identify possible linkages between internal war on the one hand, and game and bargaining theory on the other. In this essay the important point is made that the outcome of internal wars can never be an unqualified gain for either the Western or the Eastern bloc. On the contrary, their analysis makes it clear that the great powers, following the principle of "strategic rationality," are likely to recognize that deficits as well as assets accompany the victory of a favored faction in an internal war. Thus it is to be expected that a complex set of profit-loss calculations will receive no less attention than moral considerations when nations decide how and when to intervene in the internal conflicts of other societies.

In emphasizing the contribution which each essay makes to filling the gap between international and internal war analyses, we do not mean to imply that this symposium exhausts the subject. At most we have only opened it up for more extensive and systematic inquiry. As indicated in Appendix A, there are no less than sixteen distinctly different aspects of the subject and we have certainly not covered all of them. At the very least, there are two major international aspects of internal war that have not been explored in these essays. One is the role which international organizations can and do play in the outbreak, course, and conclusion of internal wars. While several of the essays—notably those by Falk, Halpern, and Modelski—inferentially suggest that certain types of internal war situations lend themselves to participation and management by the United Nations, a more direct and intensive investigation of the subject is clearly in order. Empirical studies of the United Nations' role in the Congo and other internal wars are available, to be sure, but a comparative and theoretical analysis would surely be of value.

A second gap which this symposium fails to fill is the impact of international variables upon the conduct of internal wars. All the contributors to the symposium are students of international relations and law. Quite naturally, therefore, the essays share a preoccupation with processes that move outward from war-torn societies into the international community. Presumably the processes that move inward are just as dynamic, and certainly they are just as important if strife-ridden societies serve as the unit and focus of analysis. Consideration of these processes is essentially the task of social and political analysts rather than of students of international phenomena, but undoubtedly the latter could provide the former with valuable insights if their expertise were brought to bear on the external factors which direct and intensify the inward-moving processes.

Perhaps this is another way of saying that the international aspects of internal war are not the only ones worthy of analysis and that they are not even the most important aspects. On the contrary, as indicated above, these essays form only one cluster of several that have been generated by the Internal War Project. Other members of the Center of International Studies have been looking at the subject from the perspectives of military strategy [4] and social theory.[5] Communist practices with respect to internal war have served as the focus for another symposium [6] and the attention of still other projects has been confined to historical analyses of particular cases.[7] To those who have participated in one way or another in all these diverse efforts, it is clear that no single dimension of the subject is most important; that, in fact, all the dimensions are thoroughly interdependent; and that only for analytic purposes is it appropriate to treat them separately.

[4] Andrew C. Janos, "Unconventional Warfare: Framework and Analysis," *World Politics*, xv (July 1963), pp. 636–46; Klaus Knorr, "Unconventional Warfare: Strategy and Tactics in Internal Strife," *The Annals*, Vol. 341 (May 1962), pp. 53–64; and Peter Paret and John W. Shy, *Guerrillas in the 1960's* (New York: Frederick A. Praeger, 2nd edn., 1962).

[5] Eckstein, *op.cit.*

[6] Cyril E. Black and Thomas P. Thornton, eds., *Communism and Revolution* (Princeton: Princeton University Press, 1964).

[7] Charles Tilly, *The Vendée Counter-Revolution* (Cambridge: Harvard University Press, forthcoming).

CHAPTER 2

The International Relations
of Internal War

BY GEORGE MODELSKI

I. *Introduction*

INTERNAL war is a drama that unfolds when a political system
undergoes violent fission. All the essential structures of the political system—the structures of authority, solidarity, culture,
and resources [1]—split in two, as it were, and both the incumbents and the insurgents find themselves in due course en-
dowed with a new set of at least rudimentary political structures. These two sets of political structures which emerge in
the course of internal war I call, for short, the structures of
internal war. It is my argument that in internal war the structures of at least one party to the conflict already have, and the
others acquire, international components. The incumbents always and by definition have international connections, simply
because they are in charge of the legitimate machinery of the
state, which includes the diplomatic and other international
networks; the insurgents, by virtue of having to approximate

---

[1] I assume that, in their static aspect, political systems are composed of
the structures of authority, solidarity, culture, and resources. Each of these
structures has a substructure devoted to maintaining the main structure
and enlarging it. Thus the resource structure has an "investment substructure" whose function it is to replenish, and add to, the "resource capital."
(Analogically and illustratively, the steel industry, conceived as a resource
structure, has a substructure devoted to repairing, overhauling, and maintaining existing facilities and to planning, designing, and constructing new
steel furnaces, rolling mills, coke and iron-ore treatment works, and the
relevant transportation networks; in other words, the industry has a substructure devoted to the investment function.) "Culture" has such "investment substructures" as the educational system. Each structure of the political system produces inputs fed into the system, and thus helps to sustain
it; part of the output of every political system is consumed by the need to
maintain existing structures and to construct new ones.

the incumbents as closely as possible in order to supplant them, must develop the same machinery.

Take the structure of authority, and in particular those who perform the duties of authoritative decision-making, be it for the incumbents or for the insurgents. By reason of the nature of their work, and because of the kind of men they are, political decision-makers always are—and properly so—exposed to and subject to international influences. (1) Both the incumbents and the insurgents operate in that network of external relationships which constitutes the international system. The incumbents deal with foreign representatives and travel abroad in the normal course of their everyday duties. The insurgents gain their most intimate acquaintance with the international system during the prolonged spells of exile with which their careers may be punctuated, but, in the course of an internal war, they too must maintain a foreign policy and a network of relationships with foreign powers. Engaging in these contacts, neither side can avoid entering into a close political association with at least a few other states. (2) For certain areas of decision-making, the process of recruitment tends to favor men with foreign experience or background, and this even more so during an internal war. According to Lyford Edwards, "It is a matter of common knowledge that in every social upheaval the party attacked claims that the trouble has been stirred up by outside agents and agitators." [2] As he points out, the presence of an external agent may indeed be an indispensable precipitant of change. Agrarian states almost as a matter of routine brought, at intervals, new foreign dynasties into their political systems and, in between dynastic changes, royal intermarriages effected and symbolized an international circulation of elites. Today's political processes—most strikingly so in the case of the small states —attract into positions of authority men with foreign experience

[2] Lyford P. Edwards, *The Natural History of Revolution* (Chicago: University of Chicago Press, 1927), p. 24.

gained through periods of service, travel, or training abroad. Furthermore, we must not forget the revolutionaries of the type of Lafayette or Che Guevara who join up with an insurgent movement irrespective of their original political affiliation.

Consider the structure of political solidarity or, in an alternative formulation, the incumbents' or insurgents' "reference group" or "political community." Only in the most exceptional case does the structure of solidarity coincide with the boundaries of a political system such as that of a nation-state. Normally it is both smaller and larger than such boundaries would suggest. Those who are united in interest with either the incumbents or the insurgents never all belong to one political system; the activation of the solidarity structure and the conversion of potential into actual support, especially abroad, are therefore among the chief tasks of the leaders of internal war. Among the external components of the reference group should be counted foreign governments [3] and organizations (including, for example, private individuals and corporations) who aid and support either side; foreign members of political and ideological movements with which the parties in the internal war may be affiliated; and others who together with the incumbents or insurgents form a solidary grouping on whatever basis is relevant (for instance, for an "African" insurgent, all other "Africans"; for a "royal" incumbent, the "international of kings"; for a "democratic" regime, all "democrats"). The solidary group of either side does not, however, include the partners to "specific" or "opportunistic" deals (for instance, the purchase of arms).

Next, take the structure of culture and communications. The cultural connections of the incumbents and of the insurgents at all times extend beyond the confines of one political system;

---

[3] International alignments tend to develop into alignments with particular incumbents; they benefit the government in power and to that extent at least become a matter of domestic dispute, the opponents of that government tending to gravitate toward an affiliation with the enemies of the incumbents' allies.

the language and the style of an internal war are, as frequently as not, borrowed from abroad. The ease of communication which is the product of the cultural structures is an essential cement of political organization; it welds together the political elite and facilitates the coordination of their followers; it brings mass and international support to the fighting forces. Some of the most crucial communication lines of an internal war run abroad and as such become the targets of the most vociferous attacks because, if they are cut, the other party has scored a victory and may have achieved the isolation of its opponents. The stereotyped picture of a modern revolutionary as a cosmopolitan fluent in several languages, the frequenter of capitals, of Paris, London, Vienna, or New York yesterday, of Moscow and Geneva, of Cairo, Peking, and Accra today, illustrates the complicated international communication systems of internal war.

Last, let us consider the resource structures of internal war. The resources of both parties normally extend beyond the frontiers of one political system. The incumbents have their alliances and other political associations and the military and economic aid that these produce. They have commercial and noncommercial connections and enterprises abroad. Their arms are supplied, as often as not, by foreign public or private manufacturing enterprises. But the insurgents' external resource base is even more important, primarily because it represents that section of their assets which is beyond the control of their opponents. A foreign base of operations is usually indispensable as a source of funds, manpower, and supplies, and as a final refuge in the event of ultimate defeat. For the insurgents, an external base is the embodiment of hope; yet such a base can never be acquired against the opposition of the host country and its denial becomes the major goal of the incumbents. However, the precise importance of the base (as of all the other international structures) depends on the size of the internal war system: internal war in a great state can more easily maintain itself with indigenous resources than can internal war in a small power.

Let us remark in passing that the presence of an international component in one of the internal war structures sets up pressures for "internationalizing" the other three structures. Thus, for example, the availability of a foreign resource base creates (and depends upon) external communications facilities and cultural empathy, enlarges the bonds of solidarity, and influences recruitment and training for positions of authority. The tendencies toward "internationalization" of internal war are mutually reinforcing.

So much for the "facts" of the existence of international components of internal war structures. These "facts" are empirical in the sense that the existence of the external elements of internal war structures must be empirically demonstrated in each concrete case. Depending on the character of the internal war in question, the relative importance of internal and external elements may vary, and by itself might be an important determinant of the outcome of the entire process. However, no concrete study of internal war can begin work on the assumption that such structures are unimportant; no study can omit to ask questions about external structures of internal war, for if such questions are not asked, answers to them will never be arrived at.

I would, nevertheless, go beyond the purely empirical stage and assert that internal wars logically and necessarily have external components in their structures. This simply follows from the fact that internal wars occur not only within a political system but also within an international system.[4] Internal wars affect the international system; the international system affects internal wars. The remainder of this chapter is designed to identify the mechanisms which account for the existence of the

_____

. [4] Conversely, the model of internal war which holds the external components to zero involves the assumption that the international system exerts no influence on internal war.

external components and which therefore "internationalize" internal wars.

II. *The Theory of Foreign Policy*

In principle, the foreign policies of internal wars present the same analytical problems as all other foreign policies. The foreign operations of both the incumbents and the insurgents attempt the same thing: to influence each other and the foreign states in order to implement certain interests with a determinate amount of power; they each seek allies and seek to destroy the alliances of the other side. Not all participants in internal wars satisfy the conditions which the model of "perfect" foreign policy prescribes for them. The five-day Guatemalan internal war of November 1960 was so brief that the insurgents there obviously did not develop much of a foreign policy. But, then, not all independent states satisfy the perfect model of foreign policy either. No one would expect Iceland, El Salvador, or Upper Volta to have a very active foreign policy. The generalization may be offered that the bigger and the longer-lasting the internal war, the closer will the foreign policy problems of the insurgents approach the "perfect" model. (The incumbents already have a foreign policy and therein lies one of the chief reasons for their superiority.) The external relations of the English Parliament in 1640–1648, of the United States of America in 1776–1783, of the Confederate States in 1861–1865, of Franco in 1936–1939, or of the Chinese Communists in 1927–1949 were among the crucial determinants of the respective internal wars, but they are subject to the same kind of analysis as all other foreign policies.

Yet, at the beginning the insurgents obviously had no foreign policy at all. What are the processes whereby the insurgents acquire an international personality and a provisional or part-membership in the international system? What are the processes which internationalize an internal war?

To account for the internationalization of internal war, let us

19

construct an "intervention" model. To satisfy our analytical purposes, this model is based on the following simplifying assumptions: first, that insurgents and incumbents have ample time for "internationalizing" the internal conflict; second, that the insurgents, the incumbents, and outside nations are roughly equal in power; third, that all decision-making groups have perfect solidarity and skill; and, finally, that there is perfect international mobility of communications and resources. These assumed conditions are not, of course, necessarily realistic when compared with actual internal war situations; and they are consequently relaxed at a later point in our argument.

Assume a system of two countries (or two international actors), one of which is either ready for or is actually experiencing an internal war. Furthermore, assume that one of the parties to the internal war is weaker than the other. Assume, finally, that the weaker party, in order to overpower its opponents (otherwise it could hardly be fighting an internal war), is seeking to increase its strength and has exhausted all the "internal" means of doing so. The only way of redressing the internal power balance is to invite outside aid. This, the demand for outside aid, is the first basic mechanism of "internationalization" of internal war; it inheres in the fundamental condition of struggle for power found in internal war.

That every internal war creates a demand for foreign intervention is thus implicit in the logic of the situation. The demand may not always be capable of being satisfied, but it is always there, and has been found to exist not only in modern political history but in all known international systems—during the revolt of the Ionian League against the rule of the Persian Empire in Asia Minor (500 B.C.) as much as in the course of the An Lu-shan revolt (755–762 A.D.) which threatened the stability of Tang rule and was suppressed only through the intervention of the Kaghan of the Uigurs of Outer Mongolia. Such a demand was strongly present, too, on the King's side during the English Revolution (1640–1648), but could not be met owing to a variety of circumstances, which included Parliament's control of the main ports and of the navy, powerful impediments to Royal communication with overseas powers.

The second mechanism follows from the first. If the weaker party may be presumed to be seeking outside aid, then the stronger party, if it is to maintain its preponderance, is driven to take international countermeasures by anticipation as much as by hard-and-fast information about external intervention in aid of its adversaries. (Such information is frequently false.) It must destroy the actual or potential alliances and the solidarity structures of its opponents, and must counter them by alliances of its own. Thus, as if by a "natural" process of alignment, the friends of your opponents become your opponents, too.

The second mechanism of intervention transforms a struggle inside one political system into a struggle between two political systems. A good example of the internationalization of internal war by this process is the way in which the Chinese civil war is still being fought out in the capitals of the new African states, each one of which upon reaching independence is sought out by representatives of both sides and must choose between granting recognition to Peking or to Formosa. The second mechanism depends logically, but not substantially, upon the prior operation of the search for outside aid by the weaker party. The natural and obvious expectation that the weak party will sooner or later summon foreign help forces the stronger side to make anticipatory countermoves even if no call for such aid has actually been sent out.

Every internal war is a contest between the incumbents and the insurgents. But every internal war, too, has a third party, also disposing of internal and external structures. Internally, the political system contains members who favor neither partisan position: the moderates, the liberals, or simply those who care little for either party and who are tired of the fighting and the dying; they may be well organized or completely dispersed through the political system. Externally, some outside states, too, may find themselves, by design or by accident, in the same position; they may be interested less in bringing about the complete or "total" victory of either party (every internal war tends toward becoming a total war) than in securing internal peace, precisely because of the dangerous repercussions which internal war has upon international relations; they may, in some cases, be dispersed throughout the international system, or else they may be capable of expressing their position through an international organization or an *ad hoc* political arrangement. In a sense, these two elements may be said to represent something of a "public interest" of the internal war system: the "common interest" of the war-torn political system—if we can assume that the moderates are closer to it than either of the participants—and the similar interest of the international system in the maintenance of order.[5]

Herein lies the third mechanism of internationalization and it follows from the preceding two. The search for outside aid and the effort to counteract that search make every internal war a matter of international concern. They complicate international alignments, add acerbity to them, and may lead directly to external war. Hence, in our two-country model, the second power may be brought in to intervene in the conflict, in aid, as it were, of the third party, and in order to perform functions of mediation and reconciliation. This role can be played, too, by international actors, including international organizations.

This, the third, mechanism of intervention is what diplomats more commonly mean by internationalization of an internal war. At present it is especially important with respect to colonial wars which a strong power may prevent from becoming internationalized—that is, subject to formal international

[5] Everyday judicial procedures formalize an analogical situation: in relation to the parties contending before it, a court of justice represents the public interest of the relevant political system.

discussion. For years, France succeeded in keeping the Vietnamese war out of an international forum; not until the impossibility of victory had been demonstrated beyond any reasonable doubt did she consent to the 1954 Geneva Conference on Indochina. For even longer she succeeded in reducing to a minimum the international interest in the cause of the Algerian rebels.

Each of these mechanisms has an active and a passive variant. Those outlined above have been of the active variety —they assumed that the parties to the internal war were actively seeking the intervention of the outside power. Each of these mechanisms may, at the other extreme, assume a passive form: the internal war parties may be "used" by an outside power for its own purposes. Thus the outside power may incite an internal war by urging on, organizing, and subsidizing a passive yet discontented body of men; it may press its aid upon a government unwilling to incur the odium of outside support; or, finally, it may force its mediatory services upon unappreciative contestants. Needless to say, most of the realistic cases lie somewhere between these two extreme variants of the intervention models.

Our three models clarify the alternatives open to the foreign policy-makers of the "second" country. Given an internal war in one state, the foreign policy of the second state faces three choices: (1) helping the weaker party—usually, but not invariably, the insurgents—and thus embarking on subversion; (2) helping the stronger party—usually, but not invariably, the incumbents—and thus engaging in foreign aid; or (3) working for a conciliatory solution of the conflict by attempting mediation.

Subversion, foreign aid, and mediation are the three modes of foreign policy reaction to internal war. Let me stress that there is no fourth alternative, no way for the "second" country to avoid involvement in internal war. Even though a country may decide not to act at all, to do nothing and to say nothing, then by this very fact it, too, helps—sometimes unwittingly—to mold the outcome of the process: for by refusing to act it helps the stronger party to suppress the weaker, irrespective of the merits of the case. This is the meaning of Talleyrand's celebrated definition of nonintervention: "a mysterious word that signifies roughly the same thing as intervention." Hence, there is no internal war without international intervention.

At this point we should differentiate between two uses of this important term "intervention." In one sense, and on the level of ascertainable social interaction, there "always" is (or tends to be) foreign intervention in an internal war. The scholar's problem is to decide what type of intervention it is (subversion, foreign aid, or mediation, depending on which party it benefits). This is the intervention of Talleyrand's description, founded upon the insight that no matter what attitude outside powers actually decide upon (either active intervention on behalf of one or the other of the parties, or passive intervention which minimizes international action), their action or inaction always crucially contributes toward the end result and benefits one of the parties more than the other.

The term "intervention" is also sometimes used in a legal or moral context, and may then signify that type of "foreign interference into domestic affairs" that is prohibited under the then current codes of international law or international morality. International lawyers have long been preoccupied with clarifying and defining rules of international behavior which would forbid, for instance, external aid to potential insurgents; but they have not seen any legal obstacles to the dispatch of foreign aid to a legitimate government, the accord of privileges to political refugees, or the authorized intervention of an international organization. Thus on the legal, moral, or even political plane it is sometimes perfectly justifiable to demand "nonintervention": that is, to demand the discontinuation of certain prohibited or unapproved types of intervention, and their replacement by some other kind of action (this, too, of course, being intervention, but of another type). In this discussion we use "intervention" chiefly in the first sense of the term.

In the present context, subversion may be technically defined as external aid to insurgents. The range of subversion is extremely wide and may extend from the mere fact of allowing exiles and refugees to cross the border, to permitting them to settle down and to organize (as the Cubans did in Florida in 1960–1961), to occasional financial or arms aid, to more extensive support by means of technicians and advisors, and to the supply of complete military "volunteer" formations (for instance, in the Spanish Civil War). Aid to insurgents carries with it the risk of external war, and extensive international arrangements may have to be made to control that risk. Discreet subversion is an age-old instrument of foreign policy, and every internal war has its share of it. Sometimes it is used as a means of weakening the social fabric of an opponent in anticipation of an external war (as in the standard case of the Fifth Column [6]) or else as a device for securing friendly or cooperative governments.

The counterpart of subversion is foreign aid, defined as external aid for the incumbents. All aid extended to a foreign state stands to benefit the government in power and to that extent all foreign aid is countersubversive. But some aid is more so. Much of United States military assistance to Latin American and Asian countries, and most of the special aid to police forces in those areas, have in the past been of the type designed to strengthen the internal security situation. The Lebanese landings of U.S. Marines in 1958 or the U.S. naval patrol in the Caribbean in November 1960—a measure intended to forestall Cuban support for possible risings in the Central American republics—are another type of external aid strengthening the hand of the incumbent government in an internal war. Foreign aid on the grand scale is a favorite preoccupation of the Great

[6] Louis de Jong, *The German Fifth Column in the Second World War*, trans. by C. M. Geyl (Chicago: University of Chicago Press, 1956).

Powers and an important mode of intervention on their part in the affairs of the weaker states.[7]

Mediation seems the most thankless of the three modes of intervention. It is a true alternative policy because it cannot be effectively combined with either foreign aid or subversion unless the lines of communication are kept secret; it presupposes that the mediator must to some degree have the trust of both sides, but its result may easily be an all-round decline of confidence. Conciliatory intervention customarily antagonizes at least one of the sides to the internal war because, like "nonactivity," it tends to stabilize the situation in favor of the stronger party; incumbents additionally dislike it because it adds to the status of the insurgents. Rarely does it attain its ends fully, and yet examples of it are easy to come by. Well-known attempts at mediation in internal war include the Marshall mission of 1946—an attempt to arrange for a truce between the Chinese Communists and Nationalists—and later United States efforts to support a third, liberal group of Chinese politicians; the mediation activities of the International Commission for Supervision and Control in Laos (1954–1958), culminating in a temporary political settlement between the Royal government and the Pathet Lao (1957); and, finally, the official and thankless position of neutrality adopted by the United Nations in the internal disturbances in the Congo (1960–1962). Cyprus may have been one of the few cases where outside intervention, including discussions of the problem within NATO and the U.N., helped to contribute to a compromise solution in an internal war situation. The argument could be advanced that a functionally diffuse international organization, such as the United Nations or the Organization of American States, best approximates the required characteristics of a successful third-party mediator or representative of the nonaligned parts of a strife-torn political system.

[7] On foreign aid and the hazards of intervention, see George Liska, *The New Statecraft* (Chicago: University of Chicago Press, 1960), chap. 4.

The type of intervention actually chosen by the "second" state of our model will depend on the interests at stake and the power available for their pursuit. But, granted the pervasiveness of the mechanisms of intervention, which makes it standard practice for internal war parties to attribute their grievances and their difficulties to the activities of outside agents and provocateurs, or to a betrayal of national interests in the interests of a foreign power, what are the processes which ensure that in actual fact the amount of such intervention is smaller than might have been expected from the model? To answer this question, let us examine some of the assumptions implied in our earlier theoretical argument.

The first and crucial assumption built into the two-country intervention model is that of "unlimited time." Both the insurgents and the incumbents are supposed to have available to them unlimited time in which to internationalize the conflict, to seek out and enlist foreign support, and to make pacts and counteralliances. In internal war situations this condition does not often prevail, even though the insurgents do sometimes have the choice of the time of attack and hence the opportunity of preparing their campaign in advance in the international field as well as at home. But they face this difficulty: unless and until they have established a position of strength in their own country—that is, unless they have embarked upon an internal war that has a good chance of success—few governments outside the range of their immediate "sponsors" will wish to have dealings with them, or take them very seriously. The international system discourages the setting-up of new authorities.

Large numbers of internal wars are, however, short-lived and allow little time for the crystallization of international alignments. Successful *coups d'état*—the equivalent to those threats of force or surprise attacks which produce international *faits accomplis*—confront the outside world with the alternatives of accepting the new regime or risking war against an entrenched government. Hence a short internal war, or merely a credible threat of one, is the type of action most likely to elude international complications. But there is this countervailing tendency to bear in mind: important political changes in a great state are rarely wrought overnight; they engage a body politic for an extended period and it is during that time that the outside world has a chance of making its influence felt. The crucial internal wars of modern history, such as the French, Russian, and Chinese Revolutions, were long-lasting affairs, each one of which was in its own way extensively internationalized.

The second assumption concerns the relative power and status of the two international actors represented in the intervention models. The model assumes equality of the two actors; yet the parties to an internal war in a great power have little to gain by seeking the assistance of a small power; events in a small country would, on the other hand, be decisively influenced by the actions of a great state.

Finally, the third set of assumptions concerns the "technical" conditions of internationalization. The intervention model assumes (1) perfect international mobility of resources, (2) perfect international communications, (3) perfect solidarity, and (4) perfect skill on the part of the decision-makers. In other words, external support for the insurgents will not be forthcoming unless it is logistically and otherwise possible to transfer the necessary resources from one country to the other, unless communications with the outside world are satisfactory, unless there are no political or other barriers to collaboration with outsiders, and unless the leadership of the insurgents is ready, willing, and able to seek out international assistance. Conversely, too, such external intervention will not take place if the incumbents succeed in interrupting the lines of communication or the movement of supplies, or in confusing the lines of solidarity or the policy decisions of the insurgent leadership.

In brief, the actual world is always to some degree at variance with this simplified two-country model. On a number of occasions, outside intervention may in fact not occur at all. We might add that we should also presume a certain amount of initial resistance, not to external assistance as such and in principle, but to an excessive reliance upon it. No self-respecting politician likes to depend greatly upon external aid; in "internal" politics there is the feeling, common to all solidary groupings, that internal or domestic ("semi-familial") affairs should be transacted in private and without the intervention of outside parties. But then, of course, not all politicians are self-respecting or, indeed, can afford to be so; the more violent the internal conflict, the more tenuous the links of internal solidarity and the greater the opportunities for foreign intervention. Internal war is, of course, the most violent of internal conflicts and in it such opportunities are therefore maximized.

III. *The Theory of International Systems*

We have so far analyzed internal war from the standpoint of foreign policy and, through the two-country model, have demonstrated the pressures toward its internationalization. The same processes can, however, be analyzed from the opposite and equally important standpoint—that of the international system. Only from that second point of view can we satisfactorily explain why certain insurgents fail where others succeed.

The success or failure of an internal war is always dependent upon the behavior of the international system. To grasp this basic proposition from which the second part of our argument begins, consider the power situation of every internal war: it is an event that occurs in an nth part of the international system (for n, substitute the number of members in a given international system; the system of 1960 contained at least 100 members). Right from the outset, then, the cards are stacked against the insurgents: no single member of the international system— no $\frac{1}{100}$th part of it—can stand up against the united opposition of the whole system, and even less so an insurgent party which, at the onset of the internal war at any rate, is weaker than the incumbents, and therefore amounts to anything less than ½ of the nth part of the system (that is, to $\frac{1}{200}$th part of the system in 1960).[8] Successful internal wars are therefore something of a miracle and in each such case the question most pertinently arises: how has it come about that the other members of the international system allowed this and not another course of events to occur?

To satisfy those who might argue that members of the international system have no legitimate grounds for concerning themselves in the internal affairs of a political system, let me point out that the device through which the interest of the international system in these matters is institutionalized goes by the name of "recognition." Every extraordinary change in the political status of a state or a government—resulting, for instance, from the overthrow of the incumbent government, or the establishment of an insurgent government, the proclamation of a status of belligerency by the insurgents, or the setting-up of a new state—is subject to the judgment of the other members of the international system, inasmuch as the incoming or the new government is not legally entitled to presume that the relation instituted by its predecessors will in fact be maintained. It has to seek and to receive the recognition of other states—in practice, that of the Great Powers above all—either as the *de facto* or the *de jure* authority of the country. It may also run into difficulties in connection with the seating of its delegates at international conferences, and at the U.N. in particular.

The recognition of a new state and a new government is always subject to extensive political and diplomatic debate. In the case of political turmoil in a small state—let us say, after the Thai military coup of September 1957—the recommendation to

[8] This is merely one of the ways of posing the question of the influence of the international system upon national policies or, in Morton Kaplan's technical terminology, the problem of system dominance. Early Communist thinking about the Revolution was similarly impressed by international system-dominance. Those who, like Trotsky, argued after the Russian Revolution the necessity of immediate world-wide proletarian uprisings could not conceive of the success of their own national enterprise in the face of the hostility of the whole outside world.

extend recognition to the new government may be considered on the spot by a conclave of the ambassadors of the most closely interested and most influential states. (In the Thai case, it was discussed at a meeting of the ambassadors of the United States, Australia, Nationalist China, New Zealand, and the Philippines held at the American Embassy on the morning after the coup.) [9] In the case of violent convulsions in the body politic of a great state, such as Russia or China, the recognition of the new government may become a major political issue that occupies the international system for decades. Through the device of recognition the result of every internal war is subject to international ratification.

We might add here that recognition is no academic problem involving the technical determination of whether a regime "exists" or not. For a nation, securing international status and position is as vital a matter as is gaining admission to an exclusive local club, and to the attendant share in community decision-making, for a man newly arrived in that community.

The processes whereby the international system influences internal wars may be classified under three headings: those of (1) diffusion and encouragement, (2) isolation and suppression, and (3) reconciliation. Once again, the fourth alternative of nonactivity or nonintervention does not exist, because inactivity or nonintervention must be interpreted as encouragement of the stronger party in the internal war, and hence as the activation of processes (1) or (2).

In some cases, the international system diffuses or encourages internal war. In other words, it strengthens the hands of the insurgents, builds up their morale, keeps up their hopes, facilitates the flow of supplies to their armies and, above all, isolates and demoralizes the incumbents. Most of these processes are covered by the vague term "climate of international opinion"

---

[9] One of the first actions of the "Military Group" which seized power was to send a letter to the foreign embassies affirming the intention to uphold Thailand's international obligations.

—which, at any given time, favors or condemns certain types of national endeavor. The most striking contemporary example of the diffusion effect is the current international attitude toward colonial wars. In recent years, near-universal acceptance has been gained for the view that colonialism is a thing of the past, that all colonial territories ought to be granted independence, and that colonial wars are therefore justified. The countries which support this view claim to represent the majority sentiment of mankind, while the colonial powers cannot but help feeling on the defensive. The climate of world opinion not only reinforces those who are currently fighting internal wars—as it did, for instance, the Provisional Algerian government; it also prevents internal wars in cases where the colonial power, in view of the international situation, decides to pull out without putting up a fight—as France did in much of Africa—and encourages the outbreak of colonial wars in territories whose metropolitan powers refuse to make concessions—for instance, in Portuguese Angola. The colonial issue is only one instance of the operation of the diffusion effect. Other instances are the encouragement of democratic regimes after World War II—an interesting example being the seizure of power by Pridi Panomyong, known to be friendly to the Allies, in 1944, on the eve of Allied victory in Thailand; the noticeable trend toward fascism throughout the world in 1938–1941—not only in such obvious cases as Spain and Rumania, but also in Japan, France, Iraq, Thailand, and Argentina; and the growth of national states in Central and East Europe between 1859 and 1921, partly through internal war.

In some other cases, the international system isolates or suppresses internal wars. In other words, it works to the disadvantage of the insurgents, and in such instances the world climate of opinion may be said to be unfavorable to them. The international system reinforces the incumbents, bolsters their confidence, arranges help to threatened governments, and may even institute collective intervention on their behalf. More importantly still, it isolates and discourages the rebels, and deprives them of international respectability.

In cases where members of the international system find it impossible to deal with a *fait accompli*, the isolation effect amounts to the ostracizing of the new regime of the victorious insurgents, as England was counted out of European politics during the period of the Long Parliament, the USSR was "sent to Coventry" after 1917, or Franco Spain was isolated shortly after World War II. It is the hope—more often justified in the case of a smaller state—that the unacceptable regime will in due course collapse or, perhaps, reform to a certain extent, without in the meantime upsetting the international order. Or else the isolation effect may involve the active discouragement of insurgency and its suppression by joint action. The most celebrated and, in another sense, notorious instance of this process was the so-called Holy Alliance, more correctly the Concert of European Great Powers after 1815. In the years following the Congress of Vienna, the Great Powers took it upon themselves to authorize collective intervention in several cases of internal war, and in particular in reply to the assumption of power by liberals in Spain and in the Kingdom of Naples in 1820. Among other examples of this effect have been the attempt to restore the Bourbons following the beheading of Louis XVI in 1793 and the success of the enterprise in 1814–1815; the intervention of European Great Powers in the Boxer rebellion of 1900; and the operation of the Western international system ever since 1918, tending to obstruct the success of Communist insurgents, be it in Hungary in 1919, Iran in 1946–1947, or Greece in 1944–1950. The most spectacular example of this last tendency has been the case of Korea, but the same process has also operated in respect of the rebellions which started in Malaya, India, Indonesia, Burma, and the Philippines in 1947, in all of which the tendency of the international system has been to build up the incumbents. The process has been so effective that to this day no nationalist fighting a colonial war willingly admits to a Communist affiliation—realizing that such an admission would assuredly disadvantage him both internally and externally. The isolation effect does not in the main rely upon outright force; mere anticipation of it tends to discourage some internal wars and hastens settlement in certain other potential conflicts.

The last series of cases concerns the reconciliation which in some circumstances the international system may impose upon the participants in an internal war. This mechanism operates principally in those instances where neither diffusion nor isolation is called for, and where the outcome of the war itself is less important than the very fact of the occurrence of violence and the potentialities it has for spreading. The general international interest then seems best satisfied by an effort at reconciliation, and of this the action of the Concert of Europe in the Belgian question, bringing about a peaceful resolution of the problem of Belgian independence by negotiations among all the interested powers (1830–1836), and the international attempt to bring about a settlement of the Laotian question (1961–1962) may serve as examples. A number of the ordinary rebellions or insurrections potentially fall into this category, before they have had time to develop international ramifications, and might be more easily disposed of by reference to an international organization.

Such are the processes through which the international system either encourages or discourages certain types of internal war. But how can we foretell what kind of treatment an internal war will receive? The answer is: by looking at the cultural structures (or the "formula") of the international system, and at the structures of authority and the concomitant stratification system [10] (or, crudely, the "ruling class" of the international

[10] That international systems possess structures of culture and authority has been argued elsewhere; see the author's "Agraria and Industria: Two Models of the International System," in the special issue of *World Politics*, xiv (October 1961), that was subsequently published as *The International System: Theoretical Essays*, ed. by Klaus Knorr and Sidney Verba (Princeton: Princeton University Press, 1961), pp. 120–24, 132–39.

system) which they legitimize. The international system favors those parties to internal war which accord with the current "formula" and which reinforce the current structure of authority; and it discourages their opponents. Furthermore, those great historic processes which transmute the "ruling minority" of the international system and bring about changes in the "formula" also bring in their train changes in the political systems of member states. Some of these changes occur peacefully, but others give rise to internal wars.

There are variations in the precise mechanisms through which changes in the structures of authority of the international system translate themselves into violent changes in political systems. On occasion they amount to no more than imitation of developments that are occurring in the political system of a prestigious member of the international system. For instance, General de Gaulle's accession to power in 1958, in circumstances close to an internal war, encouraged and gave ideas to a number of other military men around the world; within a few months, Marshal Sarit Thanarat of Thailand assumed a constitutional position similar to de Gaulle's after a coup of his own in October 1958. On other occasions they may amount to direct subversion—the encouragement, by fair means or foul, of internal wars in countries which resist a change in the international climate of opinion, or which stand in the way of a rising power. In March 1939 Hitler successfully disrupted Czechoslovakia by inducing the Slovaks to proclaim independence from Prague.

The most powerful mechanisms through which changes in the "ruling class" of the international system are translated into violent domestic upheavals have in the past been external wars and may in future become other spectacular tests of international strength (for instance, outer space contests). Wars have, in the past, always brought about a rearrangement of the relative status and position of the contending parties. The great coalition wars of the Western state system have been occasions

35

for attempting and executing changes in the international structure of authority. Wars have promoted countries to the rank of a Great Power—for instance, Japan after the victory over Russia in 1905—and they have tumbled powerful and ambitious states into defeat and reduced them to the rank of an international pariah—for instance, Germany after 1945. The victors call the tune for international society; the losers imitate them: they may be forced to do so or else they may wish to assure themselves of the benefits of an "obviously superior" example (for instance, Soviet successes in outer space have forced a reappraisal of programs of scientific education throughout the world, including the United States). The exhaustion of the war years and the confusion of postwar society create ideal conditions for internal war; the influence of the victors ensures that significant changes follow the lines of the approved "formula."

Changes in the international structures of authority may be either evolutionary or revolutionary. Both kinds of change transform political systems, but they differ with respect to speed and thoroughness. The great revolutionary convulsions—for instance, those of the French Republican and Napoleonic period—compel general attention, but the evolutionary and almost imperceptible changes of international status and authority that go on all the time may be just as important. Gradual changes in the relative status of the Great Powers affect at least a part of the international system. For instance, the rising status of Britain and France after 1830 and the dominance of their liberal parties lent prestigious support to liberalism in Europe for at least two decades and readied the field for the revolutions of 1848. German ascendancy in the last quarter of the nineteenth century strongly influenced the political character of the new national states carved out of the Ottoman Empire in the Balkans, including Rumania, Serbia, Bulgaria, Montenegro, and Greece; a majority of them acquired German princelings as rulers.

The revolutionary changes in the international structure of authority are more radical; they aim at the very foundations of international order and seek to bring about a complete replacement of one "ruling class" and one "formula" by an entirely new "ruling class" and "formula." They represent, moreover, a mechanism through which the insurgents' success in an internal war is transformed into a crisis of the international system.

Here are the conditions which account for such a process. First, assume the occurrence of an internal war. Assume also that it occurs in a Great Power. Finally, assume that the insurgents radically challenge not only the domestic "ruling class" and "formula," but also those of the international system. Two results can be expected in view of our earlier models; the isolation effect on the part of the international system, and the countervailing tendency of the insurgents to evade the pressure through the universalization of their interests. Depending on further conditions relating to the success of the insurgents, the perseverance with which they hold onto the "formula," the number of states they succeed in bringing in on their side, and the degree to which they themselves are absorbed into the international "ruling class," the situation which at the outset amounted to international intervention in an internal war may assume the character of a contest for the control of the international system. The French and the Communist Revolutions have been the obvious examples of such a process, with the significant difference that the French Revolution, in its external aspect, did not significantly advance beyond a self-centered, nationalistic phase and soon transformed its international aspirations into the struggle of one man and one Great Power for European mastery and for a world empire. The Communist system, too, has had its Russian-oriented, nationalistic period, but as of now it embraces two Great Powers and for that reason its contemporary expansion presents problems of vastly different proportions.

The revolutionary struggle for the control of an international system has two interrelated but separable facets: the geographical aspect of the territorial expansion of the revolutionary core of the system, and the structural aspect of the replacement of one set of structures of the international system by another.[11] Both are aspects of the same process: to be complete, control over the system must be both geographical and structural; territorial expansion brings structural control and vice versa. In internal war, too, we can recognize these two aspects of the struggle for political control: the attempt to seize territory, by expanding from a fixed base, and the attempt to capture or destroy the rival authority and communications centers and to remold the structures of solidarity and resources. In both instances, a geographically oriented policy of containment, focused on the "frontiers of expansion" of the revolutionary core, must be supplemented by efforts to counteract the danger of capture or destruction of the key structures of the international system.

Internal war plays an important part in the geographic aspect of the transformations of the international system, for it affords opportunities for carrying the revolutionary "formula" to new countries. Disaffected minorities throughout the system are "naturally" attracted by the prospects of aid and support, and by the opportunity of countering the domestic legitimacy of the incumbents by the external legitimacy of the revolutionary international system. The revolutionary core may be seen to exercise pressure upon the rest of the system and, under its weight, the weaker and more exposed sections of the system may crack up. Countries such as Laos, Greece, Iran, and Vietnam become trouble spots of the international system and experience internal wars not because their political systems are con-

---

[11] On the notions of the expansion of the core of an international system and the availability of alternative structures, see the author's *The Communist International System* (Princeton: Center of International Studies, Research Monograph No. 9, 1960), *passim*, esp. pp. 75ff.

spicuously weaker than those of other states, but because they find themselves unhappily placed in the front lines of a revolutionary contest.

So much for the processes which translate the problems of the international system into internal wars and vice versa. If we were to push this argument to its logical conclusion, we would have to suppose that every internal war endangered the stability of the international system, and that every change in the international system threatened to provoke a series of internal wars. Since this is manifestly not so, there must be mechanisms built into every international system tending to inhibit the spread of internal wars and to discourage extensive international interest in these affairs. The social system isolates and confers a special status upon the sick; [12] the international system, too, needs devices for insulating these powerful sources of disruption.

The specific reasons for such insulating devices are not far to seek. External intervention in the internal affairs of a state is profoundly unsettling for the entire international system. However justified and necessary such intervention may be in particular cases, the generalization of such practice would strike at the very roots of the independence of states. A country consumed by a civil war is weak and powerless to ward off the designs of outside powers. Internal wars have been the favorite pretext of "the men who came to fight the war" for staying on —an excellent example being the Manchus who conquered Ming China after being invited to help defeat a brigand chieftain who had seized Peking in 1640. A prolonged civil war eliminates a country as an effective member of the international system and may lead to a severe curtailment of its independence. All intervention, moreover, establishes undesirable precedents; "do not unto others what you would not have done unto you": political leaders prefer not to enter upon policies

[12] See Talcott Parsons, *The Social System* (Glencoe, Ill.: Free Press, 1951), chap. 10.

which might in the future impede their own freedom of action.

The circumstances which discourage international intervention vary. Apart from the technical difficulties involved in external intervention which were discussed in the preceding section, every attempt at interference has to surmount initial resistance in the form of a reluctance to become involved. This reluctance can be traced directly to certain prevalent values of the international system—values attributable to a desire to "contain" internal wars. A system designed for the maintenance of independence cannot but assign high priority to values inhibiting attempts to tamper with that independence. Traditional international law forbids "interference in internal affairs" (especially that which we have technically defined as subversion) and places on those making the demand the burden of proof as to what matters are not internal. The Charter of the United Nations excludes from its jurisdiction matters "essentially domestic." The values which inhibit interference do not, in fact, prevent all, or even most, intervention (and much of it, foreign aid in particular, does not contravene international law), but they do affect publicity policies and increase the reluctance of states to admit to being involved in the internal wars of others.[13] They also strengthen the reluctance of internal war leaders to admit their indebtedness to external aid and succor.

The other inhibiting factor in international intervention is the frequent lack of international authority of any kind for such action. Although possibly the forerunner of things to come, the United Nations' action in the Congo, initiated on the unanimous decision of the Great Powers, stands out because it is an exception to the rule. Other important instances of such unanimity have occurred toward the end of the great coalition wars. More often, the Great Powers which form the concert of authority fail to agree on a desirable course of action. The

---

[13] Hence they also increase the difficulties of researchers anxious to trace the external ramifications of an internal war.

post-1820 inactivity of the Holy Alliance owing to England's refusal to sanction intervention is the prototype of this type of stalemate.

In cases where the international system effectively insulates an internal war, it does so with an implied purpose—leaving the decision to the stronger party—and it does so in cases where the outcome of the war is a matter of indifference to the international system, or where the "approved" party is expected to win. The rule of noninterference is perfectly rational and amounts in operation to the isolation effect. In ordinary circumstances the incumbents are at an advantage and the rule benefits them more than the insurgents. In this sense, therefore, the devices insulating an internal war from the international system are in reality at the same time also stabilizing devices for the *status quo* and, as such, likely to be thrown overboard in a revolutionary period.

IV. *Internal and External War*

Every war has two faces; it is a conflict both between and within political systems: a conflict that is both external and internal. Every external war provokes internal conflict, up to and including violence: the mass deportations of Japanese-Americans after Pearl Harbor can be adduced as one instance of violence stimulated by World War II, and the Vichy-de Gaulle contest (1940–1944), the overthrow of Mussolini in 1943, and the anti-Hitler coup in 1944 as others. Every internal war has wide international ramifications and, as we have shown at some length on this occasion, may lead to and include external war. And by being embroiled in an external war, the internal war does not lose its peculiar characteristics.

There are considerable similarities between internal and external war. Both involve the use of violence against legitimate domestic order. Both influence the structure of the international system. Both can be used as instruments of foreign policy. Both, too, can be understood in terms of the working of an international system. The international implications of both are very similar. Frequently, one shades into the other.

But significant differences also exist in the international attitudes toward these two types of conflict. While external war is at present almost wholly condemned, internal war is held to be permissible in certain circumstances. Yet, on the other hand, while international interest in an external war is recognized as legitimate, corresponding concern with internal wars tends to be inhibited.

The differences in international attitudes toward external and internal war, combined with the inherent difficulty in classifying certain types of conflict as either one or the other—since many important cases are on the borderline and may be assigned to either category—means that in actual life in a number of significant cases there will be disagreement as to what a particular war should be called, and that political advantage may accrue to the party whose view as to the nature of the conflict prevails. Semantics have a political function here.

As a general rule, those who wish to bring about the internationalization of a violent conflict find it desirable to call it an external war; their opponents, on the other hand, may wish to isolate the conflict and for that reason may prefer to describe it as internal war. Hence, depending on the point of view and the interests involved, many important yet violent clashes may be described at one and the same time as an internal and an external war. For instance, an attack on Formosa by the Chinese Communists would be regarded by them as a continuation of the civil war, but the United States, under its Mutual Assistance Treaty with the Republic of China, would call it external aggression. France regarded the Algerian war as a purely domestic affair and resented all outside intervention; the Algerian Provisional government did all it could to internationalize it and was even reported to be contemplating union with Tunisia to achieve that end. The Dutch government described its military operations in Indonesia in 1947 and 1948 as "police actions" and opposed all foreign interference; the United Nations Security Council chose to regard them as armed attacks upon the "Republic of Indonesia" and as a threat to peace. On a number of important occasions, Communist governments have used the technique of describing a conflict as "internal" or "revolutionary" precisely in order to eliminate, or at least to minimize and to confuse, foreign attempts at intervention in cases where the war could equally legitimately be described as external. They first developed this technique in the process of bringing under their control the authorities in the borderlands of Russia which had proclaimed their independence upon the disintegration of the Russian Empire in 1917 and in implementation of the Communist-proclaimed principle of national independence. Thus in the cases of the Ukraine in 1918–1919, of Azerbaijan, Armenia and Georgia, and Khiva and Bokhara in 1920–1921, and in the case of the Polish war in 1920, in each single instance the entry of Soviet troops on national territory was timed to coincide with the setting-up of a Communist-led government or revolutionary committee, whose existence was then held to legitimize the activities of the troops, thus turning an external attack into an internal war.[14] In November 1939, coincident with the attack upon Finland, the Soviet Union set up its own Finnish government and concluded a treaty of assistance with

[14] In the Ukrainian case, typical of the others, the Soviet Commissariat of Foreign Affairs thus replied to the Kiev government's protest about the Soviet invasion: "We must advise you that your information concerning the advance of our troops into the territory of the Ukraine does not correspond with the facts. The military units which you have perceived are not ours. There is no army of the Russian Soviet Republic on Ukrainian territory. The military operations taking place on Ukrainian territory involve the army of the Directory [the Kiev government] and the army of Piatakov [head of the Ukrainian Soviet government formed in Kursk]. Between the Ukraine and Soviet Russia there are at present no armed conflicts. The Directory cannot be unaware that the government of the Russian Socialist Republic has no aggressive intentions against the independence of the Ukraine. . . ." A later Ukrainian ultimatum was turned down on the grounds that the war in the Ukraine was a civil war and not a war with Russia. See Richard Pipes, *The Formation of the Soviet Union* (Cambridge, Mass.: Harvard University Press, 1954), pp. 141, 142.

it, again seeking to convert an external into an internal war. In 1950 North Korean troops proceeded to occupy South Korea on the excuse of fighting a civil war, with the transparent hope of thereby warding off foreign intervention. The Communist Chinese invasion of Tibet in 1950 was represented successfully as a case of internal war. And, finally, when the Soviet Union decided for the second time to intervene by force in Hungary in November 1956, it did so after setting up Kadar's government, which dutifully requested Soviet help in "restoring order" to the country. Yet this intervention could with equal or even greater legitimacy—in view of Premier Nagy's appeal to the U.N.—be represented as external aggression.

Our analysis suggests that, despite these ambiguities, significant differences nevertheless exist between internal and external war. Of course, the most important of these is the fact that, irrespective of its international ramifications, internal war is essentially a conflict whose violence unfolds within, and is restricted to, one political system. This suggests furthermore that internal war is not so much a conflict that differs "inherently" from other violent clashes, as a type of war whose peculiarity resides in its success in limiting itself to one country. Internal war is, above all else, a limited war, a war limited in its geographical scope. For a Great Power, the choice between waging an internal or an external war may boil down not to some inherent obstacles but to the question whether the conflict is intended to be, or is capable of being, limited or unlimited in its impact, and to the subsidiary problem of whether such preliminary conditions as the availability of a government to be supported have been complied with. It is therefore as a technique for the limitation of war that internal war deserves particular attention.

CHAPTER 3

Internal War
as an International Event

BY JAMES N. ROSENAU

INTERNATIONAL life is nourished and shaped by developments within nation-states as well as by relations among them. The stability and structure of international relationships are, to be sure, primarily determined by the accommodations and conflicts that mark the never-ending interactions of chiefs of state, foreign ministers, and other officials. But, irrespective of the skills of policy-makers and the dynamics of their interaction, the international system is also affected by the events and trends which comprise the domestic life of nations. If officials abroad attach importance to changes within a society, or if the internal changes lead that society's officials to press new values upon the rest of the world, then these domestic developments are certain to have external consequences. This inquiry focuses on the international repercussions of one particular kind of activity which can be—and increasingly seems to be—a mode of far-reaching and rapid change within societies: namely, political violence, by which is meant the use of force, legitimately (by incumbents) or otherwise (by insurgents), to control political behavior and accomplish political objectives.[1]

---

[1] The word "political" has been included in the definition so as to emphasize that we are not interested in all the violence that marks—and mars—the life of a nation. Our concern, for example, does not extend to what might be called personal violence, such as that which criminals employ in order to control their victims and accomplish personal objectives. While the crime rate and other forms of violence may well be indicative of social changes which can have wide international repercussions, attention here is confined to the types of impersonal violence that are designed either to alter the behavior of large groups of people or to acquire and/or maintain the nonviolent instruments of control over such groups. Ordinarily, in other words, "political violence" involves the use of force to alter or preserve the personnel, policies, and/or structure of government. The force employed

45

A balanced assessment of the international repercussions of internal violence is not easily developed. One begins with much common-sense knowledge about the importance of violence in human affairs—knowledge which may be accurate but inapplicable. On the basis of the history of the twentieth century, for example, it certainly appears true that nothing is more dislocative for the international system than violence among nations. Yet, the fact that international wars are major sources of change in the system does not mean that the same can automatically be said of internal wars. Nor is knowledge about the intrasocietal repercussions of internal violence necessarily transferable to its intersocietal effects. Substantial evidence can be marshaled to show that, in general, when a social system is dislocated by violence, the larger system of which it is a part is also disrupted: fights between husband and wife are dislocative for the family as well as for the marriage; juvenile delinquency disrupts life in the city as well as in the neighborhood; labor riots are dysfunctional for the economy as well as for the industry in which they occur; racial conflicts are dislocative for the United States as well as for the American South. Thus, by logical extension it is easy to start with the assumption that violence within a nation will have significant consequences for the international system. And, impressed with the realization that turning points in the affairs of men and nations are often marked by violence, one can readily build on this original assumption: there is, for example, a compelling symmetry to the proposition that the more intense and enduring an internal war, the greater will be its effects upon the international system.

Yet, there is no reason to assume that what is true of violent marriages, neighborhoods, industries, and regions is applicable to war-torn nations. Not enough is known about the intersocietal consequences of intrasocietal events to presume from the

---

can be of various kinds, ranging from the retaliatory repression of governments to the indiscriminate terror of extremists, from assassinations to civil wars, student riots to mass uprisings, *coups d'état* to guerrilla warfare.

outset that the processes of interchange between a nation and the international system are similar to those which obtain in other system-subsystem relationships.[2] National and international systems, having legitimate or exclusive authority over the use of force, may not be as interdependent as other, less comprehensive types of social systems. Thus the external repercussions of internal war may not be as extensive as commonsense knowledge about violence might lead one to expect: some types of internal war may have no effect whatsoever on the structure and stability of the international system; or, at the other extreme, further inquiry might even show that under certain circumstances internal wars enhance the stability of the system, thus performing an integrative function for it.

To achieve a balanced assessment of the subject, in short, preconceptions about the nature of violence must be set aside in favor of a more exploratory approach. Instead of building on ready assumptions, we need to break them down and examine their component parts, to identify the relevant variables and isolate the range within which they operate. More precisely, we need to consider such basic questions as these: What conditions maximize the external effects of internal violence and under what circumstances are the repercussions only of a minimal kind? What are the characteristics of an internal war that arouse the concern of foreign offices and the interest of foreign publics? What characteristics are likely to produce changes in the structure and stability of the international system? Are variations in the scope of violence accompanied by corresponding changes in the system? Is the duration of an internal war a relevant variable? Does the manner in which it begins shape its external consequences? In what ways does in-

[2] One of the few systematic efforts to analyze the impact which developments within societies have on the international system is provided by Kingsley Davis, "Social Changes Affecting International Relations," in James N. Rosenau (ed.), *International Politics and Foreign Policy: A Reader in Research and Theory* (New York: Free Press of Glencoe, 1961), pp. 130–40.

ternal violence differ from other forms of intrasocietal change that have intersocietal consequences?

I

The last of these questions is perhaps the most troublesome. On the one hand, it is clearly true that violence is not the only form of internal social change that can have wide international repercussions. The endless ramifications of changes in Great Britain that culminated in its readines to consider affiliation with the European Common Market would seem to be a case in point. So would any national election in which victory goes to a party that has pledged sharp and thoroughgoing policy revisions. Economic recessions in the United States, decisions of leaders in Asia and Africa to accept proffers of Soviet arms, and potential Chinese and French acquisition of nuclear capabilities are examples of other types of nonviolent change which do or can have noticeable effects upon world politics. The more one ponders the question, the more one wonders about the wisdom of regarding violence as a significant variable in the linkage between intrasocietal developments and intersocietal consequences: If any internal change can have international repercussions, how will these differ if the change occurs peacefully rather than violently? If violence is merely one form of social change, a rapid and extreme form at one end of a continuum, are not change and societal stability rather than violence the key variables insofar as international repercussions are concerned? Does not a society which borders on, but never experiences, violence give rise to the same international processes and consequences as one which crosses the boundary and collapses into violence? To state the matter graphically, if it is assumed that nations A and B in Diagram 1 are otherwise similar, will the structure and stability of the international system be affected differentially by their divergent paths through time?

On the other hand, notwithstanding the force of the foregoing illustrations and questions, one cannot resist the impres-

DIAGRAM 1

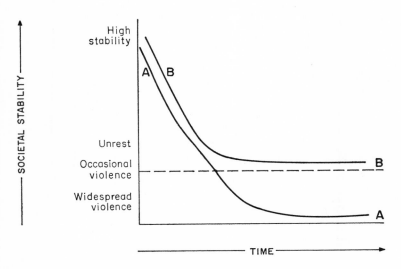

sion that internal violence is a unique form of change; that it can lead to special consequences for the international system; that, indeed, the external repercussions of the changes in nation A would, other things being equal, prove to be greater and more profound than those occurring in nation B. Such an impression is inescapable in the light of twentieth-century world politics. Leaving aside the repercussions of international war, it does not take much familiarity with recent history to discover that many of the widest and most lasting changes in the international system can be traced back to internal wars. What nonviolent intrasocietal development, for example, had such an immediate and sharp impact upon intersocietal structure as did the civil war in China? Similarly, the 1946–1950 guerrilla war in Greece, the 1947 *coup d'état* in Czechoslovakia, the stalemated, three-way war in the Congo, the successful revolt led by Castro in Cuba, the unsuccessful 1956 rebellion in Hungary, and the African and Asian wars for independence from

49

colonial rule stand out as events in the postwar world that have proved most unsettling or decisive for the international system. One could, to be sure, add a few nonviolent episodes to this list, but these additions would not be so numerous, or seem so far-reaching in their effects, as those in which the use of force was a central or pervasive phenomenon.[3] Or, if these examples do not support the impression that internal wars foster wider and more enduring external consequences than other kinds of intrasocietal change, consider the differential effects which followed from the 1917 advent of communism in Russia and the 1945–1951 advent of socialism in England—episodes which can certainly be regarded as, respectively, the most violent and the most peaceful political upheavals of this century. Both episodes did constitute rapid—as well as radical—social change. Yet the international repercussions of the successes of the British Labour Party have been virtually nil, whereas the same can hardly be said with respect to those of the Russian Communist Party.

Historical examples in support of any general proposition about international politics, however, can always be found. More is required than a simple comparison of the effects of the British and Soviet experiences if the impression that internal violence can foster especially extensive international repercussions is to be elevated to the level of an assumption in the ensuing analysis. Such a procedure necessitates identification of those characteristics of violence or of the reactions to it which are unique, which set it apart as a form of social change that has widespread consequences beyond national boundaries. Three characteristics would seem to meet this specification. In order of increasing importance—and for want of better terms—they are the morbidity and the amorality of reactions to vio-

[3] This assessment of the differing international repercussions of violent and nonviolent internal changes is confined to the "short run," to decades and not centuries, to internal changes which are "events" and not "trends." Obviously the assessment would have to be modified if the external effects of long-run nonviolent changes, such as the acquisition of Great Power status through industrialization, were taken into account.

lence, and its "explosiveness"—that is, its rapidity and uncertainty. Let us briefly examine each characteristic.

Perhaps more than any other human activity, violence exerts a strong hold over people's curiosity. There is abundant evidence of man's propensity to be fascinated by the plight rather than the pleasure of his neighbors, to take a morbid interest in their catastrophes while ignoring their normal routines. Presumably this tendency for violence to evoke morbidity also obtains on an international scale. Presumably it means, at the very least, that internal wars are likely to receive more sustained and elaborate attention and publicity abroad than any other socio-political events which occur within a country. Ordinarily international affairs seem remote and boring to the man-in-the-street. Usually he is not even aware that nation X is holding an election, much less what parties and candidates are contesting it. But let nation X experience a spectacular assassination or a brutal war for independence—the man-in-the street is likely to hear about it and even develop an interest in what it portends. One might reasonably guess, for example, that many more people throughout the world were aware of the terrorism which marked the last months of the Algerian war than of the negotiations which ended it. Of course, the man-in-the-street is not entirely to blame for this imbalance. The world's news media share his morbid concern for violence. In the case of Algeria, they clearly gave more prominent and extensive coverage to the plastic bombs that exploded in the Casbah than to the offers and counteroffers that crossed the conference table in Evian.

It is, of course, possible to exaggerate the importance of the magnetism of violence. Neither man's morbid propensities nor the publicity they foster are so all-powerful as to be prime movers in the course of events. Certainly the vast differences between the consequences of the British and Russian upheavals can hardly be explained in this way. The wide publicity which attends internal wars is not as potent a source of change in the international system as are the altered foreign policies and new alignments which they initiate.

On the other hand, this unique characteristic of violence can be underestimated. Under certain circumstances it can significantly intensify the international repercussions of internal wars. Widespread publicity regarding the purpose, course, and outcome of such conflicts may, for example, serve as a stimulant to similar activity in other societies. Such repercussions are especially likely when insurgents are spectacularly successful in their use of violence, for then groups abroad with similar goals or grievances, encouraged by the accounts of how such methods produced governmental acquiescence, may be emboldened to resort to similar tactics. Student riots are a good illustration of this process. They frequently occur in waves—as do other types of internal wars [4]—and the connection between one riot and those occurring elsewhere in the international system is often made quite explicit by its leaders. Because it inherently attracts publicity, in other words, violence tends to be contagious—far more so, certainly, than peaceful forms of political action. Aside from the adaptation of Gandhian methods by Martin Luther King, Jr., one rarely hears of groups in one country emulating nonviolent techniques of articulating demands developed by their counterparts in another country.

Nor is the contagion confined to activists. Widespread publicity can also serve to arouse otherwise apathetic publics abroad, thus enabling the insurgents—if the publicity is favorable to their cause—to procure aid more effectively from external sources. The extensive and laudatory publicity which Castro's uprising received in the United States proved to be a major factor in the overthrow of the Batista regime. Among other things, widespread American sympathy for Castro contributed to the neutralization of the United States' diplomatic

[4] For empirical illustrations, see Samuel P. Huntington, "Patterns of Violence in World Politics," in Samuel P. Huntington (ed.), *Changing Patterns of Military Politics* (New York: Free Press of Glencoe, 1962), pp. 45–46.

posture toward Cuba and, in March 1958, to the cancellation of military aid to Batista.[5] Likewise, the publicity accompanying the war in Cuba aroused wide mass support throughout Latin America, thereby subsequently limiting the ability of policy-makers in the Organization of American States to take action against the advent of a Communist regime in the Western Hemisphere.

A second aspect which differentiates violence from other forms of behavior is the amorality of reactions to it. Whatever the law may say about the right of one person to intervene in the affairs of others, it has little relevance when these affairs are marked by violence. Under such circumstances, anything, as they say, goes. If one chances upon two gangs or persons fighting each other with knives, one is entitled either to attempt to break up the conflict or to flee from it. There are no obligations, no rights, and no wrongs as long as the violence continues—and both participants and observers act accordingly.

This unique dimension of violence also obtains on an international scale. Whereas both nations and international organizations are quite circumspect in their manner of intervening in the affairs of a peaceful society, caution and discretion are readily abandoned when that society collapses into—or otherwise experiences—violence. Efforts to influence the outcomes of elections in other societies, for example, are ordinarily carried out in a judicious, if not secretive, manner. Other nations usually have strong preferences about which party they want to win at the polls, but rarely will they proclaim these preferences unqualifiedly, and even less frequently will they run the risk of seeming to intervene in the campaign. When the form of change is of a violent nature, however, the situation becomes amoral; all concerned accept the principle that both nations and international organizations are entitled to adopt publicly—

[5] See Merle Kling, "Cuba: A Case Study of a Successful Attempt to Seize Political Power by the Application of Unconventional Warfare," *The Annals*, Vol. 341 (May 1962), pp. 43–52.

even vociferously—a position of partiality with respect to the conflict. Elections are inviolable and intervention in them is wrong, but internal wars are everybody's business and overt concern about them is justifiable. Indeed, occasionally nations are unable to avoid involvement in an internal war even though they desire to remain aloof from it. Some of the neutral nations of Asia and Africa, for instance, were strongly pressed to render judgments about the Hungarian uprising of 1956.

There is, of course, an extensive body of international law on the inviolability of national sovereignty and the illegality of nations intervening in each other's affairs. Implicitly, however, even the law recognizes the amorality of internal wars. The rules and norms of intervention become obscure, "more difficult to classify," [6] when violence marks the affairs of the society in which intervention occurs. Internal wars are, as noted below, too explosive for policy-makers to be guided by legal rather than political considerations in their reactions to them. Law takes precedence when vital national interests are not challenged or when it coincides with such interests. Internal wars are challenging in this way, however, and thus nations, like the observer of a knife fight between two gangs, react to them either by intervening or by fleeing, depending upon which course is the most self-serving. In such situations, consequently, the law loses force and the distinction between intervention and nonintervention tends to be obliterated. As one observer put it in a discussion of Cuba's internal wars, "Some forms of 'nonintervention' are nothing more than acquiescence in someone else's intervention, and some forms of 'intervention' are so wrong and futile that they amount in their practical effect to nonintervention." [7] Or, as President Kennedy declared after the failure of the 1961 refugee invasion of Cuba:

[6] Richard A. Falk, "American Intervention in Cuba and the Rule of Law," *Ohio State Law Journal*, xxii (Summer 1961), p. 567. Also see his essay in this symposium, Chapter 8.

[7] Theodore Draper, *Castro's Revolution: Myths and Realities* (New York: Frederick A. Praeger, 1962), p. 113.

". . . let the record show that our restraint is not inexhausti-ble. Should it ever appear that the inter-American doctrine of noninterference merely conceals or excuses a policy of nonaction —if the nations of this hemisphere should fail to meet their commitments against outside Communist penetration—then I want it clearly understood that this Government will not hesitate in meeting its primary obligations, which are to the security of our Nation. . . .

"Should that time ever come [for an American military intervention], we do not intend to be lectured on 'intervention' by those whose character was stamped for all time on the bloody streets of Budapest." [8]

Russian Premier Khrushchev's reactions to the 1961 Cuban situation and U.S. policies toward it were no less expressive of the amoral international conditions fostered by internal wars:

"Mr. President, you are taking a very dangerous path. Think about it. You speak about your rights and obligations. Certainly, everyone can have pretensions to these rights or those rights, but then you must also permit other states to base their acts in analogous instances on the same kind of reasons and considerations. . . .

". . . If you consider yourself to be in the right to implement such measures against Cuba which have been lately taken by the United States of America, you must admit that other countries, also, do not have lesser reason to act in a similar manner in relation to states on whose territories preparations are actually being made which represent a threat against the security of the Soviet Union. If you do not wish to sin against elementary logic, you evidently must admit such a right to other states." [9]

[8] "The Lesson of Cuba," Address before the American Society of Newspaper Editors, April 20, 1961, in *Department of State Bulletin*, XLIV (May 8, 1961), p. 659.
[9] Unofficial translation of message from Mr. Khrushchev to President Kennedy, April 22, 1961, in *ibid.*, p. 665.

These quotations are especially blunt assertions of international reactions to internal war. It is much more typical for nations to cast the amorality of their reactions within the context of existing law. Ordinarily, intervening nations seek to legitimate their actions by citing international legal precedents or by claiming a higher morality than that of national security. Likewise, righteous indignation and an enumeration of laws prohibiting intervention is the usual response of policy-makers who have reason to avoid diplomatic and other kinds of involvement in an internal war. As the Kennedy-Khrushchev exchange indicates, however, the claims of both legitimacy and illegitimacy are best viewed as the payment of lip service to norms and precedents which are binding in situations where violence is not a central activity.

Much the same is true of international organizations, except that in their case a new legitimacy has emerged to justify recent interventions in the affairs of war-torn societies. The role of the United Nations in the Congo and of the OAS in Cuba represents a degree of intervention which was not contemplated when both organizations were founded. Article 2 of the United Nations Charter, for example, explicitly notes that the U.N. is not authorized "to intervene in matters which are essentially within the domestic jurisdiction of any state." Yet, this did not prevent the U.N. from intervening in the Congo in order to prevent Great Power confrontation in Africa. Rather, such action required an adjustment of international morality and the development of the principle that U.N. intervention was legitimate when peace had to be restored and order maintained.

Again a word of caution is in order. The international amorality fostered by internal wars can also be exaggerated and it is important to emphasize that this reaction to violence is unique only in degree. Nations also intervene in each other's nonviolent affairs. Programs of economic aid to peaceful societies are a form of intervention, as are propaganda campaigns, cultural exchange programs, and a host of other techniques which nations employ to shape the contents of attitudes and to control the course of events within one another's sphere of jurisdiction. Indeed, foreign ministries the world over are organized along geographic lines, with regional "offices" and country "desks," precisely because every nation regards the affairs of every other international actor as its business. Furthermore, as indicated at the outset, the interdependence of nations in the modern world makes it inevitable that each society's acts will have consequences within other societies, regardless of whether the former sought to wield influence across national boundaries and irrespective of what international law may assert about the sanctity of national sovereignty. It would, in other words, be naïve to imply that internal war is the only condition under which political considerations take precedence over legal ones. International relations, like all human relations, can range from full compliance to noncompliance with shared norms. Internal wars are distinguished by their capacity to evoke external reactions which fall toward the noncompliant extreme of the continuum—by a lack of restraint and a depth of commitment on the part of interested nations, characteristics which are not a part of situations in which normative compliance prevails. With nations overtly involved and deeply committed, it follows that internal war situations are likely to foster more extensive and enduring international repercussions than are nonviolent ones.

But why should internal wars conduce to international amorality? This question brings us to the third characteristic that distinguishes internal violence as a source of external repercussions. Internal wars constitute a form of social change which unfolds rapidly toward an uncertain outcome. This rapidity and uncertainty of violence—what we have labeled its "explosiveness"—encourage unrestrained and overt reactions abroad because they introduce conditions which place the course of events beyond the control of other nations. No situation is more threatening to nations than one whose outcome has become so uncertain as to have moved beyond their control. In order to maintain their identity and fulfill their aspirations, nations must maximize control over the outside world by adjusting their goals and behavior to their capacities and to developments which occur abroad.[10] If a neutral nation is tending toward alignment with an enemy of nation A, nation A's policy-makers will attempt to cope with—that is, control —the situation by exerting diplomatic pressure, offering economic aid, or threatening military action. If an enemy nation commits aggression, the nation under attack assesses its capabilities and responds accordingly. If new weapons are developed abroad, policy-makers press for equivalent and offsetting achievements at home.

Ordinarily, it is possible for nations to maximize, through rational calculation, their control over changes in the international environment. The capacity to control may not be sufficient to achieve the desired ends, and the controlling nation may even be subjected to more control than it exercises. Nevertheless, in most situations the leaders of a nation can calculate which courses of action are likely to result in optimum adjustment to the changes occurring abroad. Internal wars, however, present policy-makers with a unique problem. Events unfold too quickly and in directions that are too unclear for officials to calculate their responses rationally. A sudden shift of public sentiment in the war-torn society, a quick turn in the tide of battle, an intervention by another nation, an ambush of key insurgent leaders or an assassination of the chief of state, an assertion of superiority by one side and a contrary claim by the

[10] The maintenance of calculated control over the external environment may be viewed as the very essence of foreign policy. This conception is elaborately presented in my monograph, *Calculated Control as a Unifying Concept in the Study of International Politics and Foreign Policy* (Princeton: Center of International Studies, Research Monograph No. 15, 1963). In this model, control is not posited as a motivational drive of nations; rather it is viewed as a process of interaction in which foreign policymakers necessarily engage whenever they attempt to modify the attitude, behavior, or structure of objects—human and nonhuman—in the international environment.

other, an uneasy lull in the fighting, a tenuous stalemate while both sides probe each other's ambiguous terms for ending the conflict, a lack of information on whether the historic ties that previously bound the war-torn society are surviving and whether the end of hostilities will mean the restoration of stability—these are but a few of the unpredictable conditions that distinguish internal wars from other kinds of situations over which policy-makers must attempt to exert control. Faced with the potentiality of so much change at any moment, unclear as to what the next stage of the war will be, foreign policy-makers understandably become especially sensitive to violence in other societies. Maximum control over social change is not easy to exercise under any conditions—even those involving slow and sequential change—so that rapid and uncertain change may well require additional commitments (including a readiness to resort to amoral action) if interests are to be protected and some degree of control maintained.

It must be emphasized that we are not positing rapidity and uncertainty as separate characteristics of violence. A variety of nonviolent situations unfold rapidly or are marked by uncertainty. In one sense, for example, an election involves rapid change. One day a party is in power, the next day it is voted out, and shortly thereafter the winning party takes over the reins of government. Yet, elections are generally not also characterized by uncertainty. How the electorate will cast a majority of its votes is an unknown factor, but policy-makers abroad can usually anticipate what each party will do if elected and thus they can be ready to respond to any rapid changes that occur in the situation. Contrariwise, many nonviolent situations are marked by uncertain futures. What the result will be of efforts to modernize underdeveloped countries, for instance, is never clear and a host of outcomes always seem possible. Usually, however, such situations do not also unfold rapidly, and thus policy-makers are given time to adjust to developments they were unable to anticipate. Albeit a dynamic form of social change, modernization tends to occur at a slow pace and aid programs to underdeveloped nations are frequently adjusted in order to exert more effective control over the form and direction which modernization is taking. In short, nonviolent changes in societies are rarely both rapid and uncertain. Internal wars, on the other hand, are normally distinguished by the presence of both characteristics, and it is this explosive combination which makes their international repercussions so extensive.

That these characteristics must combine for internal wars to have external consequences is further demonstrated by the atypical case in which violence is not accompanied by uncertainty. Ordinarily, for example, there are few international repercussions when a military *coup d'état* occurs in societies where the overthrow of one right-wing dictator by another has become a traditional form of change. Under these circumstances other nations do not become particularly concerned about the situation because, irrespective of which faction wins the struggle, the policies of the war-torn society are not expected to change. In other words, traditional *coups d'état* pose no problem for foreign policy-makers because the techniques of maximizing control with respect to them are known and have been previously tested.[11]

II

Now that we have determined that violence does possess unique characteristics which, relatively speaking, differentiate it from other forms of internal change having external effects, let us turn to an exploration of certain aspects of internal wars which underlie variations in their international repercussions. In particular we shall be concerned with the differential effects

[11] Indeed, when the United States in July 1962 ignored prior experience in such matters and employed new techniques to cope with a traditional *coup d'état* in Peru, its efforts were to no avail and had to be undone by a hasty diplomatic retreat.

fostered by the scope, duration, and origin of internal violence. These variables will be examined first in terms of their effects upon other nations and then in relation to the structure and stability of the international system.[12] The scope, duration, and origin of internal wars, in other words, will be treated as independent variables—as causes—and developments in other nations or in the international system as dependent variables —as effects.

Proceeding in this manner, however, does not imply agreement with the view that "foreign governmental intervention more often is the result of domestic violence than is domestic violence the product of foreign intervention."[13] A case might well be made for the contrary argument that the nature and length of internal wars are more a consequence than a source of developments abroad. Our own view is that little is gained by taking a stand on this question. The causal process works in both directions, although here we are separating out only one of them for analysis. Moreover, we are confining ourselves to only three of the many aspects of internal wars which can be treated as independent variables. Attention is focused on the scope, duration, and origin of intrasocietal violence simply because these variables seem more encompassing and, from the perspective of international consequences, more important than any of the others.

By the *scope* of an internal war we do not mean the number

---

[12] In assessing the external effects of internal wars, we have been forced to make the simplifying assumption that policy-makers in all nations will react similarly to events in war-torn societies. Empirically, of course, the reactions of officials may be as varied as the goals, histories, and structures of the countries for whom they speak and act. In addition, throughout the analysis it is presumed that the international system is organized along loose bipolar lines, a presumption which means that the presentation is primarily applicable to internal wars in the post-World War II era. As Kaplan points out in Chapter 4, the general reactions of policy-makers to internal wars would obviously be based on different criteria if a balance of power rather than a loose bipolarity characterized the structure of the international systems.

[13] Huntington, *op.cit.*, p. 44.

of persons or communities actively involved in combat. Nor are we referring to the intensity of the violence or the form which it takes. Such variables are central from the standpoint of combat strategy and postwar internal stability, but they do not seem particularly crucial with respect to the international repercussions of a conflict. When viewed from an international perspective, they would seem to be subsumed by the purposes for which an internal war is perceived as being waged, and it is this variable which we shall treat as the key measure of scope. Aside from humanitarian considerations, other nations are mainly concerned about the posture which a war-torn society will take toward the outside world once order is restored and a government is able to govern. Hence it is the goals which the contesting forces are perceived as pursuing, and not their perceived size nor the perceived intensity of their struggle, which arouse anxiety among foreign leaders and publics.[14] Normally, to be sure, the more encompassing the goals of a war, the larger will be the number of persons and communities involved in it and the greater will be their commitments and efforts. We have chosen to focus on perceived goal variations as the primary measure of scope, however, because from an international perspective the exceptions to this rule can be as important as the rule itself. A small band of rebels fighting to

[14] Although the perceived and "real" aspects of internal wars may often be identical, throughout this chapter we shall have in mind only the former kind. Our concern is with foreign reactions to internal wars and, irrespective of the "true" situation in the war-torn society, these reactions can occur only on the basis of perceptions of what is taking place. In the case of policy-makers, of course, "perception" involves not only the unfolding of a mental process, but also the operations of intelligence agencies and the processing of intelligence estimates. In perceiving the goals of the warring factions, therefore, officials abroad rely on far more than simply the publicly proclaimed purposes. A perception of a goal may also be based on estimates of the prior experience and training of key leaders, of who wields how much influence with—or within—a faction's leadership, of how stable the leadership will be after it has triumphed and crisis-inspired unity has waned, of how wartime commitments and postwar conditions are likely to affect the transformation of proclaimed war goals into operating postwar policies, etc.

remodel the socio-economic bases of a society, for example, is likely to stimulate more interest abroad than will a large mob which riots in order to satisfy a highly particular grievance such as a shortage of food or a resumption of nuclear testing.

Although a host of purposes can initiate and sustain internal violence, and while the purposes can, as noted below, shift during the course of conflict, the goals of warring factions can be fruitfully viewed as giving rise to three main kinds of internal wars, which we shall designate as personnel, authority, and structural wars. Empirically, of course, no war corresponds exactly to any of the three kinds. These are ideal types which sufficiently approximate particular situations to serve as useful tools of analysis. They can be differentiated as follows:

PERSONNEL wars are those which are perceived as being fought over the occupancy of existing roles in the existing structure of political authority, with no aspiration on the part of the insurgents to alter either the other substructures of the society or its major domestic and foreign policies. Latin American *coups d'état* in which one junta replaces another are examples of personnel wars.

AUTHORITY wars are those which are perceived as being fought over the arrangement (as well as the occupancy) of the roles in the structure of political authority, but with no aspiration on the part of the insurgents to alter either the other substructures of the society or its major domestic and foreign policies. Struggles to achieve independence from colonial regimes, or those based on efforts to replace dictatorships with democracies, would ordinarily be classified as authority wars.

STRUCTURAL wars are those which are perceived as being not only contests over personnel and the structure of political authority, but also as struggles over other substructures of the society (such as the system of ownership, the educational system, etc.) or its major domestic and foreign policies. A war involving a Communist faction exemplifies a structural war, as does an agrarian revolt and possibly the present situation in the Union of South Africa. It is difficult to imagine structural wars which are not also personnel and authority wars, and thus this is the most comprehensive type.

It does not take much reflection about this formulation to recognize that a direct relationship exists between the scope of an internal war and its external repercussions—namely, the wider the scope of a conflict, the greater will be its repercussions.[15] This linkage would seem to obtain both geographically and in terms of the degree to which nations become involved in an internal war: the wider the scope of a conflict, the greater will be the tendency for more nations in more parts of the world to resort to more varied and direct techniques of exercising control with respect to it. As can be seen in Diagram 2, however, the association between scope and repercussions is not constant even though it is direct. As one variable increases so does the other, but the rate of increase varies, with the sharpest change in the slope occurring between personnel and authority wars. The reasons for this S-like pattern can be readily outlined. The international repercussions of personnel wars will ordinarily be minimal and confined to nearby nations because such conflicts encompass issues which have only local significance. The contending factions in a personnel war will, by definition, adhere to a common posture toward the great questions of world politics, so that the hostilities will not create much uncertainty abroad and more distant nations will not care particularly which faction triumphs. However, in order to justify the resort to violence, the two factions are likely to accentuate their differences on local matters, and when these include external issues such as boundary disputes or price wars, officials of adjacent or nearby societies will become sensitive to the struggle and

[15] It must be emphasized that this linkage and its graphic presentation in Diagram 2 have been derived from deductive reasoning and not from systematic empirical inquiry. Along with the other linkages and diagrams presented below, it should be regarded more as an hypothesis than as an established finding.

Diagram 2

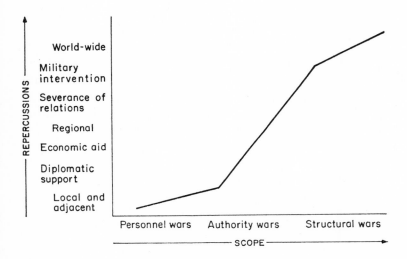

concerned about its outcome. Furthermore, the contending factions in such a war are much more likely to turn to neighboring countries for the kind of logistical assistance—such as arms, bases, and even political asylum—that more distant nations cannot easily supply.

Now let us suppose that the scope of the war expands to a contest between an authoritarian regime and a democratically oriented group of insurgents. In such a case the likelihood of other nations' developing an interest in the course of the conflict increases sharply as a universal value (self-government) rather than local issues becomes central to the fighting. To the extent that this value is of pressing concern to other nations, either as a matter of contention at home or as a key feature of policies abroad, then to that extent they will develop a stake in the outcome of the hostilities. Authoritarian regimes elsewhere in the world, for example, are likely to become fearful that an authority war may be contagious, that the aims or successes of the insurgents may encourage dissident groups within their own society to take similar action. (Portugal's reactions in the U.N. to wars of independence in British territories have clearly reflected concern about the situation in Angola and exemplify international repercussions of this sort.) Conversely, insurgents in authority wars are likely to attract the sympathy, if not the overt support, of newly independent nations or of those with foreign policies in which self-government is a core value. In addition, because distant diplomatic support may be as important in authority wars as close logistic support, warring factions will engage in more wide-ranging activities abroad than they do in personnel wars, thus further expanding the international repercussions of such conflicts.

As an increasing number of universal values divides the combatants in an internal war, the conflict is likely to have greater relevance for the internal affairs and foreign policies of other nations. Thus they are likely to attach more significance to the course and outcome of a structural war than of any other kind. Such a reaction is fostered partially by the possibility that the insurgents in a structural war are likely, if they triumph, to effect drastic alterations in socio-economic policies at home and thereby challenge other countries to do the same for their own populations. Structural wars, in other words, are more contagious than any other type. More segments of a population can find more reasons to emulate the insurgents than is the case in authority or personnel wars. Whereas contagion in an authority war is usually limited to intellectuals and middle-class groups who care about the value of self-government, the infectiousness of a structural war can extend to peasants, workers, and other groups whose way of life is at issue in the conflict.

The extensiveness of reactions to structural wars also originates with officials abroad. Their sensitivity to this type of conflict is likely to be heightened not only by a fear of unrest at home, but also by a concern about the foreign policies which the war-torn society will pursue when the hostilities are over.

66

Structural wars are especially conducive to such uncertainty because they are, virtually by definition, fought over some of the same socio-economic values which are at issue in the ideological struggle between East and West. Hence there is always the possibility—and this is why policy-makers abroad, irrespective of the side they favor in the conflict, become especially sensitive to it—that in their desire to overhaul basic societal structures the insurgents may, upon gaining power, adopt a radically new posture toward the external world, including a retreat into neutrality or even an entrance into a new alliance system. Such extreme consequences do not ordinarily accompany the downfall of governments in the other types of internal wars. The values for which insurgents fight an authority war, for example, are not likely to be so all-encompassing as to lead them, if they are victorious, to change sides in the cold war. Recent conflicts of this sort in Turkey and Pakistan are illustrative. The newly triumphant junta in the former did not withdraw from NATO, nor did General Ayub take Pakistan out of SEATO. On the contrary, in both cases the typical pattern of an authority war was followed when the two juntas hastened to announce that they would honor the treaty obligations of the constitutionally elected regimes they had overthrown.

Since other nations tend to anticipate that insurgents in a structural war will adopt new policies subsequent to the seizure of power, their responses to this type of conflict are likely to be more amoral and varied than to any other type. Having a special stake in either preventing or promoting victory by the insurgents, other nations will be disposed to employ a wide range of techniques, including covert military intervention, to maximize control over the outcome of the struggle. Lesser internal wars may evoke external statements of concern, threats of economic reprisal, and calls for U.N. action; but structural wars are characterized by the breaking of official ties, the imposition of embargoes, and the commitment of arms or troops to battle. American reactions to events in Cuba provide a cogent illustration of how increases in the scope of a war foster corresponding extensions in the form and degree of external intervention. While Castro was fighting an authority war against Batista, U.S. intervention took the form of permitting the shipment of supplies to the former and canceling military aid to the latter. But when the conflict became a structural one, with Castro in the role of incumbent rather than insurgent, the U.S. responded by suspending sugar quotas, severing diplomatic relations, and, ultimately, mounting a refugee invasion of the island. Similarly, rebels fighting for independence from colonial regimes rarely receive large-scale aid from abroad, but wherever Communist guerrillas are active, as in Greece in the late 1940's or in Southeast Asia more recently, the response of both East and West includes tactical weapons, military advisers, and helicopter pilots—not because of the kind of war that the guerrillas are waging, but because they are Communists who will alter the policies of the war-torn society if they are triumphant.

Of course, the purposes and postwar commitments of the insurgents in a structural war may not always be explicit or discernible. Frequently, in order to triumph in a prolonged struggle, insurgent movements must appeal to a wide variety of diverse and conflicting publics at home and abroad. Building such a coalition is a delicate process. As the behavior of American political parties in an election campaign clearly demonstrates, the mobilization of support among overlapping interests requires a minimum of specificity about intentions and a maximum of generalization about aspirations. To avoid offending any potential sources of assistance, domestic or foreign, the insurgents are unlikely to make detailed pronouncements about how they will proceed when they triumph. Rather, if they are not already inextricably linked to an outside nation or bloc, they will be inclined to espouse ambiguous values, such as freedom and self-government, and to claim, perhaps correctly, that prosecuting the conflict does not allow time for postwar planning. In short, structural conflicts often appear to be authority wars, a fact which foreign policy-makers recognize and which thereby narrows the difference between the international repercussions fostered by each type. The pattern depicted in Diagram 2 levels off at the top not so much because authority and structural wars are essentially the same, as because diplomats abroad may well regard them as similar. U.S. intervention in Cuba's war against Batista illustrates this point. Rightly or wrongly, American officials responded cautiously to the conflict—although they might have been expected to champion democratic rule in Cuba more vigorously—because, among other reasons, they were unsure of Castro's motives and the scope of the war he was waging.

Let us turn now to a second aspect of internal wars, their *duration*. A number of observers have proceeded on the assumption that the international consequences of such conflicts are directly related to this variable. Huntington, for example, asserts that "the longer the domestic violence continues [in a society], . . . the more likely are foreign governments to become involved on one side or another." [16] Empirically such an assumption seems entirely warranted. Certainly the internal wars of this century which have had the widest impact on world politics—such as those in Russia, Spain, China, and Cuba —lasted several years, whereas those which have not greatly affected the international system—such as the frequent *coups d'état* in Latin America—ended soon after they began. Similarly, there are many instances in which internal wars produced wider repercussions as they progressed through time. The Algerian conflict, to cite a recent example, was strictly an internal French affair at the outset, but the longer it lasted, the greater became the involvement of other nations in its outcome. What the dynamics of this relationship are, however, is far from clear.

[16] *op.cit.*, p. 44. For other assertions of this assumption, see Kling, *op.cit.*, p. 44, and Charles T. R. Bohannan, "Anti-guerrilla Operations," *The Annals*, Vol. 341 (May 1962), p. 25.

In what way does the length of a war matter insofar as its international consequences are concerned? Is the linkage a simple and direct one, with each increase in duration fostering an increase in consequence? Are the effects of internal violence cumulative? Or are there particular stages in an internal war which, when they are entered, have unique characteristics that alter and intensify responses abroad?

One is tempted to answer these questions by analogizing to the impact of internal violence on a national system or of international violence on an international system. In both cases the role of passing time is reasonably clear. The longer fighting persists in a society, the more it feeds on itself; each sequence of violence creates new issues and deepens old antagonisms, with the result that previously uninvolved groups are increasingly brought in on one side or the other and eventually, if the conflict persists long enough, the entire society polarizes around the two warring factions.[17] Likewise, as the two world wars of this century clearly illustrate, the longer an international conflict endures, the more unyielding do the war aims of the antagonists become and the less are other nations able to adhere to a neutral position. Yet, the fact that the passage of time fosters polarization within either system does not explain the dynamics by which the duration of violence within a nation affects the magnitude of its international repercussions.

Time is a reflection of two aspects of internal wars—the relative capabilities of the combatants, and the compatibility of their goals. Violence will persist as long as neither side is able to eliminate the other or force it to negotiate a settlement. Negotiated settlements, however, are primarily a function of the compatibility of the objectives of the losing side with any armistice terms that may be offered. If the differences between the warring factions are great, then the imbalance of capabili-

[17] For a stimulating analysis of the process of polarization, see James S. Coleman, *Community Conflict* (Glencoe: Free Press, 1957), pp. 9–14.

ties must be correspondingly large before one side will be ready to accede to the peace terms of the other. Indeed, if they are divided by completely incompatible aims, then the capability balance becomes irrelevant to the duration of the conflict as the losing side assumes a "fight to the finish" attitude.

Long wars, in other words, are those in which either balanced capabilities prevent a military conclusion or incompatible goals inhibit a political resolution; conversely, short conflicts are characterized by imbalanced capabilities or compatible objectives. Neither of these two factors, however, remains constant during the course of the fighting, and it is the changes in them which create the linkage between the duration and the external repercussions of internal wars. Capabilities tend to change in the direction of greater balance and goals in the direction of greater incompatibility. The latter change reflects the processes of polarization: as time passes each side accumulates more and more grievances against the other and then revises its military and postwar objectives to account for the new grievances, with the result that both sides become increasingly less willing to negotiate a reconciliation of their differences. Capabilities tend to balance as time passes, because each side, spurred on by its intensified inclination to achieve a total victory, procures new supplies and support by making new commitments—at home and abroad—which increasingly offset those obtained by the other. If both the insurgents and incumbents survive the initial days of combat, internal wars are almost bound to pass into a prolonged stage marked by stalemate and irreconcilability. At such a point in a conflict, with both warring factions continuously revising their goals and extending their commitments, other nations are certain to become increasingly interested and involved in the course of the war. Each goal revision and each new commitment deepens their uncertainty about the outcome of the hostilities and the subsequent posture of the war-torn society. As time passes, therefore, the international repercussions of internal wars are destined to mount as other nations increase their support for one of the factions or press more vigorously for negotiations between them.

Interestingly, the external consequences of internal violence reach a climax toward the end of the fighting and not during the prolonged stalemate. Stalemates tend to be stable and uneventful: the hostilities of the war-torn society are in balance, with each side knowing the limits of what it and the other side can accomplish. While the international repercussions of the conflict are intensified by the efforts of both sides to obtain new support and overturn the stalemate, the situation contains an element of stability in the sense that all concerned—other nations as well as the warring factions—know that each side is at least able to maintain control over a specified segment of the society. Violence and tragedy mark the stalemate, to be sure, but their occurrence is certain and thus the immediate future seems clear and predictable. As internal wars move out of stalemate and near an end, however, uncertainty mounts—both at home and abroad—with the knowledge that the war-torn society is soon to reassemble and redirect itself. And the actual cessation of hostilities, rather than bringing a relaxation of internal tensions and a decline of external reactions, is in fact the point of greatest uncertainty. Neither officials abroad nor participants at home are able to anticipate what will transpire when, with the conflict formally concluded, the two warring factions are forced to live side by side. Whether the conflict was terminated by negotiated agreement or because one side defeated and absorbed the other militarily, the situation is bound to be fluid and uneasy as the victorious faction undertakes to govern and fulfill its aspirations.

The wounds of internal wars do not heal easily. The reconstruction of individual and group ties tends to proceed less smoothly and at an even slower pace than after international wars. In the latter case, relations between—not within—societies have disintegrated. Stretching across cultural and national

72

boundaries, these intersocietal ties were not very strong prior to the outbreak of conflict, encompassing only a small portion of the lives of individuals and groups. For most persons caught up in an international war, the enemy is a distant and unknown entity who has loyally exercised his right to fight for national goals. Being long-range and tenuous, therefore, the relations destroyed in an international war are, relatively speaking, susceptible to quick and full restoration. Unless the victorious nation permanently subjugates the defeated one, ties again become remote and partial when the former withdraws its occupying forces from the latter and, under these circumstances, hostility can diminish and memories can fade. Such a process can be discerned, for example, in the changing attitudes of Americans toward their enemies of World War II. American wartime hatred of Germany and Japan could hardly have been more intense and unrelenting. Yet since that time it has virtually disappeared and in its place have developed cordial and cooperative relations, both at governmental and unofficial levels. The ties broken down in an internal war, on the other hand, cannot be reassembled so speedily or fully. In this kind of conflict, disintegration occurs in the close-at-hand relations that constitute the daily routine of life. Instead of the enemy being distant and unknown, he may be one's colleague or boss, possibly one's brother. Instead of serving time-honored loyalties, the conflict has caused them to be abandoned and betrayed, replacing them with suspicion and deceit. Furthermore, the longer and the more intensely the fighting has been waged, the deeper and more poisonous will be the wounds opened in intrasocietal relations. If the hostilities last more than a few weeks, and if the war grows in scope, socio-economic, ethnic, ideological, and religious differences are bound to be exacerbated. And, as the hostilities become ever wider, family ties are likely to be affected, as are relations within neighborhoods, factories, villages, and cities. To heal the wounds of internal war, in other words, is to recreate an old social system or to create a new one, and such a process is inevitably slow and painful. Victors and vanquished must live side by side and be constantly reminded of what each did to the other. Little wonder, then, that decades elapse before the scars of internal wars disappear. No better example can be cited than the persistent manifestations in American life today of the schisms created by the Civil War of a century ago.

In sum, even if one side in an internal war has clearly trounced the other, and even if a formal conclusion has been proclaimed or signed, it is never quite clear whether the conflict is actually over. The immediate postwar situation is at best unstable and at worst it threatens to explode again into violence. Both at home and abroad, all concerned have good reason to wonder whether the violence has so scarred the society that its members cannot maintain peaceful relations with each other. Ambiguous truce terms may cause a breakdown, negotiations leading to a peace treaty may sharpen rather than settle differences, some defeated leaders may go into exile and successfully call for renewed fighting, differences within the victorious faction may emerge and prove irreconcilable through peaceful means [18]—these are but a few of the possible ways in which violence within a war-torn society can resume, or, more accurately, persist. The situation in the Congo is perhaps the most obvious recent example of an internal war that lacks a clear-cut termination point. Indeed, it seems likely that years of "peace" will be necessary before the Congo conflict can be regarded as over. Similarly, it would be naïve to regard the settlement negotiated at Evian as the end of violence in Algeria,

[18] The likelihood of violence developing within a victorious faction is greater than it might seem. As one observer puts it, "No political leadership can satisfy all aspirations of guerrillas and saboteurs; consequently, each movement relying on violence contains a potential seed of future counterrevolution in those of its own rank and file who emerge from the struggle dissatisfied and who are conditioned to use violence as a means for solving their problems."—J. K. Zawodny, "Guerrilla and Sabotage: Organization, Operations, Motivations, Escalation," *The Annals*, Vol. 341 (May 1962), p. 15.

the 1962 Geneva agreement as closing the Laotian episode, or the victory of Castro's forces in January 1959 as the end of Cuba's internal war.[19]

If the situation within war-torn societies is most fluid as their conflicts seem to approach an end, the involvement of other nations is also likely to reach a climax at this time. In the first place, they must decide whether or not a conflict is over and, if they decide that it is, must then establish some kind of relation with the victor. Aloofness and neutrality are no longer possible inasmuch as the outward forms of normalcy require a return to international morality and diplomatic protocol. If the settlement is a negotiated one, nations that supplied the antagonists must turn to overt diplomatic participation in order to protect the interests which their supplies were designed to promote. If the war ends through a total victory by one side, then the nations which supported the victors must seek to obtain

[19] In terms of empirical research, the question of when an internal war ends constitutes a troublesome methodological problem. Some kind of cut-off point has to be fixed if manageable data are to be gathered and analyzed. From a societal perspective, intermittent violence can properly be treated as a single and continuous sequence of events, but from an international viewpoint this cannot be done so readily. If the international repercussions of internal war are to be differentiated empirically from those of internal nonviolent but rapid social change, then it would seem necessary to develop a clear conception, even an operational definition, of the terminal point of internal wars. Such a conception should be fairly easy to formulate in the case of wars that end as a result of negotiated settlements, but situations in which violence ceases because one side has defeated the other are somewhat more difficult to handle analytically. Consider more closely, for example, the last several years in Cuba. Is this country still experiencing the same internal war that started when Castro landed on the island in December 1956? Or did that war end and is a new one now in progress? The need to establish cut-off points is further illustrated by the problem of how the activities and successes of Castro's organization elsewhere in Latin America are to be treated. Are these developments, along with the anti-Castro activities of Cuban refugee organizations and the governments of most Latin American countries, to be viewed as the aftermath or the substance of an internal war? Were the 1962 OAS meetings that took up Cuba's role in hemispheric affairs simply a characteristic event in international politics, or should they be analyzed as an international repercussion of an internal war?

fulfillment of the obligations which their support was intended to incur; conversely, those that supported the vanquished will probably feel compelled to salvage what they can from the situation and, in any event, they must come to terms with the faction which they sought to defeat. Secondly, the no-war-no-peace phase that marks the culmination of internal wars is the point at which the future domestic and foreign policies of a war-torn society begin to take shape. Shaky as its existence may be, the new regime turns to making choices which can be crucial to other nations: the choice between breaking or reconfirming old alliances, establishing or resisting new ones, expanding or contracting trade relations, altering or reinstating the distribution of wealth and land, adopting democratic institutions to solidify political support or curbing opposition through authoritarian means. Turning points such as these can, through indirect contagion or official contacts, undermine or enhance the ability of other nations to maximize control over both their internal and external environments, and thus it seems probable that their involvement in a war-torn society will increase as its violence diminishes. International reactions to recent wars in Hungary, Laos, the Congo, and Cuba certainly reflect such a pattern. Indeed, the only exceptions to it are *coups d'état,* where the inception and termination of conflict are too close together for any pattern to develop.

The association between the duration of internal violence and its external repercussions does not, however, follow the same pattern for all types of conflict. Although in all cases the linkage is a direct one, the pattern does vary according to the scope of the war. Diagram 3 presents generalized patterns for personnel, authority, and structural wars. Here it can be seen that while all three types foster sharply increased international repercussions as they near a conclusion, the external effects of authority wars evolve at a different pace than do those of personnel and structural wars. The last two are widely separated quantitatively, but qualitatively they are highly similar. Until

Diagram 3

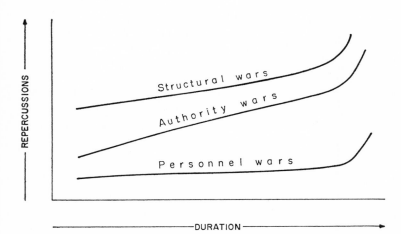

the closing phase of conflict, the repercussions abroad produced by both types increase at a slow rate—structural wars, because their external effects are already high when they commence; and personnel wars, because the geographic range of their consequences is limited. A personnel war would, of course, have sharply increased effects abroad if its warring factions revised their goals to include substantive policy issues, but such a change would mean that the conflict had escalated into an authority or structural type and thus the evolution of its effects could no longer be traced along the same slope. The international repercussions of authority wars, on the other hand, increase at a fast rate through time. The slope for this type of conflict is much steeper than for the other two because authority wars can start as localized struggles, but, if they do, they quickly arouse concern abroad as the fact that a fight for self-government is being waged becomes widely known. Castro's fight to oust Batista, for example, followed this pattern until it escalated into a structural conflict, and so did most of

77

the recent wars for independence from colonial rule in Africa.

The foregoing analysis of scope and duration as independent variables has been cast in terms of societies which lack the structure and experience to effect peaceful change and which therefore, through the processes of polarization, collapse into violence of their own accord. Internal wars, however, do not always begin in this way and variations in their *origins* can foster differences in their repercussions abroad. Most notably, violence in societies can stem from external instigation as well as from internal collapse. Although, as previously noted, little is to be gained from efforts to estimate whether collapse is a more prevalent cause of internal war than instigation, we cannot ignore the implications of the fact that intrasocietal conflict does originate in the latter way. The "just wars of national liberation" promoted by the Communists are the outstanding example of instigated violence and their occurrence is enough to necessitate distinguishing the origin of internal wars as an independent variable.

The distinction between instigation and collapse is, of course, a relative one. The origins of internal war can be placed on a continuum, and where a particular conflict falls depends on how intra- and extra-societal factors combine to precipitate it. At one extreme are wars that are due entirely to internal polarization and a lack of intrasocietal unity. Conflicts located along the middle of the continuum are of mixed origin and come into being through a combination of external interference and internal disunity. At the other extreme are wars which start because some nationals of a society have been encouraged and assisted by a foreign power or bloc to take up arms against it. The number of insurgents involved at the outset of such wars, however, need not be great. As Communist activities in Laos have demonstrated, a small band of guerrillas trained and armed abroad can initiate and sustain an internal war. Such conflicts can be externally instigated, moreover, despite a maximum of intrasocietal harmony and the absence of a polarizing process. As has often been noted, "the prerequisites for spontaneous revolution need not exist for revolution to break out." [20]

From an international perspective, cases of violence due to instigation and those that are due to collapse differ in the extent to which they produce repercussions at the outset of hostilities. When other nations perceive that an internal war has been externally instigated, they are likely to attach particular significance to the conflict and react immediately. If a society collapses into violence of its own accord, on the other hand, policy-makers abroad proceed cautiously until the situation clarifies. In such a case, time must usually elapse before the nature and direction of the war become clear. Not until then can policy-makers abroad identify both their own and their competitors' stake in the conflict. That is, the motives of other nations toward a situation which has collapsed into violence can hardly be manifest at the outset because they evolve only as the potentialities of the conflict emerge. Furthermore, since ordinarily other nations do not actively intervene at the outset of violence in a collapsed society, they must accept the terms and patterns of warfare which have been established by the time of their entry and thus they are limited in their ability to control the course and results of the fighting. In an instigated war, however, the threat—or opportunity—is clearly discernible from the start to policy-makers abroad. More importantly, it is clear from the outset that something in addition to an explosive situation has developed, that, indeed, another power or bloc is attempting to expand its influence over the war-torn society by promoting chaos within it. Clear, too, is the realization that by participating in the war at its inception the instigating power has a much greater chance of controlling the direction and outcome of the fighting than if it took no part until a later stage in the conflict. Thus other nations are likely to react sooner and more vigorously to instigated wars than to those which result

[20] Russell Rhyne, "Patterns of Subversion by Violence," *The Annals,* Vol. 341 (May 1962), p. 73.

from collapse. The U.S. response to the Greek war instigated by the Communists in 1947, for example, was quick and direct (the Truman Doctrine) in contrast to the cautious, wait-and-see attitude that characterized the American reaction when Algeria collapsed into violence in 1954. Similarly, the responses of other Western Hemisphere nations to rioting fomented by Castro's agents in one of them have been considerably quicker and sharper since 1958 than was the case when Castro initiated violence in his own country in 1956.

After the initial flurry of participation in an instigated war, of course, such a conflict tends to stabilize as it passes into the stalemate stage. Consequently, with the situation balanced as a result of their quick response, other nations are able to cut back on the extent and vigor of their intervention in it—or at least they can do so as long as the stalemate continues. Then, for the same reasons noted above in the case of wars that result from collapse, the involvement of other nations reaches a peak again as the conflict nears a military or negotiated conclusion. In graphic terms, the external effects of instigated wars that last more than several days form a U-like pattern with the passage

DIAGRAM 4

80

of time. Furthermore, as can be seen in Diagram 4, this pattern characterizes both authority and structural wars that are instigated from abroad, but it does not obtain in the case of personnel wars, since an outside power would have no reason to initiate such a conflict.

III

Thus far, the international repercussions of internal war have been analyzed in terms of the reactions of "other nations." There is, however, another set of repercussions which need to be noted—namely, those affecting the international system as a whole. While our treatment of the motives and responses of other nations is admittedly a simplified one—their reactions to intrasocietal violence are certainly more varied and complex than we have indicated—it has facilitated identification of the major aspects of internal war which have external consequences, and it therefore enables us to move on to consider briefly these larger questions: Do internal wars necessarily alter the structure of the international system and reduce its stability? Are there ways in which such conflicts actually make the system more stable? Do variations in the scope, duration, and origin of internal wars foster corresponding changes in the system's structure and stability? Do internal wars have effects upon smaller international systems (such as a region or a bloc of nations) similar to those they have upon the global system?

For analytic purposes, let us regard the structure of the international system—or of any smaller system composed of two or more national or supranational actors—as comprising those relations and interactions between nations which recur with sufficient frequency for a pattern to be discernible. Thus, for example, antagonism between the United States and the USSR is a structural element of the system, as is the North Atlantic Treaty Organization, the avoidance of alignment of many nations in Asia and Africa, the rivalry of India and Pakistan, the cordiality of China and Albania, the foreign aid programs of nations and international organizations, the European Common Market, and so on. The system is lacking in structure, on the other hand, to the extent that international events are unique or transient. Efforts to exert military control over space illustrate an activity within the system which has yet to acquire structure, while the crash of a plane carrying the Secretary-General of the United Nations is a unique event which is not part of a recurring pattern. It follows that when a pattern alters or ceases to exist, or when a new one comes into being, the structure of the international system can be said to have changed. Ordinarily the creation of a new alliance exemplifies structural change, since it usually means that some nations—the allies—modify their mode of interacting with each other. The system also undergoes structural change when a new nation is established, when an old one revises its basic foreign policies, or when a nation's capabilities grow or diminish to the point where other members of the system alter their responses to it.

Taken as a whole, the various structural elements of the system form what might be called its global structure—that is, its most dominant pattern which either subsumes all the others or is not inconsistent with them. A balance of power, for example, was the global structure of the system during the nineteenth century. At present the overriding pattern is that of two predominant blocs of nations, led by the United States and the USSR, which attempt to expand at each other's expense and through competition for influence among a large number of uncommitted nations. Unless otherwise noted, the ensuing discussion will focus on this global system, which has been appropriately labeled one of loose bipolarity.[21]

Although a gross oversimplification, let us define the stability of the system in terms of the readiness of either bloc to

[21] The "rules" and characteristics of the balance of power, loose bipolar, and four other global systems are elaborated in Morton A. Kaplan, *System and Process in International Politics* (New York: John Wiley & Sons, 1957), chap. 2. Also see his discussion in Chapter 4 of this book.

employ military action in order to preserve or alter its structural elements. The system tends toward stability when the blocs are inclined to employ peaceful means of competition, and toward instability when the probability of warfare between the blocs increases.

Changes in the stability and structure of the system do not necessarily accompany each other. As the emergence of the European Common Market demonstrates, changes can occur in the strength of one of the blocs without lessening international stability. Conversely, instability in the system need not result in structural change. The Korean War and the 1948 crisis over Berlin constituted breakdowns of the international order, but they did not alter the structure of the system in any appreciable way. In the case of most international events, however, the stability and structure of the system co-vary: primarily because the thousands of routine interactions which occur daily between nations alter neither the stability nor the structure of the system, but also because, on a rare occasion, an event will produce change in both of its aspects simultaneously. World War II, for example, initiated a completely unstable period and also precipitated far-reaching structural change that culminated in the transition from a balance of power to a loose bipolar system.

The relevance of the foregoing formulation to the international repercussions of internal wars is obvious. It suggests that only structural wars can produce change in the interaction patterns which comprise the international system, since such change occurs only when the victorious faction alters the foreign policies of the war-torn society to the extent of shifting it from one bloc to the other or from one bloc to a position of neutrality. Not every structural war, of course, produces such change: if the *status quo* faction prevails, the structure of the system will be maintained even though such an outcome may prove quite unsettling for it in other ways. Personnel and authority wars, on the other hand, can never effect structural change because in neither type are the factions committed to profound policy alterations.

Our discussion further implies that the impact of an internal war upon the structure of the system is not determined by its duration. Lengthy wars may render the system more unstable, since their continuance tends to increase the involvement of a greater number of other nations; but they will not affect its structure as long as their scope does not escalate into substantive policy matters. Contrariwise, short wars can result in major structural change if their scope is sufficiently extensive. The *coups d'état* which took Czechoslovakia into the Eastern bloc in 1947 and Iraq from a pro-Western to a neutral status in 1958 clearly illustrate this point. The contrast between these examples and the similar shifts that resulted from the prolonged wars in China and in Algeria sharply demonstrates the absence of a linkage between the duration of internal violence and its structural repercussions.

For similar reasons, it seems clear that the manner in which a war originates does not affect its impact upon the structure of the system. Externally instigated wars are especially conducive to instability, as noted above, but they will be no greater a source of structural change than those that originate through internal collapse as long as their scope is confined to the personnel and authority of government.

At a subsystemic level—within the blocs and among the neutrals—significant structural change may be fostered by those aspects of internal war which do not produce alterations at the global level. A conflict's duration, for instance, can have important consequences for the solidarity and capabilities of a bloc, with the amount of structural change increasing the longer the hostilities continue. Consider the 1956 uprising in Hungary: each day that passed further weakened ties within the Soviet bloc and, even though the rebellion was crushed and the global structure preserved, the structure of the bloc has not been the same since that climactic episode. Perhaps an even more striking example of subsystemic structural change is the 1946–1949 war in Greece: it did not result in alterations of the global structure, but its length facilitated the establishment of a pattern of American foreign aid to beleaguered nations which has certainly had profound consequences in terms of the relative strength of the two blocs. Similarly, the longer the Algerian conflict lasted, the more it weakened the ability of the Western bloc to build military defenses in Europe. The structure of relations among uncommitted nations can also be affected by the duration of a conflict. As the war persisted in the Congo, for example, certain groups of nations—the "radicals" and the "conservatives"—increasingly came to recognize common interests in the conflict and, consequently, the members of each group tended to draw closer together in an effort to adopt a unified stance toward the two blocs as well as toward the Congo.[22] Indeed, this hardening of alignments acquired formal structure when both groups convened conferences to ratify a set of policy resolutions, the conservatives at Brazzaville in December 1960 and the radicals at Casablanca in January 1961.[23]

From the viewpoint once again of the global system, it should be noted that internal wars which result in structural change at this level do not necessarily lessen international stability. To be sure, conflicts which portend the shift of the war-torn society from one bloc to the other are likely, for reasons noted below, to heighten the readiness of both blocs to resort to military action, i.e., to promote instability. There is, nevertheless, one type of internal war which will probably have structural repercussions without a corresponding increase in interbloc tension—namely, a brief *coup d'état* which is not ex-

<hr>

[22] For a listing of the members of each group and a cogent analysis of how the conflict in the Congo affected the structure of the uncommitted world, see Robert C. Good, "Congo Crisis: The Role of the New States," in *Neutralism* (Washington, D.C.: Washington Center of Foreign Policy Research, 1961), pp. 1–45.

[23] The resolutions of the Brazzaville and Casablanca conferences are summarized and contrasted in *ibid.*, pp. 21–23.

ternally instigated and as a result of which the war-torn society shifts from a bloc alignment to a neutral status. Under these circumstances, neither bloc has time to intervene in the conflict and the one suffering the loss of a member is not likely to be so dismayed by the shift to neutrality as to employ military means to reverse the outcome. The 1958 coup in Iraq is illustrative in this respect. Upon seizing power General Kassim severed relations with the Bagdad Pact and took his country out of the Western bloc into neutrality, but the stability of the global system was not greatly affected by these events. The United States did respond shortly thereafter with the dispatch of troops to nearby Lebanon, but these were soon withdrawn as clarification of the local situation revealed that Iraq had not taken up membership in the Communist bloc.

It is true that the Communist equivalent of such a shift, one in which the war-torn society departed from the Eastern bloc and adopted neutralist policies, has never occurred. Conceivably, as their reaction to the Hungarian uprising would seem to suggest, the Soviets might not accept such an eventuality and international stability might thus be diminished. Of course, the Hungarian revolt was not a *coup d'état* and, in any case, Russian intervention was not immediate. It might not have occurred at all had the rebellion ended and neutrality been proclaimed within, say, five hours. Possibly, too, their reaction might have been less vigorous if the same events had transpired at a greater distance from the center of the bloc. As previously implied, geographic location may affect the degree to which structural changes lessen international stability. Empirically it would seem that the greater the distance between a member and the leadership of a bloc, the greater the likelihood that its sudden shift to neutralism will appear more tolerable to the leadership than the risks of recovering its allegiance. The United States, for example, was more willing to accept Iraq's shift in 1958 than Guatemala's brief change in 1954. The Russian reaction to events in Hungary, therefore, may not be a prototype. One suspects that if a sudden coup should take Cuba from the Communist bloc to an uncommitted status, the Soviets would not respond with much more than testy accusations, a reaction which no longer serves to heighten international tensions.

What the Soviet bloc would do if a war to oust communism from Cuba were to unfold over a period of months or years is, of course, a different matter. The longer a war involving a possible shift to neutrality lasts, the more likely are the two blocs to develop contradictory stakes in the outcome and thus to intensify their readiness to resort to military action. Indeed, lengthy structural wars, plus all types of instigated ones, constitute the only conditions under which international stability is endangered. As the preceding analysis has shown, other types of conflicts can have a variety of external repercussions: foreign publics will develop sympathies for one or another side; officials abroad will be concerned about the welfare of their citizens and property in the war-torn society; diplomatic sanctions may be employed and economic aid programs may be curtailed or expanded. Yet high involvement, even active intervention, by other nations in internal wars does not necessarily mean an increase in tension between the two blocs. Both East and West, for example, are likely to be attentive to an authority war in a neutral country, partly because they have particular economic, regional, or ideological interests in it, but mainly because neither side can allow the other to develop advantageous relations with the winning faction. Such a conflict, however, is not so ominous for the structure of the system as to invite irrevocable commitments by the blocs. Competition is instead confined to such acts as inviting official visits, granting formal recognition, offering long-term assistance—in short, to control techniques which have become accepted features of cold war maneuvering and which therefore do not lessen the stability of the system.

To be sure, if an authority war breaks out within one of the

87

blocs, its leadership is likely to react swiftly and extensively —even to the point of military intervention—in order to preserve bloc solidarity. But the unaffected bloc, although hopeful it may benefit from the disruption of its adversary, is not likely to respond in a similar manner and become overly committed in a situation which does not involve its vital interests. Thus, for example, the Hungarian uprising of 1956 did not noticeably lessen the stability of the global system, because only one of the blocs made an extensive military response to it. Not only was there no increase in the readiness of the West to resort to military action in Hungary, but the bloc's leadership took great pains to demonstrate its restraint and to prevent any incidents which might convey a contrary impression.

We do not mean to minimize the importance of the limited number of internal war situations in which a direct military confrontation of the two blocs—or members of each—is likely to occur. Lengthy conflicts which either start as or escalate into structural wars are, unfortunately, numerous enough to sustain international tension even if settlements should be reached ending the arms race and the Berlin crisis. As long as members of both blocs maintain extensive commitments in a Vietnam or a Cuba—as they did previously in Greece, Malaya, Korea, Indochina, and Laos—the danger that an internal war will trigger a larger international holocaust is present.

For two reasons, moreover, the kinds of internal wars which conduce to international instability can be expected to recur in the future, possibly with even greater frequency and intensity. In the first place, as has often been observed, the acquisition of long-range nuclear weapons by both blocs has reduced the effectiveness of direct military threats and has therefore reinforced Communist efforts to expand their influence by instigating or taking advantage of intrasocietal violence in the uncommitted world. Secondly, the susceptibility of the uncommitted nations to internal war is, quite apart from what the

Soviet bloc may do, likely to increase rather than decrease as dynamic social changes accompany their efforts to modernize. As Huntington notes: "Without a constitutional tradition of peaceful change some form of violence is virtually inevitable. In the underdeveloped areas the alternatives, broadly speaking, are not constitutional change or violent change, but gradual change through a succession of reform coups d'état or tumultuous change through revolutionary wars or revolutionary coups d'état." [24] But, to repeat, the Soviet bloc is not likely to stand aside while violence persists in the uncommitted world. Rather, as one observer has cogently put it, "The close proximity of Communist power all along the vulnerable arc from Iran to Korea invites external support of internal disorder, and the external and internal threats feed upon each other. Potential and half-promised intervention from powerful neighbors stimulates the rise of underground movements, invites local Communist aid to them, and inhibits popular expressions of resistance against them. Once formed, such movements offer pretexts for increasing intervention in the interest of liberation." [25]

Nor is the West likely to remain detached from future structural conflicts in the uncommitted world. Its postwar military strategy has also been rendered obsolete by the nuclear standoff. Having found its newest and deadliest weapons insufficient to prevent the Soviet bloc from capitalizing on internal wars in Asia and Africa, the West's readiness to intervene actively in such conflicts has also increased. Each Communist success in this regard, whether instigated or not, has stiffened Western resolve to contest the cold war in this way. Furthermore, greater resolve has been accompanied by the acquisition of means to implement it. Recent years have witnessed the development of elaborate counter-guerrilla strategies and capa-

[24] op.cit., p. 39.
[25] Rhyne, op.cit., p. 73.

bilities on the part of the West.[26] Since the new arsenal of internal war weapons includes a capacity to airlift guerrillas or troops quickly into battle anywhere on the globe, from Vietnam to the Congo, bloc confrontation in the internal wars of neutral countries is likely to occur with increasing frequency and intensity in the foreseeable future.

Although bloc confrontation in internal wars renders the international system more rigid and more unstable, and while such situations always contain "a serious danger of escalation" [27]—of the losing side's resorting to conventional and nuclear weapons to avoid defeat—there may be ways in which conflicts of this sort actually enhance international stability. A structural element of a system can be both functional and dysfunctional for it and, upon reflection, internal wars do seem to perform certain integrative functions for the international system. They provide a means for the two blocs to compete through an intermediary—the war-torn society—and as such they enable both sides to ascertain each other's intentions, strengths, and weaknesses at a relatively low cost to global stability. Acquisition of this knowledge by both blocs is essential if a total collapse of the system is to be avoided. Coser puts it this way: "Conflict consists in a test of power between antagonistic parties. Accommodation between them is possible only if each is aware of the relative strength of both parties. However, paradoxical as it may seem, such knowledge can most frequently be attained only through conflict, since other mechanisms for testing the respective strength of antagonists seem to be unavailable." [28]

[26] Cf. Franklin Mark Osanka (ed.), *Modern Guerrilla Warfare: Fighting Communist Guerrilla Movements, 1941–1961* (New York: Free Press of Glencoe, 1962), esp. part 9.

[27] Peter Paret and John W. Shy, *Guerrillas in the 1960's* (New York: Frederick A. Praeger, 1962), pp. 65–66.

[28] Lewis Coser, *The Functions of Social Conflict* (Glencoe: Free Press, 1956), p. 137. See also Robert C. North, Howard E. Koch, Jr., and Dina A. Zinnes, "The Integrative Functions of Conflict," *Journal of Conflict Resolution*, IV (September 1960), pp. 355–74.

The war-torn society certainly pays a high price for this low-cost technique of maintaining the global system, as the South Koreans, Laotians, Vietnamese, and Congolese well know. But such conflicts are cheap for the system in that they allow greater flexibility of commitment and greater room for compromise than do situations, such as the contest for West Berlin, in which there are no intermediaries. In Berlin the lines are drawn tight. The forces of both blocs are directly involved and fully committed. Neither side can test the other's resolve without attacking it. In internal wars, on the other hand, both blocs can avoid firm commitments. By sending in "volunteers" (as the Chinese did in Korea) or "advisers" (as the United States is doing in Vietnam) they can probe each other's intentions or act to preserve the structure of the system without becoming inextricably involved. If need be, they can even retreat and lessen their involvement by blaming the loss on weaknesses of the war-torn society. Internal wars are thus a testing ground in which East and West convey to each other the extent of their aspirations and the depth of their resolve. They are, as it were, a form of communication. Even more, to the extent that they end through negotiations, as in Korea and Laos, they are a form of cooperation—a roundabout way of coordinating mutually exclusive objectives in order to preserve a modicum of international stability.

CHAPTER 4

Intervention in Internal War:
Some Systemic Sources

BY MORTON A. KAPLAN

I. *Two Models of the International System*

THE causes of internal war, one would suspect, are themselves internal in the sense that their origin is likely to be found in the social and political structure of the nation involved. The German campaign against Poland in 1939 was fought entirely in Poland, yet such a war would not be defined as internal. We would refer to a war as internal only when the dissatisfaction that produces violence on some scale large enough to be called "war" arises within the territorial area where the fighting occurs and when the fighting is carried on predominantly, if not necessarily exclusively, by locals. Thus, in a sense, to relate internal war to world politics might seem at first to pursue the peripheral, if not the pointless.

On the other hand, German and Italian aid to Franco, English support for the Greek rebels in the nineteenth century, Communist subversion, and American support to Guatemalan revolutionaries illustrate the important role that external nations have played in organizing, supporting, and helping to carry out internal wars in other nations. Outside nations may incite internal war, make use of an existing internal war, insulate the stricken nation from outside intervention, agree to intervene on the request of rebels or government, or engage in a combination of some or all of these activities.

If the factors cited above are aspects of the means by which the external impinges on the internal, the causes, insofar as they are generalizable, may stem from the form of the international system—that is, the system may by its nature encourage or discourage intervention—and from the characteristics of external social systems. For instance, in the latter case, a militant new social creed may inspire its supporters to export that creed. They may do so merely from the desire to have others emulate them, as in the support that British democrats gave the Greek rebels; from the desire to enhance national power, as in the relationships between Nazi parties in Germany and abroad; or from the desire to spread a new supranational doctrine and political organization, as in the case of communism. Or states may attempt to inhibit change elsewhere from the fear that revolutionary movements in other states might eventually produce revolution at home, as did legitimist dynastic regimes in the early years of the nineteenth century. Generally the motivation is mixed and probably some such mixture could be found in all the cited examples.

It is not as easy to cite examples of the way in which the form of the international system is related to the incitation of or intervention in internal wars, for this requires some form of theoretical analysis.[1] For this purpose a comparative, if brief, discussion of two different models of the international system—the "balance of power" and the loose bipolar models—may be helpful. Social science models of the type required in the study of international politics abstract from reality. These models are of the "if-then" type and give rise to reliable predictions only when a large number of parameters are held constant. In the real world, the parameters vary greatly and sometimes wildly. At best the conclusions of our models are tendency statements that may or may not apply to particular cases. They are not descriptive accounts of the efficient causes of events or of the concrete chain of events that produces a particular result. If,

---

[1] A discussion of this problem from the standpoint of international law occurs in Morton A. Kaplan and Nicholas de B. Katzenbach, *The Political Foundations of International Law* (New York: John Wiley & Sons, 1961). For a discussion of the framework of research within which the present essay takes its place, see Kaplan, "Theoretical Inquiry and the 'Balance of Power,'" *Year Book of World Affairs, 1960* (London: Stevens and Sons, 1961), pp. 19–39.

however, they serve to elucidate an important aspect of events, to distinguish between different periods, to explain observed differences—even if not with exactitude and infallibility—and to help to predict other aspects of situations that might not have been expected or might not have been related to those investigated, they serve a useful purpose.

The "balance of power" model of an international system is one in which the nation-state is the only significant type of international actor. The stability of the system depends upon the number of major nations (or essential actors), their economic and military potential, and their incentive to abide by certain essential rules or norms of the system. Too great a disparity in economic and military potential, for instance, may permit one particular state to establish hegemony over the system. Clearly, two essential states, as the only essential participants in the system, would be in unstable equilibrium, for any momentary advantage would permit one to conquer the other. Even a system of three essential states would be in unstable equilibrium. Suppose there were a war of two against one. If the defeated state were divided or made subordinate, there would be a reduction to a two-state system. Therefore one of the victorious states would have an incentive to form a coalition with the defeated state to prevent its dismemberment. But there might be some doubt about which state had this incentive. Each victorious state might overestimate its ability to gain more from the victory than the other. Political leaders might decide irrationally or might be deterred from rational decision by internal regime considerations. Moreover, each might reason that if the defeated state were preserved, it might be left out of the next coalition and, because of the uncertainties noted above, it might be dismembered by a future victorious coalition. If the two members of the victorious coalition adopted such a policy, there would be no other major states capable of combining with the defeated state to redress the "balance." Thus there is at least some incentive to prefer the present gains from a policy of dismemberment, despite the future instabilities involved, to the greater uncertainties of a future time when the state might be the loser in a three-nation war.

As the number of states is increased, there comes a point at which the probability of a future coalition that would guard against dismemberment becomes sufficiently high to contra-indicate clearly the policy of dismemberment for a victorious coalition. Maximizing the gains from war then involves risks that are too great and the security of the state can best be protected by a policy that secures the survival of other major states of the system.

It is now possible to derive the most essential behavioral rules of a "balance of power" international system. There would be an incentive to increase the capabilities of the state—by peaceful means, if possible, in order to minimize uncertainties and instabilities, but by war, if necessary. There would be an incentive to limit the objectives of war in order to optimize future potentialities for gaining coalition partners in order to protect against future dismemberment. Even if one state had no such incentive to limit its own gains, the other states would have an incentive to make it limit its objectives in war; and it in turn would have an incentive to oppose other states that sought complete victory. The states of the system, within certain limits, would have an incentive to encourage the formation of new states that could play an essential role in the system. And states would have an incentive to treat any other state, even the enemy of today, as a potential coalition partner. To act otherwise would limit the future availability of coalition partners and therefore would be inconsistent with the attempt to achieve a margin of security.

Alignments would be flexible and would shift on the basis of short-term interests. States would have an incentive to oppose any state or coalition of states that appeared capable of achieving dominance in the international system, and the weaker members of a potentially dominant coalition would have an incentive to leave the coalition for fear that, if it were successful, they would lack any real security in the ensuing state of the international system. Finally, states would have an incentive to oppose any other state's adopting supranational appeals, for such appeals or organizational forms would be inconsistent with the flexibility of alignment—according to which any state is a potential coalition partner—that is necessary for the stability of the system.

If we turn to the loose bipolar model, we immediately apprehend importantly different system properties and therefore have different expectations concerning the behavior of the actors of the system. In this system two blocs dominate in a military sense. Such a system can arise in any number of ways. It is relatively easy to determine why bipolarism developed when and in the form it did. The major reason lay in Communist forms of organization. The formation of a bloc around a strong nation employing a supranational form of party organization forces other important states into a bloc, for reasons of self-protection. These blocs are not mere alliances. They are not transient in interest or organized to satisfy short-term goals. Instead, long-term interests cement the bloc—often at the expense of short-term ones. Usually, organizational changes of a supranational character occur that tend further to stabilize the bloc structure because of the costs of dismantling the organization and because of the real and perceived community of interests that develop within the bloc.

A bipolar system in which the two blocs have a predominant share of the military capabilities has less stability than a "balance of power" system. A large-scale war between the blocs could easily produce a transformation of the system, since there would be no independent set of actors capable of intervening to restore the system to its previous condition of equilibrium or some analogous equilibrium. Hence the inherent tendency of states in the "balance of power" system to limit the objectives of war, to restore essential national actors, and to align with any other actor in accordance with short-term advantages is not present in the bipolar system. If the bipolar system occurs at a time of nuclear plenty, other factors may induce the blocs to limit wars in order to avoid mutual destruction. But they have no systemic incentive to preserve the integrity and independence of the other bloc if they should be in a position to dispose of it militarily at little cost or risk.

This point can be understood by reference to the period of the breakdown of the "balance of power" system. After the Franco-Prussian War, the passions aroused in France over the Alsace-Lorraine question precluded a Franco-Prussian alignment, at least for some eighty years. Therefore the principle of flexibility of alignment could not operate and the incentive of either France or Germany to limit its objectives in warfare with the other in order to optimize its potentiality for future alignments was not operative. Other strains in the system—in particular, those over the Eastern question—reinforced this development. Thus the system had an increasing tendency to rigid, if not bloc, alignment and to total war, since in the absence of nuclear weapons, mutual destruction was not highly probable.

Loose bipolar systems also contain a large number of uncommitted states in addition to two blocs. These are unlikely to possess major military power of either a nuclear or non-nuclear kind. Their major function in the system is mediatory. That is, they serve as communication bridges in the system. They may also attempt to ameliorate disputes, to prevent armed conflicts between the blocs, to bring peripheral limited wars involving the blocs to settlement, and so forth. Part of the power of the uncommitted states stems from the fear felt by each of the blocs that these states may be driven into the other bloc. And although the uncommitted states do not possess great military potential themselves, a shift of population, territory, and resources might influence the outcome of the struggle between the blocs.

However, a larger part of the power of the uncommitted

states stems from the nature of the modern nuclear bargaining situation. If we project to a time when both the Soviet Union and the United States can destroy the other in a second strike after absorbing a surprise attack, the ability to compromise an issue depends to a considerable extent upon the bargaining psychologies of the two opponents. If they cannot coordinate their demands during war, the war will be total. If either accedes to the demands of the other in order to reach agreement, it encourages the other to raise its demands. The problem is a very sensitive one. The penalties for failing to reach agreement, for demonstrating bargaining weakness, or for being stubborn at the same time that the other nation is also stubborn, are all potentially very heavy.

Each of the leading bloc nations has an incentive to create or to use cues or signposts that have some air of "objectivity," "fairness," and the like in order to weight the coordination process in its favor. Precedent, psychological expectations, legal norms, the opinions of impartial bystanders, and so forth, play a role in the coordination or agreement process, by tending to change the expectations of each of the leading bloc actors in regard to the behavior of the other. Thus, if one nation can cite a precedent and the other cannot, the second nation tends to expect the first to insist on an agreement not entirely out of line with the precedent, and the first nation expects the second to expect this and this reinforces his expectation. Since the second expects the first to expect him to expect the first to be firm, there is a reinforcement of expectations occurring at successive levels of intellectual analysis.

Other "givens" may influence the coordination process differently, but the role such "givens" play is illuminated by their effects upon the expectations and counter-expectations of the players. An important power of the uncommitted nations is their power to enunciate seemingly impartial criteria for settlement. As long as such counsel is not substantially divided, the blocs must be influenced by it; otherwise they run a grave risk that they will not coordinate their expectations. And the cost of this may be quite high. Moreover, even in the case where the counsel of the uncommitted nations is clearly not impartial, the mere fact that it is offered alters expectations to some extent consonantly with the counsel, although not as strongly as when there is at least the appearance of impartiality or fairness. As long as the argument can be made that such counsel represents impartial judgment, the opinion of mankind, or something else of the same sort, the players must reckon with the possibility that expectations have been changed consonantly; and this fact alone will influence expectations.

The United Nations, as a universal type of supranational organization, also plays predominantly a mediatory role in the loose bipolar international system and therefore performs some of the same functions as the uncommitted nations, but by means of formal and regularized political structures. The organization serves to dampen quarrels and—at least in the model of a bipolar system—to promote universally applicable and stabilizing rules of international order because the security of a predominant number of the nations represented in the General Assembly is optimized by such rules. The office of the Secretary-General serves to dampen conflict and to mitigate the destabilizing—as opposed to the stabilizing—consequences of bloc activity.

The model of the loose bipolar system, then, is obviously less stable than the model of the "balance of power" international system. To a considerable degree, the stability of the system is dependent upon the military and political struggle waged between the blocs. But, because of the bargaining situation mentioned earlier, the positions taken by the uncommitted nations, both within and without the United Nations organization, could be expected to have considerable impact on the struggle between the blocs, which, unlike the nations in the "balance of power" system, have a strong incentive to attempt to eliminate the other bloc, provided only that the immediate military costs are not too great.

II. *Normative Consequences of the Models*

A number of normative consequences that are directly relevant to the topic of internal war can be derived from the models of the two international systems. These will be discussed first in their most general form, under the assumption that states are indifferent to the social and political institutions of other states. Later this condition will be relaxed and the discussion appropriately adapted.

In the "balance of power" system, major states have an interest in maintaining the independence of other major states of the system, for only thus can be maintained the flexibility of alignment that protects them against future dismemberment. A major state that falls under the domination of another major state in effect enters a permanent coalition and is not free to participate in alliances opposed to the dominating state. Interference by one major state in the internal political quarrels of another thus is potentially unstabilizing. By favoring a particular contending political group and aiding it to obtain power, a state either may create political ties that make for long-term alignment or may even gain control over the ruling faction. For this reason, dominance of one major state by another threatens the security of all other major states and the stability of the "balance of power" system, and provides them with an incentive to oppose the intervention. There is also a risk in interference: backing the wrong side may cause such resentment that the state is not available as a coalition partner at some crucial future period of time.

Thus there is a strong incentive within the "balance of power" system to insulate internal political quarrels—including internal wars or revolutions—from external manipulation. There is an incentive to treat the internal political situation within a state as indifferent to other states, except when that internal political situation itself gives rise to unstabilizing international behavior. Internal conduct is the concern of the state; external conduct is the concern of the international community. Hence both the maxim that politics makes strange bedfellows, and warnings against the substitution of sentiment for interest, can be applied to international politics.

One possible response to internal or civil war within a major state in a "balance of power" system would be to insulate that state from any form of external aid or assistance regardless of whether the government or a rebellious faction was involved. This, however, would force other states to ignore existing agreements in many cases and would be contrary to the interests of all existing governments that would themselves desire aid if subjected to revolutionary attack.

Moreover, could the government of a state be cut off from aid and assistance merely because warfare had erupted within the state? If normal forms of commerce, including arms commerce, were cut off the moment a small rebellion occurred, the nations so acting would doubtless irritate gravely the state so treated. Indeed, it would be most unreasonable to permit rebels to sever the state from its normal ties merely by the act of revolting. The only reasonable solution of the problem would be to treat the government existing at the time of revolt as entitled to aid and assistance. Only after the rebels had clearly gained predominance and control could they be recognized as the lawful government of the state and receive aid and assistance from other states. All states would be expected to act uniformly, although independently, with respect to these matters. No state could easily take advantage of this form of behavior to obtain influence or power within the warring state. And neither the rebel nor the previous regime—regardless of which won—would have overriding reason to resent actions by other states that were taken in conformity with universally applied rules of international behavior. Although there would be no logical necessity to apply these rules to minor states, the more widely these rules could be applied, the less dangerous twilight-zone violations would be.

If we turn to historic counterparts of the "balance of power" model, we find situations that conformed reasonably well with it and which thus can be potentially explained by it. Rebel regimes, for instance, although not eligible for foreign aid until clearly in control of the situation, were not regarded as outlaw regimes. These were potential governments and might at some future time be required to play participating roles in the international system. As rebellions gained sufficient success to control part of the territory of a state, actions of a governmental nature would receive some forms of recognition from other states. They might acquire belligerent status and their ships at sea would not be subject to seizure by other states. They might even acquire some limited access to trade and commercial activities, although not on the same favorable terms as recognized governments. On the other hand, they would not thereby necessarily gain access to the formal arenas of state interaction.

Recognition of a new government resulting from revolution primarily involved acceptance by that government of the obligations flowing from the previous agreements of the state and those arising from international law. Failure to recognize was primarily a sanction designed to secure from the new government or regime behavior in conformance with international requirements. Non-recognition did not outlaw the regime but merely denied it access to modes of intercourse between states that flowed from international law, treaty, comity, and custom.

The problem of the new state—as opposed to the rebel regime —or the rebellious portion of an old state that asserted independence was not so very different in the historical system. The same factors that militated against premature recognition of a rebellious government militated against premature recognition of a rebellious new state. When independence actually was achieved, the major nations of the system had an interest in protecting the independence of the new nation against all nations other than the state from which it had seceded and in getting that state to recognize the new situation. This was roughly the procedure that the United States followed with respect to the Latin American revolutions against Spain. If the old state attempted to maintain its claim and could not do so effectively, the new state might nonetheless be recognized by other states of the system in order to increase the system's stability. And the growth of nations out of principalities was encouraged for similar reasons (among others), as in the case of the national unification of Germany and Italy.

The territorial integrity of nations was not an absolute requirement of the system. The inability of the Ottoman Empire to maintain order in its provinces—as well as sympathy for the Christian subjects of an Islamic state—played a role in undercutting support for the integrity of the Empire. Here there was some encouragement for national independence movements. Protectorates over parts of the Empire were established by Britain and France, but Russia's attempts to annex parts of it —attempts that might have interfered with the stability of the European system—were successfully resisted. The more normal course, however, was that followed during the nineteenth-century Hungarian revolution. There was no substantial outside support for Hungarian independence and Russia actively opposed it. There was good reason for such attitudes. Hungarian independence would have truncated a viable major nation to produce two minor nations. This would have been inconsistent with the stability of the "balance of power" international system. In other cases, such as that of Belgium, the nation was incapable of playing a stabilizing role in European international politics and an attempt was made to insulate it in order to eliminate unstabilizing consequences.

As the last few instances indicate, the principle of non-intervention did not necessarily apply to minor states. Yet intervention, if not logically necessary, could have had unstabilizing consequences for the international system. This would have been particularly true had such interventions been connected, not with *coups d'état,* but with genuine social or political revolutions. In addition, the more broadly the rule against intervention was phrased and the smaller the danger that twilight-zone violations would threaten serious interests of the major states of the system, the easier it would be to mobilize action against interventions and the greater the inhibitions against engaging in them. Thus even where such interventions occurred, they were differentiated from interventions in sovereign states by doctrines of dependent or non-sovereign statehood. And the closer the intervention to the critical areas of the international system, the greater the efforts made to limit interventions to specific matters that had nothing to do with internal war, such as debt collections or fiscal management. The nineteenth-century system was basically a European rather than a world system, and interventions in the case of internal wars were genuinely inhibited for the most part at the vital centers of the system.

The "balance of power" international system, however, could not be expected to operate in the same way in the non-European areas that eventually were colonized. Here there was no potentiality for modern nationhood—at least in the near future. Indeed, the nations presently arising in these areas—the new and uncommitted nations—owe their birth to the political, economic, and social changes produced by colonial regimes. Moreover, these colonial areas in Asia and Africa were important from the standpoint of trade and resources, although other motivations also played a role in colonization. Therefore they could not be excluded from the competitive struggle of the major nations of the "balance of power" system. Division into spheres of influence was the most practicable solution of the problem. In the sensitive China area, where an old civilization and state was breaking down and where in the absence of countervailing moves by other states a great Russian—or Japanese

—advantage conceivably might have been gained, spheres of influence were carved out reciprocally to prevent national advantage. In other areas, such as Africa, reciprocal spheres of influence, although sought, did not play the same role, but attempts often were made to preserve at least the trading interests of the nonholding state in African colonies. The degree of control or intervention in Asian and African areas ranged from colonies, to "dependent states" in which foreign affairs, finance, and some police power were controlled, to cases where only sporadic influence was exercised. The pressure on such entities may have been direct and continuous or intermittent and indirect. The financial reforms forced on Egypt in the nineteenth century are a case in point, but so are the interventions in the efforts of Egypt to split away from the Ottoman Empire. And, in the case of Panama, the independence movement came close to being an American intervention. The great difficulty lay in the fact that these non-European areas were highly important economically and in other ways, but they lacked state systems capable of playing an independent and stabilizing role in international politics. They could not be ignored or left alone. And hence some behavioral inconsistencies developed that were camouflaged as well as possible by the doctrine of the time.

Thus we can see that the "balance of power" system operated virtually the same way with respect to both new governments and new states arising out of internal violence. In both cases the major states of the system attempted to insulate the affected state from external interference or intervention. Support for the rebels would have been considered interference whether it was granted before the outbreak of violence and helped to incite the internal war, or whether it occurred during the course of the war. Only after the rebel regime had either secured control of the state or had carved out a new state would recognition of or support for the new regime or state be regarded as legitimate within the normative structure of the system. And, despite major exceptions, the general behavior of the states of the system conformed with the norms because the same interests that produced the norms made conforming behavior generally consonant with state interests.

Clearly, the loose bipolar system could not be expected to operate in the same way. As we have seen, flexibility of alignment and the maintenance of optimal potentiality for coalition formation are not features of a bipolar system. Consequently the factors that militate against interference in internal war in the "balance of power" system are not present in a loose bipolar system. The organic relationships within the blocs in the form of joint military commands, supply facilities, production plans, division of functional responsibility, flows of manpower and material, and so forth, are inconsistent with fully independent action by the member states. This does not imply that differences of policy are absent within blocs or that on particular issues a member of one bloc will never support the leading nation of another bloc. But blocs are not short-term alliances and, in a system of blocs, the integration of the bloc—and not merely the "sovereign" independence of its members—is an important factor making for stability in the system.

Each bloc of the bipolar system has an evident interest in opposing or preventing internal changes within the political systems of its members that would move the state out of the bloc or, what is worse, into the other bloc. And each bloc has an interest in attempting to bring about changes in the political life of the members of the other bloc that would remove them from that bloc and that might possibly produce a switch in bloc affiliation. Although in a nuclear age there is concern not to act in a way that will precipitate nuclear war, nonetheless some incentive exists either to incite changes in relationships in the opposing bloc, to encourage revolutions that have broken out, or to intervene in one form or another against revolutionary changes in one's own bloc that would be inconsistent with maintenance of the bloc. Obviously, in the real world, this task is somewhat easier for the Soviet Union, which can manipulate informal party relationships, than for the United States, which must resort to formal—although occasionally clandestine—governmental agencies. This conflict involving intervention in internal war is most acute in such divided nations as Korea, Vietnam, and China, but it also has occurred in virulent forms in Laos and Cuba.

Now, even in terms of the model, it is not evident that the blocs have a major interest in attempting to incite or to exploit internal wars in uncommitted nations—at least in an overt manner. Either bloc would run the danger of alienating the nation involved if the attempt failed, and—more important—of alienating most other uncommitted nations even if the attempt succeeded. Because of the role specialization of the loose bipolar system, most uncommitted nations would have an incentive to treat actions of this kind as though their interests were the same. Local differences or ambiguities might tend to obscure this joint interest in particular cases, but in general the uncommitted nations would pursue their interests best by insulating themselves from bloc quarrels and perhaps also by exploiting bloc differences. In terms of the model, the uncommitted nations would have an interest in opposing intervention in internal wars by other uncommitted nations, for such intervention would tend to undermine a normative rule forbidding intervention by the blocs. As we shall see, however, other considerations contra-indicate this statement when we turn from the model to the real world.

It seems reasonable that the less uncommitted a nation is, the less will be the interest of the other uncommitted nations in protecting it from bloc intervention, and the less the principle of bloc nonintervention in uncommitted areas will be impaired. Although one might argue that intervention anywhere by the blocs—even intervention against members of the other bloc— impairs the principle of nonintervention and therefore ought to be opposed by the uncommitted nations, the argument is not completely compelling. If the situation is such that the uncommitted have sufficient bargaining power to impose considerable penalties on intervening actors, and if the difficulties and costs of intervention are high enough, it is possible that strict support for a universalistic rule of nonintervention becomes a sound policy for uncommitted states. But in at least some cases—for example, intervention by a leading bloc actor in the affairs of a member of the bloc—the attempt to enforce the principle might prove abortive. Such failures might undermine the entire principle. On the other hand, some exceedingly fine distinctions could be drawn by means of which any particular interventionary act could be defined as one not in violation of the essence of the principle. And it is intuitively obvious that this also could undermine the principle.

III. *Other Factors Making for Intervention*

The models we have employed so far give insight into some of the most striking differences between the "balance of power" and the loose bipolar international systems in regard to the propensity of external nations to intervene. They do not, however, exhaust the subject or account for all cases of intervention or nonintervention. Some of the factors accounting for particular cases are themselves so individualized that they have no relevance for an analysis of this type. Others result from rather general causes—although they are not included within the models—and therefore have considerable interest.

Every student of history is aware that the discussion so far does not account for the Holy Alliance—the most striking example of collective intervention during the "balance of power" period. Clearly the behavior of states at that time was at least manifestly inconsistent with the model that predicts nonintervention. It should be noted, however, that the collective intervention of the Holy Alliance was a reaction to two seemingly connected phenomena: the Napoleonic wars and democratization. The Napoleonic wars had threatened the stability of the "balance of power" system. Napoleonic France, because of the organizational and military genius of Napoleon, threatened the independence of the other European states. France was also a messianic state. The attraction of the French political system for the awakening middle classes created potential fifth columns. This made much more difficult the forging of military counteralliances elsewhere. Thus France had an internal drive and dynamism that gave it an advantage, and other states were handicapped by internal sympathies for the French Revolution and the state it had spawned.

The conservative nations of Europe had a natural fear that other democratic states might present the same kind of threat to the international system and thus to their national security. There was, however, an additional and most important consideration. The spread of democratic doctrine threatened dynastic regimes. Our models are constructed as if there were no conflicts of interest within a nation. But this is merely an initial assumption to be modified in subsequent analysis. Dynastic rulers had to balance regime interests against national interests. In this case, there did not appear to be any grave conflict between the two sets of interests, as the democratic states—assuming the Napoleonic model—also threatened international peace and national interests. Even so, intervention posed considerable dangers for national interests—since it was partly inconsistent with the need for flexibility of alignment—and also for the dynastic interests of those dynasties whose nations might lose out in the European struggle.

Despite the strong motivation of the conservative regimes to intervene against democracy, they had to balance this concern against the dangers of intervention. Collective intervention was the attempted solution. Just as some small European areas were neutralized or insulated against the play of European politics, and as some Asian areas were divided to minimize individual "unbalancing" gains, or as the spoils of war were divided for similar reasons, all the conservative nations intervened against revolutionary democratic regimes to prevent any of them from securing some form of permanent advantage or governmental tie or alliance. Collective interventions, however, are of dubious workability. Some particular nation is likely to secure an important advantage despite the collective nature of the intervention. In addition, British opposition and the nondynamic nature of some of the new democratic regimes took much of the steam out of collective intervention. So did social and political changes in the conservative and intervening nations. Eventually both the reason for intervention and the ability to intervene caused the demise of the Holy Alliance. And, in succeeding years, practices with respect to intervention resembled much more the predictions of the model.

The attempts of the Holy Alliance to put down democratic revolutions were in any event somewhat counterbalanced by English sympathies for popular revolutions in Greece and by American sympathies for popular revolutions generally. The support for such movements ranged from encouragement to diplomatic recognition, volunteer recruits, and so forth; but it rarely, if ever, included direct military support or other overt forms of direct intervention in internal warfare.

During the period of the breakdown of the "balance of power," alliances tended toward rigidity and the rule governing nonintervention had considerably less force. This period coincided with various movements that threatened to sweep across national boundaries. Some, like the pan-Slavic movements, were of little consequence and need not be mentioned. But the Fascist movements during the later interwar period were of great significance. Although nationalistic in the sense of stressing national power and glory, these movements tended to disrupt the fabric of nationhood externally as well as internally. And they extended assistance to kindred movements in other national areas.

The techniques of fascism ranged widely. In Spain an internal revolt led by Franco received massive support from Nazi Germany and Fascist Italy, ranging from diplomatic aid, including early recognition, to financial aid, the supply of arms, and even of elite military units. Pressure was placed on the democratic nations not to aid the legal government of Spain, at the same time that aid was extended by fascism to the revolution. Fear of communism and sympathies based on class ties that crossed national boundaries, as well as the influence of the Roman Catholic Church, tended to support the efforts of the Fascist states to intervene and to inhibit support for the government of the Spanish Republic. In addition, pacifist and peace movements that were afraid of the possibility of war, although usually opposed to fascism and to the Spanish Revolution, opposed rather successfully the internal measures, including the strengthening of the military arms of their governments, that would have permitted those governments to play a more active role in international politics if they had had the will or the desire.

The conquest—or *Anschluss*—of Austria in 1938 was accompanied both by threats of military action and by an internal *putsch* by local Nazis. The campaign against Czechoslovakia that preceded the Munich Pact was supported by local Germans and other separatist groups acting under orders or suggestions from the Nazi regime. In these cases internal violence had a primarily external genesis. And other states of the international system were unable or unwilling to intervene to protect the norms stressing nonintervention. The system of rigid alignments of the period also limited the interest of states in supporting these norms as general rules. And in addition, although the democracies had an interest in supporting the norm against Fascist revolution, internal political dissension, pacifism, and fears of communism served to inhibit them.

Indeed the fear of communism, although exaggerated in terms of communism's effectiveness, was justified in terms of its methods. The new revolutionary system in the Soviet Union, based on Leninist techniques of organization, established a world-wide conspiratorial and revolutionary system operating under directives from the Comintern, which in turn was dominated by the Kremlin. A world-wide system of shadow governments inconsistent with the organization of normal state-systems and with that of international politics was established. Plans were organized for revolutions, strikes, other forms of violence and economic pressures, and for the infiltration and subversion of ostensibly non-Communist organizations and movements. Directed from the only Communist state, these external Communist movements were designed to immobilize bourgeois states when pursuing objectives contrary to the interests of the Soviet Union and to enlist bourgeois states in support of Soviet objectives.

To the extent that Communist organizations were successful in wielding influence—even apart from other destabilizing factors already mentioned—the "balance of power" system was inhibited from successful operation. Thus the bourgeois states were correct to fear this threat, although such fears may have blinded them to temporarily greater dangers. In any event, the rise throughout the world of political movements that did not recognize national boundaries interfered seriously with the stability of the "balance of power" system and made it difficult, if not impossible, to implement its norms—particularly those dealing with nonintervention in internal wars.

Following World War II, the dangers of Fascist subversion of national states were eliminated. However, the Soviet Union emerged as one of the world's two most powerful states. Communist regimes were established in Eastern Europe behind the protection of the Russian armies. Large Communist movements in France and Italy were serious fifth columns and for a period seemed capable of taking over governmental control. Even after their representatives were removed from important Cabinet positions in both nations, the Communist organizations remained serious political dangers and, under Cominform directives, for a period of time in the 1940's were responsible for disruptive strikes and violence. And, in the late years of the decade, the Communist parties in Japan, India, Indonesia, and other Asian areas resorted to direct violence in an effort to topple non-Communist governments and to establish regimes that would join the Communist bloc.

Although revolutionary communism exaggerates the normal tendencies of a bipolar system toward intervention, it does not give rise to them. They are an expected aspect of the system. It would also be expected, however, that the uncommitted nations would tend to oppose such intervention and to dampen it as offensive to their own national interests. And, no doubt, to some extent this has happened in the postwar period. This general prescription for the uncommitted states nonetheless assumes that they are indistinguishable from other states, that they have no history that sets them apart and that establishes different motivations to make their interests at least appear different. It may be a historical accident—at least from the standpoint of systems theory—that the uncommitted states are largely ex-colonial or that, even when not of such origin, other factors identify them with such states. But this accident is of great importance in understanding and predicting their behavior in the contemporary world of international politics.

Most of the uncommitted states were at one time colonies of members of NATO. Even though their nationhood and their ability to govern themselves may in many cases be the product of colonial rule, their national image was formed in opposition to the colonial power, which, to many of these countries, is seen as a continuing threat to their independence or a barrier to the independence of similarly situated areas. Their sympathies are with the areas still striving toward independence and—at least until the process is completed—their image of the imperial powers is not likely to be modified greatly.

Still another important factor is involved: color. The people of the colonial states are different in color from their former European overlords. And although they may differ in color from each other as much as they do from Europeans, the Europeans were able to define the color issue in terms of "white" and "colored." This does not imply the absence of prejudice among colored peoples toward each other, but it does establish a common antipathy toward the previous overlord and his present allies.

A third factor plays a major role: the uncommitted nations are almost invariably underdeveloped areas. Whether accurately or inaccurately, they blame this lack of development on imperialism and foreign capitalism. Their subjection is seen in economic as well as in political terms. And they are unlikely to feel free until they have also developed economically and are economically independent of external nations.

In the underdeveloped "non-Western" areas, however, economic development requires social change. Unfortunately the NATO nations pose, or seem to pose, barriers to the kinds of social change that the local elites often deem necessary for modernization. And it has been these regimes that the West has tended to support. This has the additional disadvantage of shifting these nations into the center of cold war tensions and of raising the specter of hot war. In turn, involvement in the cold war reduces the ability of these regimes to bargain with both East and West for aid and diverts their attention from modernization.

The West has itself fostered the unnecessary linkage of external and internal anti-communism, and it has by its policies tended to link both with reactionary domestic policies. Thus the West appears to many elites in the developing nations to represent a threat to their development and to their insulation from the distractions of the cold war. The interest of the West in relations with these nations tends to be regarded as a form of imperialism. And the success of Western policy in moving any developing nation into its camp appears a threat to the other developing nations in the same way that the shift of a state to the Communist bloc appears a threat to the West. It is viewed as part of a process which, if it is not stopped, could cause the collapse of the values these elites are pursuing.

For these reasons, many of the elites and counterelites in the developing nations cooperate in opposing Western policy. And this in turn leads to intervention against those conservative or reactionary elites supported by the West. Revolutionary elites in the developing states seek and tend to receive aid from sympathetic uncommitted states, many of whom see their own interests as dictating intervention in these struggles. In Africa, Asia, and Latin America, growing movements espouse revolutionary changes throughout these continental areas. Despite the other dangers involved, their sympathies and desire to protect their own revolutions thrust them into positions where intervention of various kinds in internal war appears desirable.

Such intervention is normally anti-Western in orientation. So strongly does this factor operate that responsible and pro-Western modernizers are regarded as traitorous or radical and anti-Western demagogues take on the guise of heroes. Not only is there an incentive for the uncommitted nations to intervene and thus further weaken the rule against intervention in the loose bipolar period, but they also have an incentive to intervene in ways that are favorable to Soviet interests and unfavorable to NATO interests—thus introducing a further unstabilizing element in the system.

The loose bipolar system is therefore one in which intervention in internal wars is to be expected. The range of intervention is extremely great. Thus, for instance, the Cairo radio has often incited the Transjordanian populace to revolt against King Hussein. It has incited revolt in Iraq, Yemen, Syria, and Iran. Ibn Saud evidently at one point attempted to have Nasser assassinated. Pan-Arabism has been employed to incorporate Syria in the United Arab Republic, and these tendencies were manipulated at one time in an effort to incorporate Iraq. Secret agents are employed, arms distributed, money spent. Similar campaigns have been waged against Tunisia. Within sub-Saharan Africa, however, expansionist regimes such as those of Ghana and Guinea have apparently not gone beyond personal persuasion and mass propaganda, although a non-African state, Yugoslavia, has aided the Cameroon rebels with arms. The more conservative African states—in particular, Nigeria and most of the members of the French Association—are attempting to mitigate and control these activities. Israel has less protection against external forms of subversion because many Asian nations regard it as a European rather than an Asian nation. Conservative regimes generally are less likely than radical regimes to receive support from the uncommitted states when subjected to intervention. And so are European nations as contrasted with non-Western nations. An attempt to catalog these considerations or to predict their effects, however, would go well beyond the bounds of the present essay.

In these uncommitted areas there are many potentially explosive situations that invite bloc conflict. Bloc intrusion might well threaten the interests of the uncommitted states by bringing the general area into the cold war. Moreover, because of the degree of political and social disintegration, the conflicts arising in these areas may threaten to involve the blocs in war without compensating advantages. Under some conditions efforts may be made to involve the United Nations, as in the case of the Congo. Such United Nations involvement necessarily leads to involvement in the internal wars from which such areas suffer, for even an effort to produce stability favors some elements and injures others. Therefore United Nations involvement shifts to U.N. organs some of the political struggle to determine the outcome of these cold wars.

IV. *Bloc Intervention*

The most dramatic forms of intervention are bloc interventions. The two most striking cases to date have been Hungary and Lebanon. In the case of Hungary, Russian troops were used against the legal government when it attempted to adopt a neutralist position. In Lebanon, American troops entered at the request of the legal government and presided over a political compromise between the warring factions that placed Lebanon in the neutralist camp—although not with the evangelistic fervor manifested by the United Arab Republic. Hungary was a committed nation that the Soviet Union used force to retain within its bloc. Lebanon was a mildly committed nation torn by religious and other quarrels. It was not a member of any American-led bloc and its lapse into neutralism did not threaten any important American interests; indeed, had it not been arranged at that time, the transition might have occurred in a much more detrimental fashion later on. Still, the two cases emphasize the difficulty the United States may encounter in attempting to retain a nation in its bloc by force. In the absence of a political instrumentality such as the Communist Party, the alternative instruments of control are unstable and inconsistent with the image the United States seeks to project. Thus there is a basic asymmetry which, in some circumstances at least, might incline the United States to give support to a norm of nonintervention.

Intervention within one's own bloc clearly is less inhibited than intervention in the opposing bloc or in uncommitted nations. Thus American intervention against Communist revolution in France or Italy—particularly at the request of the government—would seem somewhat more acceptable than intervention in Hungary or Guinea in favor of democratic revolutionists. Although Latin American states may be uncommitted in some senses, the existence of the Monroe Doctrine differentiates that situation to a certain degree from the African, where no protective pretext of this kind exists. Such differences often reflect matters of history and national expectations. Where intervention in this sense appears to have more justification, it can more easily be accepted. Thus it appears reasonable that leading bloc members will not accept radical changes in the political structure of bloc members that threaten bloc stability.

Direct military support for a rebellion in the territory of a member of the opposed bloc is unlikely. In Vietnam, for instance, the Viet Minh infiltrate in areas difficult of access and where the infiltration—as opposed to indigenous armed rebellion—is not easily susceptible of proof. Indochinese elements are employed rather than Russian or Chinese. In Laos in 1962, recognition of Souvanna Phouma as premier gave a legal cloak to Soviet air drops. Although it is not clear that the American response would have been different in the absence of this guise of legality, at least it reduced the probability of direct American intervention, including possibly resort to nuclear weapons.

The closer to a bloc area the intervention is, the easier it is to deter counter-intervention by the opposing bloc. Thus the U.S. position in Laos (if the possibility of a strike against North Vietnam is disregarded) and the Soviet position with respect to Cuba are logistically and tactically inferior. On the one hand, this lessens the probability of intervention of any kind, but, on the other, it may raise the probability of a resort to nuclear weapons should a decision to intervene be made, for that may be the only means of intervention carrying any hope of success. The attitudes of uncommitted nations may play a role in the delineation of acceptable and unacceptable forms of intervention. Thus, in Laos, Indian and Cambodian attitudes may have bolstered the subtler forms of Soviet intervention, while the United States would have to change the attitudes of the Latin American nations to achieve any likelihood of carrying off intervention in Cuba without Soviet countermoves. Collectivizing the intervention would raise this probability still more.

If expectations can be changed appropriately, the probability of intervention or of deterrence of intervention may change also. Thus there is much room for encouraging ambiguity. For instance, a Communist revolution in Italy would be less likely to bring about American intervention if it occurred after a popular front government had taken over and pulled Italy out of NATO, than if the present government of Italy were the victim of a Communist-inspired revolution. In terms of contemporary expectations, the authoritarian governments of Spain and Portugal have less legitimacy than the totalitarian government of Yugoslavia. Thus there would be less resistance to intervention in favor of revolution in the former, and to intervention against revolution in the latter.

The modes of intervention are not exhausted by the military techniques for intervention. Recognition policies as applied to China, the divided Koreas, Germanies, and Vietnam, for instance, are political weapons designed insofar as possible to influence political events in the areas to which they are applied. Economic aid policy can be used to bolster existing regimes. Aid can be withheld to induce political change. It was so used in the Indonesian struggle for independence. The prospect of aid was not without influence in 1947 in the cabinet changes in France and Italy. Military aid was not without influence when the Taiwan land reforms were administered and also played a role during the Korean ouster of the Rhee regime.

The factors mentioned above help to determine definitions of legitimacy and of acceptability with respect to the resort to and the extent of external interventions in internal wars. And these expectations influence the ability to deter such interventions. So too does the willingness of a nation or bloc to resort to intervention, or its stubbornness in pursuing its objectives. Such a nation or bloc then becomes almost a force of nature to which other nations must adjust in order to avoid war and the danger of a nuclear holocaust. Or, if it is not quite like a force of nature, at least its stubbornness increases its bargaining power and influences the nature of the accommodations likely to be reached concerning the use of intervention in internal wars. Thus, for instance, the Soviet leaders' belief in the dialectic of history creates expectations on the part of others that reinforce the so-called dialectic. Others expect the Soviet Union to intervene, thereby influencing their expectations concerning the points at which coordination will have to occur if the danger of nuclear war is to be reduced. And this in turn helps to redefine the rules of the game and considerations of legitimacy in the struggle. These matters are of great importance and deserve much more detailed attention than the cursory treatment they have received here.

Intervention will continue to be a feature of the loose bipolar period. But some efforts will be made to give legal color to the intervention and much of the political struggle in this period will lie in the effort to define acceptable norms of intervention in ways favorable to one bloc or the other. Thus there is the continued probability of the incitement of internal wars and of bloc aid to internal wars that have begun for indigenous reasons. This is an age in which bloc conflicts necessarily give incentive to aiding or to inciting internal war. But this is also a revolutionary age in which new and modern nations are appearing on the scene. These nations also have incentives to intervene in internal wars. And the instability of the social, economic, and political structures in these areas provides ample opportunity for those who have the desire and the incentive.

To some extent, these revolutionary opportunities also existed in the nineteenth century, but in that period of the "balance of power," supranational political organization was not operative and the major nations of the system had an overriding incentive to dampen such interventions. In contrast, there is great incentive in the bipolar age to intervene. The danger of nuclear war and some interests of the uncommitted states are the major dampening agents present. But these factors serve not so much to prevent as to regularize and to normalize intervention, while defining the conditions and opportunities under which it may be resorted to. These conditions cannot be stated precisely and they are subject to change. They are established as a conse-

quence of political bargaining and of international "legislation." Much of the stuff and flavor of contemporary international politics lies in the regularization of the process of
intervention, including intervention in internal wars.

CHAPTER 5

International Settlement
of Internal War

BY GEORGE MODELSKI

I. *The Termination of Internal Wars*

THE outright win, the complete and unqualified victory of either the incumbents or the insurgents, is the most usual outcome of an internal war. The government's win in the Greek Civil War (1946–1949) and the speedy defeat of the Saigon paratroopers' revolt in November 1960 are good examples of an outright victory by the incumbents; General Franco's victory in the Spanish Civil War of 1936–1939 and General Kassem's Baghdad coup of 1958 are instances of unqualified and unhampered victories by the insurgents.

Short of the outright win, there is a range of intermediate solutions to internal wars, the two main types being separation and settlement. In both of these, negotiation of terms is an essential part; in both, too, the political identity of the incumbents and the insurgents remains intact. However, we shall describe as *separations* all those endings which result in the establishment of a new state. Separations may be either "secessions," such as the independence achieved by the United States in the Treaty of Paris (1783)—and these are the typical endings of colonial wars won by the insurgents—or else "partitions," such as the *de facto* division of Vietnam agreed to at the Geneva Conference of 1954.[1] *Settlements*, by contrast, are war endings in which the existing political system remains intact and the identity of both contestants is maintained on the basis

---

[1] The opposite of separation is *unification;* this is an outcome of certain types of insurgents' win (e.g., a possible outcome of the present war in Vietnam). Correspondingly, a certain number of incumbents' wins represent the defeat of attempts at separation.

of an explicit agreement. Neither side has prevailed and the outcome, usually a compromise, may represent various degrees of partial success for both sides; frequently it embodies a stalemate and an equal division of authority. Good examples of such settlements are the events in Laos (1961–1962) and the solution of the Lebanese crisis in 1958.

Basic to the subsequent discussion, thus, is a distinction among three types of internal war endings: (1) outright win, (2) separation, and (3) settlement. The distinctions correspond broadly to Kenneth Boulding's three types of "ended conflict": conquest, avoidance, and procedural resolution.[2] In relation to internal wars, conquest must indeed be viewed as an outright win for one of the parties, and avoidance as separation. Procedural resolution is what we understand by "settlement," for it is the distinguishing characteristic of settlements that, unlike outright wins, they devise and employ unmistakable procedures (both negotiation and "award"—the imposition of terms) for bringing conflicts to a close. But we would stress once again that the ultimate criterion for distinguishing among internal war endings is the fate and survival of the rivals for control of the political system. Internal war is a violent contest for such control, and political violence that does not have this aim need not detain us here. Control over the political system being the stake of internal war, its final disposition is the appropriate criterion for classifying internal war endings.

A survey of 100 internal wars since 1900—covering, in fact, most of the well-known incidents of domestic political violence in this century—yields a number of useful points about outcomes and helps us to put into perspective the relative frequency and importance of the various types of endings (see Table I). It confirms the common-sense notion that the great majority of internal wars (some four-fifths) end in the victory of either one or the other party. Indeed, the figures in Table I

[2] Kenneth E. Boulding, *Conflict and Defense: A General Theory* (New York: Harper and Brothers, 1962), chap. 15.

demonstrate an equality (39:39) of wins for the two sides, suggesting that once the issue has been joined in actual combat the insurgents have a good chance of winning. (It would be unwise to describe that chance as even because our sample is almost certainly weighted in favor of successful insurrections,

TABLE I

OUTCOME OF 100 INTERNAL WARS, 1900–1962 *

INCUMBENTS' WIN	39
INSURGENTS' WIN	39
SEPARATION	11
SETTLEMENT	6
UNRESOLVED	5

* See Table II at the end of this chapter for a listing and classification of the 100 Internal Wars.

more attempts being nipped in the bud than are widely known and reported.) But the figures also demonstrate that intermediate solutions of the negotiated type are not negligible and comprise a significant quota both of separations (11) and of settlements (6).

This evidence confirms our earlier comments on the stakes of internal war. The prevalent notion that such wars represent a fight for a total victory finds confirmation in the fact that a large proportion of conflicts does reach such an outcome. The prevalence of this idea adds to the difficulties, often close to being insuperable, of negotiated settlement. Another unquestioned notion is that power—the exercise of governmental authority—is indivisible. The empirically confirmed phenomenon of settlement in internal war forces us to rethink this assumption and to examine conditions in which power-sharing becomes possible.

Statements about outright wins must, however, be qualified in this sense: although coups, revolts, and revolutions often fail, the causes for which blood has been shed are seldom completely defeated. What we have called an "incumbents' win" amounts most often to the destruction of the revolutionary core, its leaders and its "cadre"; the interests which the leaders stood for may, more often than not, be afterwards conciliated. Thus the Vendée, an insurrection which formed a part of the larger historical process of the French Revolution, failed at considerable cost to all concerned, and yet essential parts of its subsequent pacification were concessions in the contested field of exercise of religious freedom and indemnifications for losses suffered.[3] An uprising in Madagascar was bloodily suppressed in 1947, but thirteen years later the island attained independence. Frequently, it may be argued, the defeat of the insurgents is the necessary requisite of such desirable changes.

Thus we must bear in mind that outright wins by either side are not satisfactory indicators of the degree to which the interests at issue have in fact been frustrated or accommodated. It is this divergence between the interests of the leaders and their followers which makes for the stability of solutions to internal war that otherwise would appear unconditional. It is here, too, that the apparent simplicity of the outright-win solutions is deceptive, for it creates illusions and misconceptions which may hinder the task of reconstruction after the internal war has ended.

The dominant image of outright win in internal war recalls another influential conception, this time taken from the field of international relations: the "unconditional surrender" doctrine of World War II vintage.[4] The belief was general at the end of that war that by insistence on unconditional surrender the victors would put themselves in the position of dictating terms

[3] Peter Paret, *Internal War and Pacification: The Vendée, 1789–1796* (Princeton: Center of International Studies, Research Monograph No. 12, 1961), pp. 50ff. A settlement was in fact negotiated, but was broken within four months by the Vendée leaders; however, the concessions granted effectively separated the leaders from their supporters.

[4] This seems to have been directly related to General Grant's famous "unconditional surrender" policy in the American Civil War. Cf. Robert E. Sherwood, *The White House Papers of Harry L. Hopkins* (London: Eyre and Spottiswoode, 1949), pp. 692–93.

as though the defeated enemies had been left with no bargaining assets at all. This is now recognized as fallacious.[5] The winner can never avoid making payments proportionate to the loser's residual bargaining strength and that is why the doctrine leads to unrealistic objectives. The payments will take the form of either the winner's *unnecessary* losses, or the loser's or the third party's gains. These payments are unavoidable, but a process of bargaining (or settlement) may help clarify objectives and alter the distribution of payments to the winner's advantage (for instance, by preventing the third party from making gratuitous profits). A negotiated settlement may not always be appropriate, but in internal war, too, the method should be borne in mind as a possible and a realistic means of terminating conflict. Let us get away from the prevalent view that internal war is a process that can end only in unconditional surrender.

II. *International Participation in Internal War Endings*

While the general topic of termination of internal war deserves much more attention than it has received,[6] and constitutes a broad and fruitful field for new research, we shall in this essay limit our attention to those endings which can be described as settlements. We will, moreover, investigate in particular the role which members of the international society can play, and may realistically be expected to play, in such settlements and in their maintenance. But before doing so we shall elaborate on the proposition that, irrespective of the type of ending, international society always participates to some degree in the terminal stages of conflict.[7] This is ultimately traceable to the fact that

[5] For a fine discussion of this point, see Paul Kecskemeti, *Strategic Surrender: The Politics of Victory and Defeat* (Stanford: Stanford University Press, 1958).

[6] But see in particular Lewis A. Coser, "The Termination of Conflict," *Journal of Conflict Resolution*, v (December 1961), pp. 347–53.

[7] This proposition has been put forward in Chapter 2, above, "The International Relations of Internal War."

every internal war occurs in the context of international society; it is a disturbance in the functioning of one member of that society and it cannot but affect other members and the society as a whole.

The least degree of international participation [8] occurs in cases of outright victory for the incumbents. No special arrangements need attend the restoration of *status quo ante.* Indeed, interposition either on behalf of defeated insurgents, especially when coming from states known to sympathize with them, or else in support of peace and order in general is rarely effective or even well received. Nevertheless, diplomatic or private representations urging leniency and amnesty may be made, and even in the absence of representations insurgents may be considerately treated for fear of foreign criticism. Some states are always dependent upon the good will of others, and hence susceptible to their suggestions, especially when weakened by internal strife. In the years following the defeat of Germany, for instance, her many difficulties, such as the Kapp Putsch, the Ruhr, Hamburg, and Bavarian risings, and the Silesian insurrections, were all subject to considerable Allied influence.[9] Disturbances in areas under mandate or trusteeship have been the subject of debate in international organizations for decades now; thus, the insurrection in the Cameroons was under review by the U.N. Trusteeship Council continuously between 1955 and 1960. Rarer are the instances of foreign action in an attempt to alter the terms in favor of the defeated party, as when Russia issued an ultimatum and intervened militarily in

[8] Participation includes such processes as acknowledgment (or non-acknowledgment), approval (or disapproval), the influencing, the co-deciding, and the awarding of outcome. We further distinguish between authoritative participation (by "authorized" great and other powers) and other participation (by rank-and-file members of international society). Participation is directed to affecting the terms of the outcome, the main components of which are the disposition of resources and facilities of both sides and the fate of the interests at issue.

[9] For the role of British diplomacy in these events, see, e.g., *Documents on British Foreign Policy, 1919–1939*, First Series (London: HMSO, 1946–), IX, chaps. 2 and 3, and XI, chap. 1.

Persia in 1911 after the failure of the previously deposed Shah to reestablish himself with Russia's help.[10] These are, however, the less common instances, for most often the inertia of international life works in favor of the established order, and in propitious circumstances—for instance, at times of universal turmoil—a legitimate government can in fact dictate its own terms and achieve the destruction of its opponents with little regard for their interests.[11]

A victory of the insurgents affords somewhat larger opportunities for external participation. The formal expression of this is the requirement in international law that every unusual change in governmental arrangements, be it caused by a coup, revolt, or revolution, must be recognized by other members of the international community. Louis Napoleon's coup of 1851, the establishment of the Chinese People's Republic in 1949, and the Republican revolt in Yemen in 1962 each gave rise to problems of recognizing a new government.

International lawyers frown upon the notion of "conditional recognition," whereby in exchange for recognition newly recognized powers undertake to carry out certain obligations. They point out that "failure to discharge the obligations attached does not affect the recognition, which is an act accomplished beyond redemption . . . is irrevocable." [12] It is nevertheless true that the necessity of securing recognition—that is, in effect, confirmation of membership in the international society—and the diplomatic processes that occur at that time serve as the occasion when the terms on which the internal war is ended may be affected. It is a time for close scrutiny, for asking questions and seeking assurances, and some of the criteria of scrutiny are usually relevant to the desirable outcomes

[10] Sir Percy Sykes, *History of Persia* (London: Macmillan Company, 1951), II, pp. 423–26.

[11] Cf. France's brutal suppression of revolts in Algeria (1945) and Madagascar (1947).

[12] Ti-chiang Chen, *The International Law of Recognition* (New York: Frederick A. Praeger, 1951), p. 266.

of internal war. That is the reason, too, why in the early stages of the assumption of power, revolutionary regimes customarily adopt an attitude of dissimulation and studied moderation that is often belied by their subsequent performance.

When a group of younger military officers seized power in Bangkok in November 1947, they immediately realized that "public, and especially foreign, opinion was so strongly against the coup that their plans had to be temporarily dropped." [13] To moderate the impact of the coup they persuaded a prominent liberal, Nai Khouang Apphaiwong, to assume the Premiership. Nai Khouang lasted only six months, but in the meantime power shifted to more senior officers around Marshal Pibul. Here the adjustment of aims proceeded almost entirely by anticipation of foreign demands. But international opinion may also make itself felt through direct representations, as in 1939 when in connection with the recognition of Nationalist Spain the United States, British, and French governments sought assurances about Spanish independence, the withdrawal of foreign troops, and an end to reprisals against the Republicans,[14] or in 1959, when Fidel Castro's seizure of power brought about a wave of executions and protests were voiced in the United States.

"Separations" offer still greater opportunities for international influence, for they create not only a new government but also a new state, potentially a new full member of international society. The achievement of independence by the United States (1783) and Spanish America (1818–1824), by Greece (1830), Belgium (1831), and Bulgaria (1878), were each major diplomatic settlements involving the European and world-wide international systems. Four out of 11 twentieth-century separa-

[13] John Coast, *Some Aspect of Siamese Politics* (New York: International Secretariat, Institute of Pacific Relations, 1953), p. 41.
[14] Norman J. Padelford, *International Law and Diplomacy in the Spanish Civil Strife* (New York: Macmillan Company, 1939), p. 191. For the diplomatic correspondence, see Department of State, *Foreign Relations of the United States, 1939*, ii (Washington: GPO, 1956), pp. 744–64.

tions (listed in Table II at the end of this chapter) were arrived at through multilateral international arrangements (Upper Silesia, 1921; Indonesia, 1949; Vietnam, 1954; Cyprus, 1959). The other 7 were embodied in solutions negotiated bilaterally —most of them, however, with a large international component (as, for instance, Algeria, the subject of annual U.N. General Assembly debates for a number of years), and they too were of course subject to express international approval through the device of recognition.

Some closing observations: (1) Internal wars occur in states that are members of international society, and hence that society cannot avoid taking note of their conclusion. (2) Direct international participation is usually confined to a narrow front and is more often the result of earlier foreign intervention than an effort to make the end of an internal war the opportunity for arriving at a sound settlement of the political system. (3) In the instrumentality of recognition, certain rudimentary procedures for regularizing international participation in internal war endings are already in existence.

III. *International Settlement: Some Twentieth-Century Cases*

For a student of politics, the most interesting of endings to an internal war is the negotiated settlement that does not call for a separation. It is interesting because it is comparatively rare and also because it makes full claims on the resources of human inventiveness in social affairs. Despite this interest, literature on the subject is scant. What few statements there are on terminating internal wars dismiss negotiation as an impermanent and imperfect method of settling such grave issues. A French student of revolutionary warfare, for instance, denounces the thought of putting an end to such conflicts through talks as a "dangerous illusion." He gives two grounds for this opinion: (1) "La Révolution n'envisage pas, en effet, de victoire partielle"; in other words, it takes two to keep a settlement. (2) "L'adversaire obtient vite, grâce aux facilités que nous lui avons consenties, ce que la violence n'avait pu lui donner. La négociation accélère ainsi le processus de la guerre révolutionnaire"; [15] in other words, negotiation confers significantly greater benefits upon the insurgents than upon the incumbents. Neither of these propositions holds absolutely, even in respect of revolutionary wars (in the French sense of this term) and most certainly not in regard to internal wars in general. The second cannot hold unqualifiedly, because an end to fighting need not always and necessarily work to the advantage of the insurgents. On the contrary, and depending on the circumstances, it may advantage either party. The more convincing proposition is the first, the difficulty of treating in an atmosphere of inevitable and unbearable suspicion with a revolutionary party whose aim is total: the complete conquest of power. Experience shows that such negotiations have taken place in the past, however, and even though this experience is not unequivocal, it does not allow us to rule out this method of terminating conflicts. We must nevertheless admit that the mere opening of talks benefits the insurgents, because it confers upon them a position of equality and improves their legitimacy.

Another Frenchman, commenting on the Peace of St. Germain (1570), which ended the Fourth War of Religion in France, voices the widely held view that only an outright win can bring about a lasting settlement: "Ceux [traités] qui se prolongent sont ceux qu'un vainqueur impose à un vaincu. Ce sont les plus faciles. Ils durent les temps que le second se relève. Puis ils cessent de durer." [16]

Here is the search after the illusory solidity of a dictated solution. Yet, the stability of internal war endings should not depend solely on the capacity of the defeated side to recover. Surely, a good settlement would have anticipated this capacity

---

[15] J. Hogard, "Guerre révolutionnaire et la pacification," *Revue militaire d'information* (Paris), No. 280 (January 1957), p. 14.

[16] Francis Walder, *Saint-Germain, ou la négociation* (Paris: Gallimard, 1958), pp. 194–95; a historical novel by a practicing diplomat.

and have provided accordingly, obviating the need for new appeals for change which, in the circumstances, cannot but mean further resort to arms.

Bearing in mind the skepticism which surrounds all attempts at settlement—and the suspicions, be it of foolery or of knavery —let us survey the known twentieth-century instances of such solutions, beginning with two instances of failure to use negotiation.

The most important civil conflict of the interwar period was the war in Spain (1936–1939).[17] Lasting for close to three years, and exceptional for its ferocity (armies of over 500,000 ranged on each side and fatal casualties reaching 600,000—some 3 percent of the entire population), this war provoked international intervention (and measures of "nonintervention") of large proportions and profound consequences. The number of attempts made at composing it by compromise is therefore not surprising. Among the early mediation attempts was an Anglo-French plan (December 1936) calling for the six powers most closely concerned to declare an armistice, send a commission to Spain and, after a plebiscite, set up a government composed of men (such as de Madariaga) who had kept out of the civil war. Despite the support of the Council of the League of Nations, the plan was soon dropped because neither side in Spain nor any of the other Great Powers favored it. In mid-1937 the Republican President himself sought the help of the British Foreign Office, asking that the Great Powers impose a settlement. Late in 1937 there were rumors of peace talks for a federation of two Spains, to be achieved (once again) by persons uncommitted to either side. Peace feelers were put out by the Republican Premier on his personal initiative in 1938, and then in 1939, but failed because Franco, with the support of Italy in particular, refused to consider anything but uncondi-

[17] See Hugh Thomas, *The Spanish Civil War* (New York: Eyre, 1961), esp. pp. 334–36, 438–39, 496–97, 631–33; Padelford, *op.cit.*, esp. chaps. 3, 4, and 6.

tional surrender. President Roosevelt also contemplated a plan for a compromise peace to be launched at the Inter-American Conference at Lima (December 1938), but this too came to nothing, owing to differences among the South Americans.[18] In the event, this plethora of feelers, plans, and firm proposals yielded nothing of consequence. But it did show that, even in a conflict of the most violent kind, statesmen and diplomats never dismissed all thought of a settlement as unreasonable.

This is not the place for a full analysis of reasons for the failure. Suffice it to note that some of the circumstances did in fact favor compromise: the length of the conflict, and its seriousness, the near-stalemate prevailing for a considerable period, and the direct intervention of a number of foreign powers. Too many circumstances were, however, working against it: the blood toll of casualties and atrocities, hence the excessive polarization of the political system and the absence of a center party; the growing polarization of European international society, the commitment of most of the Great Powers of Europe to one side or the other, and the incapacity and unwillingness of Britain or the United States to impose a settlement; finally, the tendency of the international system to promote a solution favorable to Franco. In such adverse circumstances, few, if any, conflicts, could indeed have been peaceably composed. The failure of diplomatic action did show, however, that mediation pure and simple is not enough if it remains unsupported by other international action, even though it is acknowledged as a legitimate diplomatic instrument for the furtherance of international settlement.

The Civil War in China (1946–1949) is another case of failure. At stake were the respective positions of the Kuomintang and the Chinese Communist Party in postwar China. Most of the proposals put forward by competent observers (who knew that the Communists were too strong to be defeated) mentioned

[18] Department of State, *Foreign Relations of the United States, 1938* (Washington: GPO, 1955–1956), I, pp. 255–60; v, pp. 82–83.

as the basic elements of a negotiated settlement a coalition government, reduction of the armed forces of both sides, and Communist control over some areas of North China.

The negotiations had two main phases.[19] The first began in 1943, when the "inevitability" of a civil war after the defeat of Japan started to be talked about, and was marked by American attempts (led successively by Generals Hurley and Marshall) to arrive at a settlement between the two parties by means of mediation prepared for diplomatically by Chiang Kai-shek's settlement of outstanding questions with Moscow (August 1945). There was also an attempt at mediation by leaders of the minority parties of the center, the so-called Third Party Group (1946). The failure of the Marshall mission and the outbreak of full-scale fighting in the latter part of 1946 did not, however, extinguish all thought of negotiation. In this second, though much less hopeful, phase (1947–1949) the liberal group which gained some power in 1948 did not hesitate to ask for Soviet, as well as American, British, and French mediation.[20] They also held direct talks with the Chinese Communists, who by then were asking for unconditional surrender. Needless to say, success eluded these attempts, too.

Why the failure? The backlog of hostility of at least two decades and the incompatibility of the objectives of the two parties were no doubt the major obstacles to agreement. Another was the rapid shifts in the domestic and international situation at the end of World War II, the disappearance of Japanese power, and the resulting changes in the Far Eastern scene which hindered sound judgment and took all sem-

[19] Department of State, *United States Relations with China* (Washington: GPO, 1949), chaps. 3 and 4.

[20] Nanking sought Soviet mediation in exchange for (1) Chinese neutrality in any future international conflict; (2) the elimination of American influence to as great an extent as possible in China; (3) the establishment of a basis of real cooperation between the governments of Russia and China. *Ibid.*, p. 283.

blance of stability from the appreciation of events. Finally, the weakness of the third parties: the concentration of power, resources, and initiative in the hands of the major contestants and the sharpness with which their "political identities" were defined; the ineffectiveness of the domestic center group even when officially sharing power, and the inefficacy of foreign mediation, whether by the United States or by any other nonaligned power in this conflict, in the absence of readiness to commit strong forces in support of proposals.[21]

An instructive comparison may be drawn between these abortive attempts at compromise and the settlement actually achieved in China in 1936–1937. This was the direct result of an incident staged in Sian by troops then engaged in an anti-Communist offensive. Led by a group of officers which included pro-Communists and which looked to the Soviet Union for aid and support, these units captured Chiang Kai-shek and refused to continue fighting the Communists, claiming that the real dangers to the country stemmed from the mounting threat of Japanese aggression. In accord with Comintern decisions, the Chinese Communist Party, too, had in the previous year changed to a policy of an "anti-Japanese united front." Chou En-lai went to Sian, had long talks with Chiang, and the upshot of the whole affair was an internal war settlement that lasted close to ten years.

Some years later Moscow claimed credit for the moderation of that settlement.[22] This in effect created for a time a Kuomintang-Communist center bloc headed by Chiang, with Wang Ching-wei (who might have captured the Kuomintang machine

21 The United States decided from an early date against the commitment of armed forces in China, holding American interests not to be vitally affected. Tang Tsou, "Civil Strife and Armed Intervention: Marshall's Mission in China," Orbis, vi (Spring 1962), pp. 76–101.

22 Molotov's interview with Hurley, August 1944, reported in United States Relations with China, pp. 71–72. For the background of the Sian incident, see James M. Bertram, Crisis in China (London: Macmillan Company, 1937).

in the event of Chiang's death) left to treat with the Japanese, on the one hand, and extremist Communists and others calling for Chiang's head, on the other. No written treaty or agreement was ever negotiated, and yet the civil war stopped and such fighting as went on was directed against Japan. Essentially it was no more than a truce and contained within itself the seeds of its own destruction, but it worked as long as Japan served as the main target of hostility. The terms, maintenance of a separate government (the "Chinese Soviet Government" being renamed "Government of the Special Region of the Republic of China") with its own army, at the price of giving up the civil war and the confiscation of land, were inherently unstable and no more than postponed the day of reckoning. Even though the Communist army agreed to serve under the leadership of the Nanking Military Commission, the course of the war and the defeat of Japan and of Wang Ching-wei altered the relative power of the contending parties and polarized the system without adding to the links of solidarity. The center weakened and no new third party or force emerged to hold the balance.

Let us look at another failure, the Laos settlement of 1957. This was an attempt to bring to an end a time of troubles that had begun as early as 1945 and that in 1953–1954 had brought into Laos divisional formations of the Vietminh army. The Geneva agreement on the cessation of hostilities in Laos (July 1954) had secured the withdrawal of these forces, but had not solved the political problem of the Vietminh-supported Pathet Lao, and to some extent complicated it by assigning two (out of Laos' twelve) provinces to the control of that organization and its forces. A positive aspect of the Geneva settlement nevertheless was the creation of an international commission to supervise the implementation of the agreement. Chaired by India, this commission (and the international connections at its disposal) was instrumental in bringing about a political settlement when attempts at a military solution failed in 1955. In exchange for legalization, participation in a coalition government and in elections, and the keeping under arms of two of its battalions, the Pathet Lao surrendered the control of the two provinces and entered upon the process of "reintegration" with the national community.

What were the conditions of success? Stalemate, added to the conviction that the "partition" of Laos could not, and should not, last; some effective government diplomacy (seeking and obtaining direct assurances from Peking and Hanoi and thus undermining Pathet Lao's lines of support); and, above all, the influence of the third parties—domestically, the moderates within the Royal government and in Parliament; and, internationally, India, as the chief member of the international commission. In her role as the channel of communication between the parties, and through the judicial use of her casting vote in the commission, India had a major share in creating an acceptable settlement. Why, then, the breakdown, within less than two years of the agreements? The stalemate was not as firmly grounded as was supposed: the Pathet Lao made an unexpectedly good showing at the supplementary elections of May 1958 and the possibility of its victory in a subsequent general election could not be ruled out. Immediately after the May vote, the commission was asked to withdraw and its collective moderating influence was thus removed. Circumstances gave a head to younger, more intransigent forces in Vientiane and, within a year of the supplementary elections, fighting was resumed in Laos.[23]

Might it be argued that the settlement was doomed because its election provisions were the causes of its own destruction? Was violence inevitable? This conclusion is unjustified. For if we take as an example the political situation in Indonesia after the elections of 1955 and 1957 (which disclosed the rapidly increasing power of the Communists), a situation that was resolved by the abandonment of elections and resort to nonpar-

[23] For background, see George Modelski (ed.), *SEATO: Six Studies* (Melbourne: Cheshire, 1962), pp. 147–50.

liamentary government with concessions to the Communist Party, we might surmise that a similar procedure could have prevented the outbreak of violence in Laos. Elections are not unfailingly peaceful; they may serve as an occasion for violence (as they did in Spain in 1936) as much as an opportunity for compromise.

Let us pause and look briefly at the second Laotian settlement, embodied in the agreements of 1962.[24] It is much too early yet to call it a success, but at the time of writing (January 1963) the prospects are not entirely unfavorable. The situation of stalemate has now been restored and the international interest has been reaffirmed by a multilateral agreement signed in Geneva in July 1962 and based upon neutrality (the Laotian word for which is *penkang*—to be in the middle). Most importantly, a center group of not entirely negligible strength has emerged (Prince Souvanna Phouma's Neutralists) and may conceivably hold the balance between Phoumi Nosavan's Nationalists and the Pathet Lao. The condition of success is, of course, the survival of the center group (if need be, by playing off the other two groups) and the gradual consolidation of its strength (here, too, elections would upset the applecart). The situation may be powerfully reinforced by strong international support for that group, but if the Neutralists fail to gain strength and, on the contrary, lag behind the two extremes, the settlement will not last.

Two more instances of internal war settlement may be briefly mentioned here: the Colombian settlement and the Lebanon crisis of 1958.

The troubles in Colombia date from the famous Bogotá riots of 1948, which broke out when a Conference of American States

---

[24] For details of the international aspects in particular, see George Modelski, *International Conference on the Settlement of the Laotian Question, 1961–1962* (Canberra: Department of International Relations, Australian National University, Working Paper No. 2, 1962).

was meeting in that city.[25] Assassinations followed and soon the contest between the Liberals and the Conservatives engulfed the whole country, causing unrest and persistent violence, with fatal casualties in excess of 200,000. A genuine stalemate occurred, as neither party could prevail over the other, but there was no sign of a center party. Instead a military regime installed itself and precariously held onto power. In this situation the two main contestants decided to compromise and, through negotiations in Spain and elsewhere, agreed to end the use of violence, to rotate the office of President, and in other ways to share in the government and its spoils.

A civil war in Lebanon broke out in 1958 when, in the aftermath of the Suez crisis and of Syria's accession to Egypt, demands began to be voiced for closer links with the Arab world. This broke the uneasy unity maintained between the two main sections of the country, the Moslems and the Christians, but the fighting was on a moderate scale only. Yet when General Kassem's coup in Iraq suddenly threatened a revolutionary collapse in the entire Middle East, President Eisenhower responded to an invitation by the Lebanese President and landed U.S. Marines. A United Nations Observation Mission was already in the country, watching the frontiers for signs of Egyptian intervention and support for the rebels. For a brief period Lebanon was in the world's limelight, and the center of a grave crisis. The USSR maneuvered troops in the Caucasus, British soldiers returned to Jordan, and the U.N. General Assembly met in special session. But the diplomats were feverishly at work and a satisfactory solution was soon devised. A man of the center assumed the Presidency, foreign

25 For background, see John D. Martz, *Colombia: A Contemporary Political Survey* (Chapel Hill: University of North Carolina Press, 1962); V. L. Fluharty, *Dance of the Millions: Military Rule and the Social Revolution in Colombia, 1930–1956* (Pittsburgh: University of Pittsburgh Press, 1957), esp. chaps. 7–9 and 15–18.

intervention ceased, U.S. troops withdrew, but the U.N. maintained its observer corps.[26]

This has been, purposely, a twentieth-century survey in order to show that in the era of total war and unconditional surrender, internal wars have been, and can continue to be, settled by a compromise. Without delving too deeply into world history, we would further maintain that some such violent conflicts have always found solutions through negotiated settlement. To support this statement with but one example, of a most instructive kind, we turn to France at the time, not of its famous Revolution of 1789—notable for its spiraling extremism rather than for its rationality—but of the Wars of Religion in the second half of the sixteenth century. For fifteen years of that period, the Huguenots and the Catholics fought eight consecutive civil wars, and yet—contrary to what we are inclined to expect in an era of religious, and therefore presumably uncompromised, strife—each one of these ended on a note of moderation, and the final settlement, codified in the Edict of Nantes of 1598, provided the stable solution which endured for the next three generations (until 1685). Here too this favorable outcome was ensured by a stalemate, and by the uncommitted forces of the *Politiques*, allied to royalty and operating in a favorable international environment.[27]

IV. *International Settlement: Analysis*

The preceding section purports to establish no more than the proposition that settlement is a possible and, indeed, in certain well-defined circumstances—soon to be analyzed—a plausible way of terminating wars within political systems. That proba-

[26] Two other instances deserving analysis are the Nagaland disturbances which began in 1949 and reached a partial settlement by the creation of the Nagaland state in September 1962, and the negotiations for the settlement of the Kurdish rebellion following the overthrow of the regime of General Kassem early in 1963.

[27] For an outline of events, see, e.g., *Cambridge Modern History*, III: *The Wars of Religion* (Cambridge, Eng.: University Press, 1904), chaps. 1 and 20.

bilities may frequently be against it has already been demonstrated; but the historical examples show that those who on occasion urge the desirability of negotiation are neither foolish nor wholly impractical.

The cases demonstrate too that, as a rule, settlements have a large international component and may therefore usually be called international. This appellation is more apposite than, for example, in relation to outright wins (not all of which can be so described). It is more apposite, too, because international action may properly be regarded as a virtual prerequisite of settlement. International society itself creates the conditions that conduce to negotiated solutions, for it is the largest reservoir of third-party mediators. But, above all, it is the home of diplomacy, the institution whose very *raison d'être* is the notion of negotiated settlement. It is diplomats and all those others at home in diplomacy and its tireless search for compromise solutions, its disdain for absolute cures, and its age-old expertise in the art of settling wars by such firmly institutionalized arrangements as truce talks and peace conferences, who are most likely to contribute to transplanting these tested procedures into the field of settling wars within political systems.

Futile and indeed foolish would be the expectation or the wish that settlement should conclude every case of internal violence. Settlement is a type of ending that can occur only if a certain number of conditions have been satisfied. These strictly limit the applicability of this solution to a number of cases only; but these, too, are also the more serious cases of internal war and for that reason the cases that really matter.

The three preliminary conditions of a settlement concern (1) the identity of the contestants, (2) the duration of the conflict, and (3) the degree of communication. To begin with, settlement can occur only between parties whose "identity," or "personality," has been well defined. The incumbents are, as a rule, well enough known, but the insurgents' leadership and following are frequently obscure. Such outbreaks of political violence as riots, or such widespread but unfocused disorders as *jacqueries,* are not easily "settled" because there is no one to settle with. But there is this difficulty: the clearer the identity of the insurgents (and the more closely they therefore approximate the position of an efficacious alternative to the incumbents), the more reluctant will the incumbents be to treat with them for fear of conferring a status of equality.

Second, settlement is feasible only in cases of internal war of more than a certain minimum duration. Coups which either succeed or blow over in a matter of days are hardly a proper object for elaborate settlement (although settlements concluded under the threat of violence must not be ignored here). Settlements most often seem to follow upon an initial test of strength in which the several parties' capacity for mischief and violence has been demonstrated in action. A certain minimum duration, too, is a precondition of the coming into play of third-party actors, of conciliatory mechanisms, and of international plans and resources.

Both the foregoing conditions, identity and duration, amount to saying that the conflict must be of some importance if it is to deserve the trouble of being settled, especially if international action is to be involved. But if, as is likely in cases of internal wars of any consequence, international implications and repercussions are considerable, the case for a regulated settlement becomes very strong.

Third, a certain amount of contact and communication between the parties is a prerequisite of settlement. In part this is a matter of shared cultural values, such as language, other symbols, and conventions of negotiation; as, for instance, in the case of early settlers who found it difficult to negotiate with "savages." In part it depends on the sheer availability of means of communication. In either event, the ready availability of the services of a third party—for example, a common friend of the two parties, or a foreign embassy as a meeting ground for talks —helps a great deal. Breakdown of communications being one of the major consequences of violence, their reestablishment is one of the preconditions of settlement.

This brings us to the two *basic conditions* of settlement: (4) stalemate, and (5) the rearrangement of aims. Fundamental to both of these is the presence of a third party.

Stalemate is easily the most important condition of a settlement. Without it, one or both of the parties may hold justified hopes of an outright win and therefore have the incentive to go on fighting. Stalemate may be defined as the state of affairs in which neither side, given its aims, has the resources to overwhelm the other (absolutely, or without incurring unacceptable losses). Conditions of stalemate did appear at times, for instance, in the Spanish and Chinese civil wars and gave rise to hopes of settlement, and they were present in all the other cases we have noted. Stalemate creates between the parties that situation of "balance" without which negotiations cannot properly begin.

At first sight this may appear a most restrictive condition, limiting the applicability of settlement to the few cases where stalemate occurs naturally, as it were. Such cases are in fact rare, because if a conflict is allowed to last long enough, one side is bound to win in the end.

But this condition need not necessarily be restrictive, because conflict can never be allowed to run on unchecked, and herein lies the importance of international participation in settlements: a stalemate can always be contrived by international action. The international system can induce such a situation, because its resources are superior and because a sufficient amount can be diverted in aid of the weaker party for the purpose of creating a stalemate. For instance, in March-April 1961 the Royal Laotian forces commanded by Phoumi Nosavan were decisively beaten by the Neutralist-Pathet Lao coalition. Left to itself, the war in Laos would have ended in the seizure of the two capitals by the winners and thus in an outright victory. However, the threat of intervention by certain members of SEATO, including the United States and Thailand,[28] caused a truce to be declared and negotiations for a settlement were soon under way.

The smaller and the weaker the country, the more readily will a system-induced stalemate occur in its internal war; strife-torn societies are as a rule weak and exhausted. Greater resistance may be encountered in large and populous states, and difficulties will be met in situations in which one party to the conflict is obviously and disproportionately weaker than the other. However, since the object of international action would be stalemate alone (and not outright win, the more usual aim of foreign intervention), the problem is not insurmountable. Within certain limits, therefore, the basic principle holds that a stalemate can always be imposed upon an internal war system.

To support our analysis of the second fundamental condition of settlement, the redistribution of aims, let us digress a little [29] and describe the distribution of support for a range of political aims in a stable community by means of what statisticians call the "normal curve." (See Figure 1.) This figure brings out how, in a stable system, majority support clusters around a group of middle-of-the-road political aims. If the community is organ-

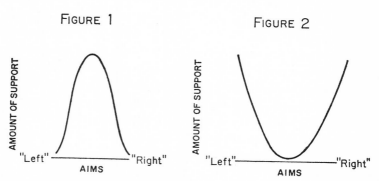

FIGURE 1

FIGURE 2

[28] See Modelski (ed.), SEATO: Six Studies, pp. 12–13.
[29] This digression is related to problems raised by Robert A. Dahl in A Preface to Democratic Theory (Chicago: University of Chicago Press, 1956), pp. 91–99.

ized into two political parties, fairly evenly divided in strength, the differences between them will be small and public debate will be preoccupied with minor shifts of opinion. By definition, extremists will be without power.

Contrast this with the graph of a strife-torn society, which can be described as a "U" curve (Figure 2). Political support clusters at the two poles of the political system and the center is either nonexistent or weak. Extremists thrive.

The two graphs thus show that the difference between the "normal" political system and its internal war variant is the composition of the center. Societies undergoing internal war lack any middle—let alone a strong middle. The problem of settlement, which in its second aspect is one of redistributing aims by attenuating their extremism, thus reduces itself (unless a separation is brought about) to one of strengthening the center.

There are, in the main, two ways in which the center may be built up (the political consensus be broadened) or, putting it differently, the gap in the distribution of aims be reduced: (1) the appearance of a common enemy, or (2) the growth of a center group. The first may be illustrated by the cessation of hostilities in the Chinese civil war which followed the Sian incident and which lasted, broadly speaking, for the duration of the Japanese danger. A different instance of the same process may be the Colombian case, in which the two antagonistic political parties composed their differences when a military regime became the main beneficiary of their conflict. It is not at all unusual to observe two parties to a dispute settling their differences when faced with third-party intervention. The chief weakness of this method is its impermanence: it depends on the somewhat fortuitous appearance of an "enemy" and operates only as long as that enemy is in sight.

The growth of an "inside" center group therefore offers greater prospects for stability. In a sense, such a group also serves as an "enemy" of the extremists and helps to bring them closer, if only in opposition to itself. More significantly, however, the middle group operates as a balancing factor and can play off one extremist group against the other. Play-off is, of course, most effective in conditions of stalemate.

Thus it is the second cardinal principle of settlement that the center can be built up by international action. At first sight this may appear less obvious than the principle of system-induced stalemate, but upon reflection it will be recognized to be as effective. Violence confers unwarranted "visibility" upon the armed minorities and it disadvantages the moderates who, even though they form the majority, may not have the chance to make their voices heard. International support for such center spokesmen as can be found in an internal war system may give them the opportunity to start building up the momentum of their own strength. Internal war settlements in Laos (1962) and Lebanon have been in essence settlements in favor of an internationally backed center group. And the pathetic story of the search for settlement in the Spanish and Chinese civil wars is one, by contrast, of the ineffectiveness of the middle. A condition of success here is a certain "elasticity" of aims and a certain "mobility" of political support. International action in favor of a settlement can be based only on the assumption that the society has not yet divided against itself into two armed camps, with no movement out of them being tolerated. But except for some limiting cases of this sort, a minimum degree of elasticity and mobility may be postulated for most societies.

By contrast with these two essential points, neutrality, in the currently accepted sense of neutralism or nonalignment in the cold war, cannot be regarded as an indispensable condition of settlement. It depends on the conflict that is to be settled. If it is a contemporary event in which the Communist Party has been involved and has received "fraternal" support from abroad, and the incumbents have benefited from, let us say, American aid, a declaration of neutrality may be an unavoidable part of the final settlement and possibly, as it has proved in Laos (and conceivably might have done in China), the key feature of the program of the middle group. But in conflicts unrelated to the cold war, as the Colombian and Lebanese cases largely were, nonalignment of this kind would be unnecessary, though nonalignment of a different kind, related to some other conflict, may be required. In Lebanon, for instance, neutrality as between the Arab and the Western worlds was necessary. In a general and positive sense, neutrality must thus be regarded as no more than an important, but not indispensable, component of a center position.

The essential role of international action in the settlement of internal wars must now be clear. The outside world is the most efficient (though not the only) provider of third-party influence which, in turn, may be essential for achieving a stalemate and for building up the center. (Though we must enter a caveat: the tasks of inducing stalemate and strengthening the middle need not be accomplished by the same power. These are different and partly contradictory functions—the first amounting to support for the weaker of the two parties; the second, to building up the moderates.) But why should external powers go to all this trouble in order to achieve, not the victory of their own preferred side, but merely a settlement? Or rather, narrowing the problem (since we can never expect *all* external powers to take such action), which international actors (states and international organizations) may we expect to take steps leading to a settlement?

To answer this question, we hypothesize the interdependence of the authority structures of the international system and those of the political systems of its members.[30] We assume, in fact, that international actors closest to the center of an *international* range of political choices (positing here an international "normal" curve) will support regimes similarly based in their own political systems, just as those inclining to more extreme posi-

[30] See also Chapter 2.

tions would support their own likenesses. They would do so because the viability of a power's position in the international range depends on the number and influence of other actors of a similar kind.

It is a consequence of our assumptions that a stable international society with a strong center may be expected to favor and foster internal war settlements which build up the middle. A polarized ("U"-shaped) international society, by contrast, has little hope of solving domestic political warfare. Conversely, international actors wishing to move to the center of international authority will also support middle-of-the-road domestic solutions. There is in this process a distinct "vicious circle" which cannot be prevented but which could conceivably be put to good use.

To sum up our analysis, the requisites for the maintenance of an internal war settlement are two: (1) the stalemate must be preserved, but (2) the center must be progressively strengthened. These requisites need not prevail forever, but for the time-span of a generation (beyond which it is meaningless to speak of the durability of a settlement) all measures that may do away with the two original parties to the internal war, or that significantly reduce their viability, or that favor one more than the other, put the whole settlement into question. The persistence of a settlement depends on the development of techniques for sharing power and its fruits equally between the parties (as, for instance, in the Colombian case, by the rotation of the presidential office). For these techniques to work most effectively, the maintenance of the spirit of neutrality may be required in order to bring about some insulation of external influences favoring either party. But measures to preserve equality are not enough, chiefly because the passage of time and the operation of other uncontrollable processes inevitably confer undue advantage on one of the parties, thus putting the other in danger. In order to endure, the settlement must therefore rely upon the continual strengthening of the center, in part by drawing support away from the extremes.

V. *Conclusion*

As a method of terminating internal war, settlement has a number of features to commend it to the student of politics. Settlement reduces the amount of violence and serves as a clear landmark beyond which the renewed use of violence becomes illegitimate. Settlement takes account of a wider range of interests and mirrors more accurately the state of political forces in society. Settlement, above all, is a rational way of ending a period of violence and the appropriate method for inaugurating a period of domestic peace.

As an internationally operated method of dealing with internal wars, settlement is preferable to the primitive remedies of earlier international society, to those built upon undiscriminating devices of insulation. "Nonintervention" is not only patently impracticable but untenable in an age that cannot turn its back on outbreaks of political violence anywhere. But it is unfortunate that, in addition to nonintervention, two rather crude methods of terminating domestic strife—outright win and separation—should be internationally institutionalized, while international settlement, potentially a much more sensitive international instrument, is not.

Settlement is not the only correct way of ending internal wars, and in a great number of such cases it is indeed inapplicable. For some political systems, nothing but the surgical remedy of separation suffices to restore order. For others, outright victory may be so easy to come by that it is unnecessary to resort to negotiations—and it goes strongly against the grain of human nature to seek a negotiated solution when one can be imposed merely by demanding it. But it is most certainly the point of this essay that settlement has been applicable in more cases than it has been made use of in the past decades.

If it is to be used more widely as a method of ending internal wars, settlement must first of all be understood and recognized as intellectually respectable. Our purpose here has been to sketch out in a preliminary fashion the grounds for such respectability. Once this is established the necessary international techniques and institutions will follow, and the field will thus be clear for a wider application of an important social innovation—regularized procedures for the international settlement of internal wars.

TABLE II

100 TWENTIETH-CENTURY INTERNAL WARS, 1900–1962

		STATUS AS OF JANUARY 1963				
Date	Event	Incumbents' win	Insurgents' win	Separation	Settlement	Unresolved
1900–1	Boxer Rebellion (China)	X				
1903	Ilinden Rising (Macedonia)	X				
1903	Obrenovic Assassination (Serbia)		X			
1903	Revolution (Panama)			X		
1905	First Revolution (Russia)	X				
1907	Shah's Attempted Coup (Persia)	X				
1908	"Young Turk" Revolution (Ottoman Empire)		X			
1908–9	Revolution (Persia)		X			
1909–10	Revolution (Nicaragua)		X			
1910	Revolution (Mexico)		X			
1911	Revolution (China)		X			
1917	February Revolution (Russia)		X			
1917	October Revolution (Russia)		X			
1918	Revolution (Germany)		X			
1918	Civil War (Finland)	X				
1918–21	Civil War (Russia)	X				
1919	Soviet Republic (Hungary)		X			
1919–21	Civil War (Ireland)			X		
1919–21	Risings (Upper Silesia)			X		

Date	Event	STATUS AS OF JANUARY 1963				
		Incumbents' win	Insurgents' win	Separation	Settlement	Unresolved
1919–22	Independence Movement (Egypt)			X		
1920	Kapp Putsch (Germany)	X				
1920–26	Rif Revolt (Morocco)	X				
1922	Mussolini's "March on Rome" (Italy)		X			
1923	Anti-Stambolisky Coup (Bulgaria)		X			
1924	São Paulo Revolt (Brazil)	X				
1926	Pilsudski Coup (Poland)		X			
1926–27	Communist Revolt (Java and Sumatra)		X			
1927–36	Communist War (China)				X	
1930	Yen Bay Mutiny (Indochina)	X				
1930	Vargas Revolution (Brazil)		X			
1931–37	Military Terrorism (Japan)		X			
1932	Constitutional Coup (Siam)		X			
1933	Hitler's Accession (Germany)		X			
1934	Sakdalistas (Philippines)	X				
1934	Nazi Putsch in Vienna (Austria)	X				
1934	King's Assassination (Yugoslavia)	X				
1934–38	Stalin's Purges (USSR)	X				
1936–39	Civil War (Spain)		X			
1936–39	Arab Revolt (Palestine)	X				
1940	Bac Son and Other Uprisings (Indochina)	X				
1941	Attempted Army Coup (Iraq)	X				
1943	"Colonels' Clique" Revolt (Argentina)		X			
1944	Anti-Hitler Coup (Germany)	X				
1944	Resistance Coup (Bulgaria)		X			
1945	Riots (Algeria)	X				
1945–49	War of Independence (Indonesia)			X		

TABLE II (continued)

Date	Event	Incumbents' win	Insurgents' win	Separation	Settlement	Unresolved
		STATUS AS OF JANUARY 1963				
1945–54	War (Vietnam)			X		
1946–49	Civil War (China)		X			
1946–49	Communist Civil War (Greece)	X				
1946–54	Huk Rebellion (Philippines)	X				
1947	Madiun Revolt (Indonesia)	X				
1947	Pibul's Coup (Thailand)		X			
1947–48	Rebellion (Madagascar)	X				
1948	Hyderabad Accession (India)		X			
1948	Prague Coup (Czechoslovakia)		X			
1948–50	Rebel Insurrections (Burma)	X				
1948–58	Civil War (Colombia)				X	
1948–60	State of Emergency (Malaya)	X				
1948–62	Darul Islam Movement (Indonesia)	X				
1949–	Naga Unrest (India)					X
1950	Coup and Installation of Boy-King (Nepal)		X			
1951–56	Tunis Troubles (Tunisia)			X		
1952	Neguib Coup (Egypt)		X			
1952–56	Mau Mau Rebellion (Kenya)	X				
1953	Berlin Uprisings (Germany)	X				
1953	Anti-Mossadegh Coup (Iran)		X			
1953–56	Disturbances (Morocco)			X		
1953–57	Pathet Lao Action (Laos)				X	
1954	Overthrow of Arbenz (Guatemala)		X			
1954–59	Enosis (Cyprus)			X		
1954–62	War of Independence (Algeria)			X		
1955	Anti-sect Action (South Vietnam)	X				

Date	Event	Incumbents' win	Insurgents' win	Separation	Settlement	Unresolved
		STATUS AS OF JANUARY 1963				
1955	Anti-Perón Insurrection (Argentina)		X			
1956	Revolution (Hungary)	X				
1956	Gomulka's Seizure of Power (Poland)		X			
1956–59	Castro Revolutionary Movement (Cuba)		X			
1957–58	Sarit's Coup (Thailand)		X			
1958	Kassem's Coup (Iraq)		X			
1958	Rebellion (Lebanon)				X	
1958	De Gaulle's Accession (France)		X			
1958–61	Rebellion (Indonesia)	X				
1958–	Guerrilla War (South Vietnam)					X
1959	Lhasa Revolt (Tibet)	X				
1959	Opposition Violence (French Cameroons)	X				
1960	Paratroopers' Coup (South Vietnam)	X				
1960	Anti-Menderes Revolt (Turkey)		X			
1960	Rebel Coup (Ethiopia)	X				
1960	Parliamentary Dissolution (Nepal)		X			
1960–62	Civil War (Laos)				X	
1960–63	Katanga Secessionist Movement (Congo)				X	
1961	Bay of Pigs (Cuba)	X				
1961	Pak Chung Hui's Coup (South Korea)		X			
1961	Secession from UAR (Syria)				X	
1961	Generals' Revolt (Algeria)	X				
1961–	Uprisings (Angola)					X
1962	Army Coup (Yemen)					X
1962	Ne Win's Coup (Burma)		X			
1962	Frondizi Ousted (Argentina)	X				
1962	Azahari Revolt (Brunei)					X
1962	Congress Rising (Nepal)	X				

CHAPTER 6

Internal Violence as an Instrument
of Cold Warfare [*]

BY ANDREW M. SCOTT

As noted elsewhere in these pages, internal war may be precipitated by internal collapse or instigated by an external power.
The instigation of internal war, however, requires access to the
target nation on the part of the instigator. This chapter will
deal with the way that the governmental officials of one country, acting through agents or impersonal media such as radio,
can reach inside another country in order to bring about various
results, including internal violence. The capacity to achieve this
kind of influence has grown rapidly during what might be
called the "era of cold warfare."

But what exactly *is* "cold warfare"? The concept, and the
reality that it refers to, have received surprisingly little analysis.
One way to approach the question is to enumerate some cold
war measures and then to analyze the enumeration. All of the
following measures and many others might be found on such
a list: collaboration among the NATO powers; economic aid to
India; military aid to Yugoslavia; a Voice of America broadcast
to Latin America or the Soviet Union; the operation of a guerrilla group in South Asia; the actions of Communist parties
and their auxiliaries in Western Europe; a *coup d'état* in the
Middle East; the maintenance of a USIA library in West
Berlin; financial subsidies to anti-Communist newspapers and
labor organizations in Western Europe. All of these measures
are undertaken to improve the position of one nation or group
of nations vis-à-vis another nation or group of nations. If we
examine the list further, it is evident that some examples, such
as alliance policy and military preparedness, are familiar and

[*] The substance of this paper was first presented at the Annual Meeting
of the American Political Science Association, Washington, D.C., September 6, 1962.

fall within the confines of traditional statecraft. Others tend to be novel.

What, if anything, do the examples in this second category have in common—the technical assistance programs, cultural exchange programs, guerrilla activities, and so on? The common denominator lies in the fact that each example involves access by the agents of one country to the population (or part of it) or processes of another country. This characteristic of the cold war measures that do not fall into a traditional pattern we shall term "informal access." Informal access distinguishes these novel forms of cold warfare from the traditional, formal, government-to-government type of relationship.

Because the term "cold war" was not coined until after World War II, the tendency is to assume that cold warfare is a product of the post-World War II conflict between the Soviet Union and the non-Communist world. This is to confuse *the* cold war with cold warfare in general. Cold warfare is a special *type* of conflict; *the* cold war of the past seventeen years is an example of this type. More or less isolated examples of informal access extend back through history; instances can be cited from the Wars of Religion and the French Revolution. It was not until after World War I, however, that informal attack in its modern form may be said to have developed. If one must pick a date for the beginning of cold warfare in its present form, 1919, the year of the formation of the Communist International, is probably as good as any. The two men who contributed most to the development of the theory and practice of cold warfare during the interwar period were Hitler and Lenin.

The existence of isolated examples of informal attack in earlier periods should not be allowed to obscure the significant differences between cold warfare as it is now practiced and anything that has gone before. Some of its present-day characteristics may be summarized as follows:

(1) A wide variety of techniques may be used simultaneously; overt and covert, violent and non-violent. A partial list

would include the use of front groups; infiltration of existing organizations; financial subsidies to newspapers, labor unions, political parties, and many types of voluntary organization; externally organized guerrilla warfare and resistance movements; passive resistance and sabotage; terror and counterterror; strikes and riots; the establishment and use of militant party formations; *coups d'état;* and various forms of psychological and economic warfare.

(2) These techniques are used in a planned and coordinated way against a variety of targets.

(3) This means that their effective employment has become a complex and specialized task.

(4) The leading powers have placed an increased emphasis on measures of informal attack.

(5) This increased emphasis, plus the growing complexity of these operations, has led to the institutionalization of cold warfare. Its conduct now involves large organizations, massive budgets, many types of specialized personnel, extensive training programs, and all the other paraphernalia of institutionalization.

(6) Some of these activities are overt and some covert. The existence of large organizations charged with covert activities tends to become widely known. Security may be maintained with regard to particular operations, but the fact that a nation is engaged in the conduct of covert informal-attack activities cannot remain a secret.

(7) The conduct of covert activities by the major powers is viewed by progressively larger numbers of persons in the country concerned as a normal and continuing aspect of foreign policy and foreign operations.

(8) Smaller nations are now becoming interested in covert informal attack.

(9) The greater the variety, depth, and geographical extent of a nation's interests, the greater are likely to be the variety, depth, and geographical extent of its cold war activities. Pow-

ers with global interests, such as the United States and the Soviet Union, regard virtually any accessible area of the globe as a proper theater for their cold war skills.

Although this is not the place to undertake an extended analysis of the concept of access, several of its main dimensions need to be identified at the outset. More precisely, we must take note of the objectives, targets, and techniques of access.

Obviously, in seeking access to another nation, a government will have certain *objectives* in mind. A given set of objectives may be limited and confined, or they may be virtually unlimited. Their variety can, of course, be very great. A penetrating nation may seek any of the following, and others as well: (a) to gather intelligence; (b) to harass and weaken the government; (c) to paralyze, influence, or dominate foreign policy; (d) to paralyze, influence, or dominate domestic policy; (e) to influence or divide public opinion; (f) to seize power; (g) to accede to power legally; and (h) to annex the target nation. In a given case there will probably be a hierarchy of objectives, ranging from a set of modest aims to more grandiose ones. If the penetrating nation cannot achieve its maximum objectives, it is likely to settle for as much as it can get, short of them.

It must be stressed that hostile intent does not necessarily underlie the resort of governments to informal access. The purpose behind the achievement of access may be friendly, unfriendly, or a mixture of the two. The objectives mentioned above are those appropriate to informal *attack*. In addition, there are those appropriate to informal *support*, such as helping the country to develop economically, speeding necessary social change; strengthening the government in resisting threats from abroad; assisting it in overcoming the threat of subversion; training its administrative personnel; and so on.

Whatever its purposes, the penetrating nation will direct its attention to certain *targets* in the nation to which it is seeking access. There is an almost infinite variety of targets: particular individuals, political parties, cultural groups, youth groups, veterans' organizations, unions, the military services, strategic industries, the opinion media, segments of public opinion, and so on.

As for the *techniques* of informal access, these are also quite variable. Some techniques are dual purpose, in the sense that they can be used either for purposes of attack or support. Once it is initiated, for example, an economic aid program provides the granting country with access to the recipient country. This access might be used in order either to assist the target nation in developing its resources or to insert advisers into the governmental system in the hope of achieving dominance over the political and economic life of the country. Other techniques, however, by their very nature, are almost always confined to attack functions—political agitation, subversion, sabotage, guerrilla warfare, resistance activities, strikes, infiltration of groups, assassination, character assassination, bribery, terror and counterterror, the organization of a *coup d'état*, and so on.

In discussing access, an important distinction to make is that between technical penetration and substantive penetration. Technical penetration relates to the actual mechanics of penetration. Is a radio program actually being received in the target country? Is it logistically possible to organize and supply a guerrilla movement in the target country? Substantive penetration, on the other hand, involves the response of the target population. Are citizens in the target country influenced by the radio program? Do they join or support the guerrilla movement?

In one situation, technical penetration might be highly successful but the audience might be completely unresponsive. In another situation, the target population might be ripe but technical penetration might be unsuccessful. Or, technical penetration and substantive penetration might enjoy the same degree of success or failure. The dynamics of access vary a great deal, depending on the purposes, the target, and the techniques involved. A great deal also depends on the technical and substantive *accessibility* of the target. If nation B is open to penetration by nation A, we may say that B is accessible to A. This does not mean that A, in fact, has access to B, but only that it could have such access if it chose to seek it. It is implicit in the distinction between access (the actual achievement of penetration) and accessibility (vulnerability to penetration) that not all targets that are accessible will be penetrated.

It may be helpful to think of nations as ranged along a scale of accessibility. At the lower end of the scale would be a country such as Japan prior to Admiral Perry's visit in 1853 or the Soviet Union under Joseph Stalin. At the upper end of the scale would be those countries that are relatively easy to penetrate. This end of the scale would fade off into outright control. The position of a state along this scale would vary over time, depending upon its internal security measures, the seriousness of the cleavages in its population, and so on. Most countries today would have to be located toward the higher end of the scale. Indeed, this mutual access of nations to one another is so omnipresent that it needs to be explicitly recognized as one of the most important features of the nation-state system today.

I. *Cold Warfare and Nationhood*

In view of the fact that cold warfare in its modern form has played a role in international politics for close to half a century and appears now to have become the dominant mode of conflict among the Great Powers, it is surprising that there has not been more interest in trying to place it in its broad historical perspective. The key to the achievement of such a perspective lies in the defining characteristic of the nontraditional forms of this new type of conflict—that is, informal access.

Throughout most of the history of the Western world, after the development of the nation-state system, the individual component units in this system were relatively immune to informal access. Conflict and cooperation between states was between units set apart in space and incapable of significant

159

interpenetration. The aggressive designs of one country upon another could be gratified only by attempts at military conquest or threats. Relationships were almost exclusively formal and were restricted to a handful of diplomatic and consular officials. One nation rarely penetrated the space of another or had access to its population. Competition between them rarely involved efforts to penetrate the space of third nations. This situation has changed markedly during the past half-century.

Informal access has important implications for the functioning of nations. One of the functions of the state has been to define territorial boundaries and to control movement across them as it chose. Today, however, most states are either unwilling or unable to control fully the movement of funds, persons, ideas, information, and material across their borders. To speak of the informal access that many nations now have to one another is only a different way of saying that territorial boundaries do not have the meaning they formerly had. Traditional lines between nations are becoming blurred. The Eastern European satellite nations provide one example of this and the developing European Community provides quite a different example. In a period of increasing informal access, a situation sometimes occurs in which the critical boundary is not geographical, but one defined by the circumstances of the market, the location of the adherents of an opposing ideology, the location of a given race or religious group, or the zone of effectiveness of a counter-intelligence organization.[1]

Another important function of the state is to defend its citizenry and repel attack. While this has not always been easy, or even possible, the nature of the task has usually been clear-cut. The country suffering aggression rarely had any doubt about the matter. Now, however, the advent of informal access of

---

[1] For an excellent analysis of military factors which have also contributed to the breakdown of the impenetrability of states, see John Herz, *International Politics in the Atomic Age* (New York: Columbia University Press, 1959).

nations to one another has introduced new and subtle forms of aggression. Conflict becomes far more varied. Aggression becomes far harder to identify and deal with. Instead of an ultimatum, there may be the quiet infiltration of labor organizations and the preparation of a series of carefully organized "spontaneous" riots and strikes. Instead of a declaration of war, there may be the formation of a militant Communist Party and the systematic infiltration of student, youth, veterans' and cultural organizations. Instead of an armed thrust across a border, an "attack" may take the form of the establishment of a government-in-exile and the organization of anti-government resistance forces. A government may receive the first indication that it is in serious difficulties when a foreign-sponsored *coup d'état* erupts. The task of a state in trying to defend its citizenry and territory has changed, therefore, and has been made a good deal more difficult by the development of the techniques of informal attack.

The state normally has a monopoly of force within a country. In cold warfare, guerrilla units, resistance forces, or the combat adjuncts of a militant party may also wield substantial force. These paramilitary formations destroy the force monopoly of the government, whether they are used against the government itself or against other parties and organizations.

Historically speaking, the rulers of one society have often challenged the claim to legitimacy of the rulers of another society. These disputes, however, have generally proceeded within the framework of an agreed principle of legitimacy, such as monarchy based on hereditary succession. In an era of cold warfare, on the other hand, the attack on the legitimacy of the government in the target country, which is usually the first order of business, frequently denies the very principle of legitimacy on which that government is based or reinterprets it in a significant way. In a colonial area the legitimacy of colonial rule will be denied. Dictatorial governments based on a military junta will be denounced on the grounds that only governments based on the free consent of the governed can be legitimate. If a country has democratic institutions, they may be undercut by the argument that the state is the instrument of the dominant class and that bourgeois democracy is not democracy at all.[2]

One of the functions of the state is to promote symbols and ideals designed to create loyalty to the nation and unity within it. The state teaches that loyalty to the nation is a value of supreme importance and most citizens respond with the complementary feeling that disloyalty is abominable. In the present period, however, a nation having access to another may offer alternative symbols in an effort to create division and to break down loyalty. While the government of the target country is trying to reduce conflicts within the populace, agents of the penetrating nation are working hard to exacerbate them. While the government is teaching loyalty, the penetrating power is busily trying to persuade the nationals of the target country that values such as justice, the proletariat, socialism, fascism, or democracy take precedence over nationalism. Treason is presented as a higher loyalty. The vertical type of loyalty—that is, to the nation—is challenged by a horizontal, or transnational, appeal that seeks to reach out to men across national boundaries. The effectiveness of this type of appeal has been demonstrated repeatedly during recent decades.

II. *Informal Attack and International Stability*

If informal access is as important as the foregoing suggests, then almost every aspect of international politics should be affected by it, including international stability. Do nations vary in their accessibility to penetration? Do they devote different proportions of their resources and energies to achieving access to other

2 The verbal formulations of the opposing sides may or may not, of course, be genuinely believed by the leaders of those sides. For example, regardless of the arguments pressed into use, the only governments that the Soviet leadership accepts as legitimate are those that take their orders from Moscow.

countries and to denying access to themselves? Are there differences in the skill, technical competence, and imagination of the nations engaging in informal attack? If the answer to these questions is "yes"—as it is—then informal access must necessarily have an effect on international stability.

The concept of "power," and the reality that underlies it, are central to the study of international politics. From the point of view of the discerning student of international relations, or the individual concerned with the conduct of foreign policy, the capacity of a nation to wage a campaign of informal attack may be of as much interest as its capacity to wage total or limited war. The essential point is that its ability to wage a military campaign is by no means the same thing as its capacity to conduct a campaign of informal aggression. To a degree, these two measures are independent variables, thus suggesting four types of capabilities:

(1) A nation may be powerful in traditional terms and also have a great capacity for informal aggression. The Soviet Union would be an example of a nation in this category.

(2) A nation may be weak in both respects. Most of the smaller nations would fit in this category.

(3) A nation may be strong in traditional terms and be weak in its capacity for informal aggression. Some years ago the United States would have provided an example of a nation in this category.

(4) Finally, a nation might be weak in traditional terms and yet be strong in the area of informal aggression.

This final category is perhaps the most interesting of the group. It suggests at least the logical possibility that a nation that is relatively poor with regard to resources, population, and military power may yet possess substantial capabilities for informal attack. Can nations be found that are examples of this? Nasser's Egypt is weak according to the traditional indices of power, and was even weaker during the early years of Nasser's regime. Nevertheless, by means of agitation, political menaces, terrorism, the propaganda of Radio Cairo, the appeal of pan-Arabism, and the conception of a United Arab Republic, this weak country has had a marked effect on the political climate of the entire Middle East. Fidel Castro, in the period immediately after he came to power—and with few of the traditional resources at his command—managed to throw a sizable portion of Latin America into turmoil by his efforts to foment revolution in neighboring countries. It seems clear that there is no inherent reason why informal aggression, including attempts at *coups d'état,* cannot be designed and promoted in Cairo, in Havana, or in the capitals of other small countries, quite as well as in Moscow or Washington.

Informal access alters the power relations among nations and, in so doing, has an unsettling effect on international politics. It is worth noting some of the factors that help to bring about this result.

(1) The techniques of informal attack can be highly effective under favorable conditions. The covert subsidy of one or two newspapers in a country might make a substantial difference in the complexion of public thought. The injection of a modest sum into the labor movement of a country at the right time and place could significantly alter the direction of its development. The organization of a guerrilla movement can create grave difficulties for a government or even lead to its overthrow. In Malaya a guerrilla movement supported from outside achieved its minimum objective of harassing the British. In Indochina a guerrilla movement (converted in the final stages of the conflict into a regular army) achieved its maximum objective of driving the French out of the area. The organization of a successful *coup d'état* of the type of which there have been so many in recent years, can change the entire political orientation of a nation. The fact of the accessibility of nations, and the existence of effective informal-attack techniques to exploit this accessibility, will be as obvious to the smaller powers as to the great.

(2) Informal attack is a relatively economical way of achiev-

ing results. To a very considerable extent, this type of attack depends upon the vigor, skill, and inventiveness of a relatively small number of persons. A nation engaging in it will seek to exploit the energies of others but it need not deploy vast armies of its own citizens. Funds and material are needed, to be sure, but the expenditure is of a different order of magnitude from that required for the development of modern military power. It allows a nation to think in terms of millions rather than billions. Political turmoil can sometimes be created in a country for the equivalent of a few million dollars. Governments of smaller countries have been overturned for not much more. Guerrilla movements are relatively inexpensive to organize and operate and their suppression is costly and difficult.

Aggressively inclined nations that would be foreclosed from playing a major role in international affairs by the cost of modern weaponry will find that informal aggression has much to recommend it. Traditionally, a nation's imperial ambitions have been sharply limited by its resources and its general power position. In the realm of informal attack, however, resources go a long way. If a small nation chooses to concentrate its efforts (or if it has access to outside support), it can become quite influential in a restricted area. That is to say, a nation may now be imperialist on a shoestring. This is a development which various nations will not be slow to appreciate.[3]

(3) The time required for developing an informal attack capacity is modest. There is a limit to the rate at which a nation's overall strength can be increased, since it involves such factors as the level of education and training of the population, the availability of resources, and the level of development of the

---

[3] The capacity to take over a country by subversion does not necessarily imply the existence of the administrative and other resources necessary to control and direct the country taken over. A nation might very well bite off more than it could chew or digest. For present purposes, however, it is enough to note that a small nation might be capable of taking some pretty substantial bites and that this could have a thoroughly disruptive effect.

economy. With relatively little time and effort, however, a nation with a small informal-attack capacity can expand its capabilities four or five times over.[4] It did not take Nasser and Castro long after coming to power to develop their capacities in this direction.

(4) Informal attack permits an aggressively inclined nation to probe for weak spots without forcing it to take overtly aggressive action. It need not deliver an ultimatum to its neighbor, nor declare war nor invade. It can attack a neighbor informally while maintaining correct relations formally. The nation attacked may be left without grounds for a military counterattack and even, perhaps, without grounds for a formal protest. Indeed, it may be some time before it realizes that it is under attack.

(5) A nation undertaking covert indirect attack usually takes some pains not to become formally involved. This allows it to disengage itself from an undertaking with a minimum loss of prestige if it seems advisable. If a project does not develop favorably, it is quietly liquidated or allowed to taper off while attention is centered elsewhere.

(6) A nation will try to avoid having its covert activities exposed, but if they are exposed the penalty is not always great. There is a period of embarrassment but the dust settles rather quickly. After it becomes widely known that a nation is engaged in this activity, and after it has been caught in the act several times, each new discovery occasions progressively less shock and surprise. The Soviet Union, for example, never experiences more than a momentary embarrassment. However, a nation, such as the United States, that attaches a good deal of importance to its moral position will suffer relatively more from

[4] Nonetheless a nation cannot expect to develop its informal-attack capacities evenly across the board. In some areas development will be rapid, while in others it will be slower. For example, a nation might find it easier to expand its paramilitary and propaganda facilities than its political warfare operations. It will also find it easier to increase its activities in some geographical areas than in others.

exposure. The U-2 exposure [5] and the abortive Cuban invasion were both grievous blows at the time.

(7) Traditionally the defeat of a nation in its policies of aggrandizement has been costly to that nation. Military defeat can alter the history of a nation or even lead to its liquidation. Defeat in an informal attack, however, while it may vary from the disappointing to the serious, is rarely catastrophic. Hence defeat in such projects may be borne with a degree of equanimity.

(8) Not only is the number of nations engaging in informal attack likely to increase, but the number of operations carried on by each nation may also increase. It is a truism of foreign policy that a nation should husband its power and not overcommit itself. But what is "overcommitment" during a period of cold warfare? In the case of traditional techniques such as alliances, solemn guarantees, and the deployment of military forces about the globe, the concept of overcommitment is reasonably clear. The techniques of informal attack, however, involve a type of power that is substantially different in its nature and its uses. We have already noted that in cold warfare a nation, characteristically, makes no formal commitments, can disengage itself with little loss of prestige, can expand its cold war capabilities rather rapidly, and can engage in these activities on a moderate budget. A nation of modest resources might, therefore, conduct three, four, or a half-dozen operations simultaneously. This means that the dangers of overcommitting a nation's power are markedly altered, and eased, when the matter is considered from the standpoint of informal aggression.

(9) Several features of the present international environment tend to encourage the use of informal aggression. These would include the emergence of new states that make excellent targets for attack and the existence of three major power centers willing

---

[5] Technically speaking, the U-2 affair involved the exposure of an intelligence operation rather than an example of informal attack, but the case is still instructive.

and able to encourage and finance the informal attack activities of a variety of other powers. Additional instability is fostered by the fact that still other nations, not aggressively inclined themselves, may be forced to respond in kind when they find themselves under informal attack.

(10) The general level of accessibility in the international system has increased in recent decades. The accessibility that exists, however, is not evenly distributed. Some nations are highly vulnerable; others are far less so. Some nations have virtually no access to populations outside their borders, while others have enormous access. The differential distribution of both defensive and offensive capabilities relating to informal attack is another factor promoting instability in international relations. When a single country, such as the Soviet Union, combines a low level of accessibility with a high level of access to other nations, it becomes a formidable factor on the world scene.

The factors mentioned above will encourage nations to probe for weak spots in the defenses of their neighbors. Why not fish in troubled waters? If a given project works, well and good. If it does not, little has been lost in the way of prestige, personnel, or material. When victories can be achieved at all in the realm of informal attack, they are likely to be excellent investments, providing a large yield in return for a modest risk. The situation is one that encourages adventurism in nations great and small.

When the factors mentioned above are taken in conjunction with one another, it is evident that the advent of informal attack has introduced an important element of instability into international politics. It had an unsettling effect on international affairs between the world wars, when Hitler's Germany engaged in cold warfare on a large scale and the Communist International was active, and this effect has been even more pronounced since the end of World War II. Furthermore, "disarmament" in the realm of informal attack would be extremely hard to achieve except in the context of a general reduction in

168

the level of tension. An army, once created, cannot be hidden. Airfields and missile-launching facilities can be detected. Covert informal attack, on the other hand, can be so shrouded in secrecy, or so confused by claims and counterclaims, that the truth is hard to come by. It is one thing for a United Nations Peace Observation Commission to police a border or to determine whether armed aggression has taken place. It would be quite another thing to try to learn the "facts" about subversion or to guard against political penetration.

CHAPTER 7

The Limits of
International Coalitions

☆

BY KARL W. DEUTSCH AND
MORTON A. KAPLAN

THE contemporary international system has been described in an earlier chapter as a loose bipolar system. Two blocs of states, centered around the United States and the Soviet Union, respectively, are competing for power and security, since each perceives the other as an actual or potential threat. A third group of states are uncommitted and share a limited common interest in dampening the conflict between the two blocs and in preventing the extension of either bloc so as to absorb any still uncommitted state.

It has been suggested that the rational behavior of states in such a bipolar system will differ substantially from that obtaining in a system of balance of power, such as prevailed at times during the nineteenth century. In a bipolar world, neither of the two competing blocs, and neither of their leading states, has an interest in keeping in existence either the opposing bloc or its leading state; only lesser states in each bloc may have such an interest, in order to preserve their value as allies for their own bloc.

The two blocs and their leading states have far fewer inhibitions in their struggle. It may pay them to strive for total victory, to wipe out their opponents, to coerce and absorb neutrals, and to intervene openly or secretly in the internal affairs of opposing and neutral states. However, the risk of driving uncommitted states into the opposite bloc, the danger of an escalating chain of acts of retaliation, and the effects of an exchange of blows with thermonuclear weapons are obvious potential factors of restraint.

Are there any other restraining factors inherent in this situation, as it is pictured by the loose bipolar model? In particular, does each of the two leading states have an unlimited interest in extending its own bloc, at the expense of the bloc of its rival or of the group of uncommitted countries, whenever opportunity offers?

By making explicit some hidden assumptions contained in the loose bipolar model, it can be shown that there may be rational limits of self-interest to the expansion of each bloc, and rational interests on the part of both contending blocs in keeping a substantial number of states in the uncommitted group.

The hidden assumption that needs to be made explicit is simply that neither of the two chief rival powers is omnipotent, and that in fact the capabilites of each of these two states are limited, if—considering the magnitude of the commitments required of it—each is to hold its own bloc together.

Under these conditions, the accession of a new state to a bloc will almost immediately not only add something to the capabilities of that bloc, and/or to those of its leading state, but will also subtract something. It will add that part of the capabilities of the new member which it can make available to the support of bloc policies, but it will at the same time also subtract from the potential power of the bloc an amount corresponding to that part of the previously existing capabilities of the old bloc that must now be devoted to defending the new member, or to holding it in the bloc by maintaining its government, or by responding to its major political, economic, or military needs.

Each new state joining a bloc, in short, contributes not only assets but also liabilities in terms of wealth, power, and attention. It adds not only some disposable new capabilities, but also some new demands that require the consumption or commitment of some old capabilities to cope with them. If its assets to the bloc exceed its liabilities, its addition would be rational; if not, not.

The same reckoning applies, of course, to the extension of

coalitions in domestic politics; to the opening or closing of branch stores or plants by a business corporation; to the inclusion or exclusion of a particular type or grade of labor in a craft union; to the adding of new staff to an organization or the cutting out of "deadwood" from its personnel; to the acceptance or rejection of territories or provinces whose populations may wish to join a state, or else to secede from it, and thus to their retention, even at the price of force, or to the bestowing of independence upon them, even though they might have been willing to remain a territory of the mother country.[1] The Swiss refusal to accept the proffered accession of Vorarlberg in 1918, or the bestowing of independence upon the Philippines by the United States Congress in 1934, might appear rational from this point of view, and so might the British consent in 1947 to the independence of India, Pakistan, and Ceylon, and perhaps also Russia's grudging toleration of Yugoslavia's secession from satellite status in 1948. All these territories, under the conditions of the respective periods, may have represented greater liabilities than assets to the states or blocs that either let them go or did not take them in, and that by so doing preserved a greater share of capabilities for their other and more vital interests.

Many of the present-day uncommitted nations may be in a similar category. They might be unlikely to contribute much, if anything, to the net disposable strength of either coalition if they should join it; and they might be costly to hold in either coalition, by reason of their poverty, or the unruliness of their population, or their unwillingness to contribute as much to a coalition as they demand from it.

It should be noted, however, that even such political deficit areas might become profitable in the more distant future. If a coalition had an abundance of ready economic and military resources, it might find it profitable to risk some of them on such

[1] Cf. William H. Riker, *The Theory of Political Coalitions* (New Haven: Yale University Press, 1962).

a highly uncertain political investment as the acquisition of a currently unprofitable ally. A similar calculation might suggest that even such currently unprofitable allies ought to be denied to the opposing coalition, lest that coalition should succeed later in transforming this costly political investment into a profitable one.

Countries with a high likelihood of recurrent or protracted civil conflict or internal war—for instance, Iraq and Lebanon in 1958—are unlikely to be worth much as unwilling allies. Even the mineral resources of Iraq would not necessarily have outweighed the logistic drain on either Western or Soviet resources that an outright occupation by either side—backed conceivably by paratroops and airlifted supplies—would have required. In the event, the United States presence in Lebanon was short-lived and the country was left to choose its own course of mildly pro-Western neutrality, while Iraq's policies in the long run proved to be not much less independent of Soviet influence.

If the neutralist group of countries succeeds in retaining a large number of such political deficit areas, they may thus make both major blocs stronger in the net result, and leave their leading powers, in an old image of Winston Churchill's, crouched rather than sprawled. Acquiring control of some of the currently uncommitted countries might then actually weaken the bloc which acquired them, since holding them might consume, or at least tie down, a greater amount of strategic resources than the bloc could extract from them.

Some calculations of this sort actually have been made in warfare. T. E. Lawrence of Arabian fame has been reported to have decided in March 1917 not to cut the Turkish railroad to Medina and not to capture the Turkish garrison of that city, but rather to allow the railroad "to be just—only just—kept in working order, so that it would be a continual drain on the Turks to the north to keep it going and to feed the troops in Medina. . . . The Allied cause would, in fact, be best served by attracting and keeping as many Turkish troops as possible in this unimportant theatre of war. . . ." [2]

Similar considerations of extending and exhausting the forces of the adversary, while keeping one's own forces in being, have been not infrequent in both British and Russian strategy, from Wellington's Peninsular campaign and Kutusov's retreats before Napoleon, to the British and Soviet strategies against Hitler in World War II. In American history, a similar strategy was followed in the War of Independence against Britain in 1776–1783.

In the postwar era, however, much of American strategic thinking seems to have followed the Napoleonic and the German conception of dramatic confrontations and annihilating blows. In World Wars I and II, the United States entered combat relatively late, after the enemy forces were already far extended and were at least beginning to be strained or exhausted, so that American strategy could take this phase for granted and concentrate principally on winning an early decision. In the long-drawn-out conflicts of the cold war, however, it would seem strategically rational to evaluate carefully the advantages and disadvantages of each possible ally and each geographic position, and of the extension and expenditure of forces and attention that its acquisition would require.

Such a rational appraisal would of course also include an evaluation of the possibility that the adversary was so superior to one's own side in the arts of political and economic entrepreneurship and management that he could take over some previously unruly and resource-consuming countries and transform them into new sources of significant strength. Where such conditions in fact apply, of course, it would be rational for the other side to deny even an unpromising country to a resourceful opponent, and to commit additional capabilities to this task, up to the level of the power increment that the adversary might

[2] Robert Graves, *Lawrence and the Arabs* (London: Jonathan Cape, 1935), p. 152.

be expected to extract. The Chinese Communists' ability to draw or wrest greater increments of power from the Chinese provinces than did their opponents, the Nationalists, is a case in point; but Albania, Hungary, and perhaps Tibet suggest that Communist abilities of this kind are neither universal nor unlimited. The Russian intervention in Hungary in 1956 was followed by quiescence, but no such results could have been expected in Tito's Yugoslavia, and Western attempts at direct or indirect intervention in Egypt in 1956, and in Cuba in 1961, revealed the serious difficulties posed by local conditions and popular attitudes.

Another rather primitive refinement of this line of reasoning would consist in taking account of time preferences on both sides. One bloc, perhaps disposing currently of more ample resources, might be able to afford a risky investment in acquiring another dubious ally, or in defending some exposed geographic position, while the other bloc, more hard-pressed for immediate resources of strategic power, might find it necessary to avoid such expensive commitments and to content itself in these marginal or unprofitable theaters with propaganda efforts, small-scale harassment, and revolts by relatively expendable local forces.

Even in the case of a strategically affluent bloc, however, its propensity to spend more of its "liquid"—or currently available —strategic resources on long-shot gambles in secondary theaters would have to be weighed rationally against the opportunity cost of each such strategic investment. What is the probable return from investing X units of manpower and resources in the doubtful country Y, instead of devoting them to consolidating the bloc's hold on country Z, or to some productive investment in the technological or scientific growth of the leading country of the bloc itself, so as to increase its future capabilities?

All these are secondary elaborations on a basic principle. This basic principle is that of strategic rationality: the need to distinguish between profitable and unprofitable investments, strength-increasing and strength-diminishing allies, power-giving and power-wasting geographic positions. Strategic rationality applies a realistic calculation of when to advance and when to retreat; which positions to hold and which ones to evacuate; and how to keep in being under all circumstances a core of one's own forces and one's own society, and never to lose the integrity of one's own essential values and motivations in the process.

Strategic rationality also requires, of course, an intuitive judgment of emotions and intangibles, of the "bandwagon effect" that further enhances the earlier gains of a popular cause, and the "counter-bandwagon effect" that arouses additional opposition to the advances of an unpopular one. All these considerations, however, do not obscure the basic point: there may be rational limits to the expansion of each bloc, to strategic investment in exposed positions; or to expenditure of deterrent power, or of any other kind of bargaining power, on partial issues.

What has been said is in some way a restatement of what sometimes was implied in the old language of national interest. Traditional diplomats and their "neo-realist" successors distinguished between "vital" and secondary interests, and were disinclined to risk as much for the latter as for the former.[3]

The traditional diplomats' discriminating appraisal of interests, allies, and territories, and their readiness to concentrate limited resources on the most important ones, have been paralleled by the strategic theory and practice of the Communist parties and Soviet regimes from Lenin's day onward. Bolshevist theory, like the strategy of the ancient Parthians, included explicitly the utilization of both strategic and tactical retreats. Both before and after World War II, the Soviet rulers have

[3] George F. Kennan, *American Diplomacy, 1900–1950* (New York: Mentor Books, 1951); Hans J. Morgenthau, *Politics Among Nations*, 3rd edn. (New York: Alfred A. Knopf, 1960).

abandoned exposed territories, allied regimes, and both geographic and ideological positions, as well as their allies in local
civil wars, whenever this seemed strategically rational to them.
A classic case was Lenin's advocacy of the Peace of Brest-
Litovsk in 1918. More recent examples include Stalin's abandonment of his puppet Kuusinen government in Finland in
1940; his abandonment of the North Azerbaijan regime in 1946;
his acceptance of the expulsion of the French and Italian
Communist parties from the governments of their respective
countries in 1947; his acceptance of Yugoslavia's secession from
the Soviet bloc in 1948 and his effective abandonment of the
Stalinite faction in that country; his abandonment of the Greek,
Philippine, and Malayan Communist guerrillas in the local
civil wars of the same general period; and his abandonment of
the pro-Soviet regime of Guatemala in 1954.

In many of these theaters, such as France, Italy, Iran, Guatemala, and in the internal wars in Greece and in the Philippines,
the combination of Western interests and Western local capabilities outweighed the local interests-cum-capabilities of the
Soviet bloc, and the Communist retreat in those areas became
at the same time an occasion for a Western advance. In other
cases, such as Yugoslavia, Finland, and Austria, Soviet retreats
were followed by the emergence of more or less uncommitted
or neutral regimes, at least partly accessible to Western economic and cultural influence.

In the future, too, it seems likely that Western capabilities
and interests will outweigh Soviet ones at some points on the
map, while the reverse may be the case in others. A flexible
strategy of rationally chosen local advances and retreats, corresponding to the actual changes in the local configurations of
interests and capabilities of the two blocs, may thus be more
to the advantage of both contenders than a mere prestige
strategy of indiscriminate rigidity with a high likelihood of a
mutually annihilating collision. The Russians, however, have a
doctrine of strategic retreat *pour mieux sauter* and the organ-

izational means and morale to implement it. The West tends to be more rigid in defending existing positions and has not yet developed a fully adequate doctrine, organizational technique, or morale for recoiling from a retreat to begin a new advance.

It would be simpler, of course, if either bloc could rely on having at all times and places a clearly firmer will and stronger motivation than its rival. Such a test of wills or of deterrence is formally similar to the game of "chicken," in which juvenile delinquents race automobiles toward each other to see which driver will swerve first from the collision course. Such a procedure is equivalent to playing two games in rapid succession. The first is a cooperative game against nature or fate, in which both players are betting that their motivations will be sufficiently asymmetrical to avoid collision. The second game is competitive and will only be played if the first, cooperative, game has been won: if collision is avoided, a reward accrues to the player who contributed nothing to the winning of the cooperative game, while a penalty will be imposed upon the player whose concession made the winning of the cooperative game of joint survival possible. If the rewards of the competitive game seem more important to both of them, both are more likely to lose the cooperative game. The more important the stakes of the competitive game, therefore, the more rational it would be to strive to disentangle them from the risk of mutual annihilation in a "chicken" or deterrence game situation.

A strategy of solvency, or a discriminating appraisal of interest, might help to avoid "chicken" situations and to promote such disentanglement. It would permit distinctions to be made as to those points where one bloc's motivation and will might be presumed to be stronger, and where the bloc could be expected, therefore, to make the more credible commitments or threats, in contrast to those other countries, issues, or geographic positions where its interests and capabilities were lesser and its commitments therefore inherently less credible, despite all artificial efforts to inflate them for purposes of deterrence and bargaining.

In our current age of mass politics, however, the language of interest is becoming drowned out by the language of international public bargaining. To enhance its bargaining power, each bloc is now supposed to describe each and every theater, every position, every ally, and every interest as almost equally important. Each is to be a "test case" of its "will," which otherwise might be thought to be faltering: "If we retreat here, how can we ever stop retreating anywhere?"

Some of this rhetoric is addressed to the opposing bloc, and some to presumably reluctant elements among the public, taxpayers, and allies within one's own bloc. Inevitably, however, this bargaining rhetoric gets in the way of factual discussion of the actual national and bloc interest in allocating a limited amount of strength to competing theaters and uses, including the ineluctable long-run claims of greater domestic economic and scientific growth.

Despite the great intellectual merits of game theory, and the promise of its application to problems of bargaining and of deterrence,[4] too many of our recent popular discussions of the strategic interest of the United States and its allies have made inappropriate use of the bargaining model. Though bargaining and deterrence models are intended to encourage rationality, their explicit use in a political context does not always do so. The techniques of bargaining often prominently include concealment and deception. The bargaining tactic of "irrevocable committal" represents a concealment of the true preference structure of the committed party, and tries to make this concealment irreversible.[5] In trying to bargain in this manner with

---

[4] For an impressive presentation of this approach, see Thomas C. Schelling, *The Strategy of Conflict* (Cambridge: Harvard University Press, 1960).

[5] Cf. Herman Kahn, *On Thermonuclear War* (Princeton: Princeton University Press), pp. 289–95.

its opponent, however, each bloc—and particularly, every democratic country in the Western bloc—runs the grave risk of deceiving itself through the cumulative deception and self-deception of its domestic publics, elites, and finally its leaders.

"Single-play" bargaining techniques reward the bargainer who pretends convincingly that one particular object or locality currently at issue is far more valuable to him, compared with other objects, than it actually is. This same misrepresentation of relative preferences, however, which is so useful in negotiating for a single short-run bargain, may be quite detrimental to a rational allocation of the bargainer's efforts and resources in the long run.

Thus in a conflict over a disputed border city or territory, it may pay each power in the short run to pretend that possession of this piece of land is more important to it than, say, the survival of the population of its capital city. This assertion and its attendant threat of thermonuclear war may indeed serve to deter the opponent, but it may also lead to an irrational lack of adequate allocation of the threatener's resources to the defense of the population of its own capital city; and it presupposes that the threatened power does not misrepresent its own interests in the same manner, but will continue to value its own capital city more highly than the border city in dispute, and will continue to allocate its resources accordingly.

Similarly, in the course of a civil conflict or internal war in a border country, such as Laos or Vietnam, or on a strategically situated offshore island, such as Cuba or Taiwan, at least one of two rival outside powers might assert that the victory of the local faction allied to it was more important to it than the loss of some of its own centers, or even its capital city. To make this assertion appear credible, the power protecting its allied faction or regime in the country or island might find it advantageous to stress the symbolic value of the territory, as well as considerations of strategy or national honor; and it might consider committing additional manpower and resources to the aid of its local ally, in such a manner that these nationals of the protecting power would become almost automatically involved if its local ally were decisively defeated. Here, too, such a policy would, in effect, sacrifice the rationality of interest calculation to the search for an increased credibility of threats. The protecting power in such a case would try to create deliberately the probability of an extreme commitment, including nuclear war, precisely for the kind of secondary objective or theater for which such an extreme commitment would not appear credible on ordinary grounds of rational self-interest.

The same considerations apply even more strongly over time. Short-run bargaining techniques often reward an actor for a very high allocation of attention and resources to an immediate objective in dispute, while his most favorable long-run strategy might be quite different. The bargaining style of behavior may require the early pinning down of resources that actually could be allocated to a far more rewarding sequence of steps toward somewhat longer-run objectives.

Both types of misallocation of effort and attention—over space among different objectives, and over time among different sequences of steps—involve a "contamination effect" of bargaining behavior. Bargaining messages are essentially addressed to the other party, who is to be deceived. To be credible, however, in any society requiring mass communication they must be transmitted in large part not only to foreigners but also to the broad internal elites of the bargaining country, down to the middle and low elite levels, and eventually to the level of mass opinion. This requirement holds not only for mass democracies, but also to a large degree—so far as can be seen—for dictatorships of the Soviet type.

Once an overevaluation of a disputed object has been widely disseminated for bargaining purposes among the elites and the politically relevant population of a country, the government itself may lose control of its own actions in the subsequent stages. A prisoner of aroused domestic opinion, it may now have to sacrifice major national objectives, resources, and values for the sake of peripheral or minor goals; or else it may have to back down somewhat awkwardly from its self-created extreme position, with possibly serious consequences in terms of the morale of its home population and its allies, and possibly the increased confidence of its opponent.[6]

In the continuing chain of clashes of interest between the United States and the Soviet Union, both powers may find themselves repeatedly in situations where their conflicting demands cannot be easily accommodated, but where neither side desires a military conflict. In such cases, the uncommitted nations—and agencies such as the United Nations—can perform a role genuinely conducive to international stability and supportive of the interests of the two blocs, if they can maintain their independence and serve as umpires or referees of bloc disputes. By opposing the extension of bloc boundaries and perhaps even by supporting some diminution of existing blocs, they can help to stabilize bloc relations in a nuclear world. By enunciating criteria for bargains that affect the expectations which each bloc has of the other bloc's demand structure, and of that other bloc's expectations concerning the first bloc's demand structure, the uncommitted states help the two blocs to arrive at a mutually acceptable bargaining solution.[7]

Some of the uncommitted nations, such as Ghana, Guinea, and Yugoslavia, have been seeking to exploit the opportunities in world politics that are offered by their situation, but they do

[6] Cf. K. W. Deutsch, "Mass Communications and the Loss of Freedom in National Decision-making," *Journal of Conflict Resolution,* I (June 1957), pp. 200–11.

[7] Such a solution then could be likened to a Nash-type bargain, and the bargain might occur somewhere on the Pareto Optimal line. See Morton A. Kaplan, *System and Process in International Politics* (New York: John Wiley & Sons, 1957), pp. 193–99, for a discussion of the Nash bargain; and "Bipolarity in the Revolutionary Age," in Morton A. Kaplan (ed.), *The Revolution in World Politics* (New York: John Wiley & Sons, 1962), pp. 262–66, for a more complete discussion of the bargaining power of uncommitted states in Nash-type bargains.

not seem to have found thus far any highly consistent or effective strategy. By emphasizing heavily their conflicts with the Western coalition over the remnants of colonialism, they have risked appearing as appendages or allies of the Soviet bloc, and have risked losing some of the benefits of their uncommitted status. Even membership in a coalition of uncommitted countries, it appears, imposes significant restraints on the national policy that can be effectively pursued, if the uncommitted countries are at the same time to promote major interests of their own, such as anti-colonialism, and yet to make the most of their potential stabilizing function in the international system.

This process would be aided by the growth of appropriate institutions of international order that helped to restrict competition between the blocs, particularly with respect to the acquisition of new members. The United Nations might perform here a particular service to both blocs in regard to many of the underdeveloped countries and the territories emerging into self-government. Most of these countries lack the capabilities to add appreciably to the strength of either bloc, while they could add much to its troubles. Moreover, many of them lack the capabilities to bear the burdens of participation on either side in the cold war without an eventual collapse of their domestic political consensus, followed by protracted and inconclusive internal warfare. Such politically fragile countries need to be somewhat insulated from the cold war, just as the major competing blocs may be better off if they do not have to divert too much of their attention and resources to these peripheral theaters. The United Nations might offer these countries a possible political haven and an honorable role, compatible with the realistic interests of both contending coalitions.

Since internal war is likely to accompany potential bloc changes involving underdeveloped countries, rules of the game that dampened both military and paramilitary competition, and placed it within reasonable limits, might well be to the interests of both blocs, given the grave disadvantages of indefinite extension of bloc size and of war. Moreover, such procedures would encourage a kind of interbloc communication that would improve the prospects for mutually satisfactory solutions to conflicts of this type. And they might permit nations such as the United States to appraise their own interests by means of that frank and continuing dialogue that is essential to democracy, most conducive in the long run to realistic policy formation, and perhaps most likely to prove effective in supporting the institutions and values of a free society.

CHAPTER 8

Janus Tormented: The International Law of Internal War [*]

BY RICHARD A. FALK

I. *The Reconciliation of Legal Restraint and Cold War Strategy*

VIOLENT encounter of major rivals in world affairs has always been primarily a matter of warfare *between* states; now suddenly it is participation in warfare *within* states. It is easy to appreciate this as an objective fact by making a survey of international affairs during the period after World War II. It is much more difficult to do something about, even to the extent of adapting our thinking to these altered circumstances. Recently a writer has given the international significance of internal phenomena a usefully wide formulation: "International affairs are affected at least as much by events which are not international as by events which are; by events, that is, which proceed within a state without proceeding or primarily impinging upon the relations between two or more states." [1]

The literature of international law has been slow to respond to this aspect of the altered condition of the contemporary world. At this stage, then, an inquiry into the international legal status of intrastate violence seems dramatically appropriate.[2]

[*] The final version of this essay has tried to take advantage of criticisms made of earlier drafts. It is especially indebted in this respect to constructive comments that were received from Manfred Halpern, Klaus Knorr, and James N. Rosenau.

[1] Peter Calvocoressi, *World Order and New States* (New York: Frederick A. Praeger, 1962), p. 101.

[2] International lawyers have exhibited interest in the significance of international law for the conduct of civil war for a surprisingly long time.

Two important studies indicate a flourish of interest in the importance of civil strife for international law at the turn of the century: Carlos Wiesse, *Le droit international appliqué aux guerres civiles* (Lausanne: 1898); Antoine Rougier, *Les guerres civiles et le droit des gens* (Paris: Larose, 1903). See also L. Stéfanesco, *La guerre civile et les rapports des*

The drama is partly a consequence of the cold war: is there much doubt that the struggle for world dominance will be resolved by internal wars between armies of the same nationality and hostile ideology? Aside from the possibilities of accident and miscalculation, a major international war seems unlikely to take place, unless it is chosen as a suicidal gesture, initiated by the losing side to make political defeat mutual. However, the implausibility of a calculated initiation of major warfare does not dissolve the problems that face American policy-makers. It is still necessary to respond to subtle forms of aggression throughout the world that tend to undermine our values and preferences and those of our allies. It is still necessary to implement policies that propose to build up the power and authority of institutions that might usher in a reign of world law at some future date. This dual challenge signifies an orientation towards the problems of international violence in an age of nuclear politics. This introductory section serves to depict the political confrontation that alters the legal environment and to disclose my own bias about the desiderata of world order.

Perhaps a question helps to identify the primary nexus of law and politics: can the United States defend its interests in the contemporary world without continuing to compromise its tradition of respect for international law? American interventionary participation in the internal wars of Southeast Asia and sponsorship of the illegal 1961 invasion of Cuba suggest the character of the problem. We find embarrassed attempts by national officials to reconcile American foreign policy with pledges to continue our adherence to the norms of noninter-

---

belligérants (Paris: Arthur Rousseau, 1903); P. Sadoul, *De la guerre civile en droit des gens* (Nancy: 1905). A resurgence of interest in the subject was occasioned by the Spanish Civil War: Norman J. Padelford, *International Law and Diplomacy in the Spanish Civil Strife* (New York: Macmillan Company, 1939); Charles Rousseau, *La nonintervention en Espagne* (Paris: Pedone, 1939).

vention.[3] This satisfies neither the cold warrior who would have us discard every restraint upon behavior that is not a product of strategic thinking nor the ultra-legalist who would paralyze our response to Communist patterns of aggression by a pedantic insistence upon asymmetrical adherences by the West to the restraints of law. It is hard to find a foothold on such slippery terrain—to sustain the relevance of law without making the victim's compliance an asset to the aggressor. This requires, first of all, some modernization of the international legal system to take account of recent changes in the character of world politics.

It is illuminating to put in preliminary focus the substantive problems that arise from attempts to achieve increasing international control of contemporary political violence. It is taken for granted that attitudes of unrestraint about international violence tend towards the employment of thermonuclear weapons. It is further assumed that the eventuality of nuclear war is perceived by dominant national actors, regardless of ideology or culture, as a mutual disaster of such extent that it significantly inhibits recourse to nuclear weapons. Such a perception tends also to discourage reasoned recourse to non-nuclear forms of international violence that contain serious risks of nuclear war. This risk accompanies aggression carried on by any major armed attack across an international frontier. Therefore, the common interest in the avoidance of nuclear war discourages recourse to explicit forms of international violence that possess a high escalation potential and serves to reinforce those existing legal rules that prohibit the use of force to resolve international disputes or to promote national objectives.[4] Legal techniques

[3] For a sophisticated argument, see, e.g., Abram Chayes, "The Legal Case for U.S. Action on Cuba," *Department of State Bulletin*, XLVII (November 19, 1962), pp. 763–65.

[4] Cf., e.g., the language of Articles 2(4) and 51 of the United Nations Charter. Of course, the extent of renunciation and the scope of the persisting right of self-defense are subject to serious debate. Nevertheless, the legal claim seems to have a clear intention: to eliminate national discretion to employ force except in situations of self-defense.

and institutions helpfully clarify and implement this common interest, guarding especially against instances of myopic disregard which, if not systematically suppressed by community action (Suez, Korea), might lead to an abandonment of this fundamental basis of universal restraint. It is generally the case that the effectiveness of law is enhanced by a convergence of the legal rule with the conscience and welfare of those subject to its claim, especially when this convergence is vividly perceived and rigorously implemented, as well as objectively present.[5]

This healthy situation, however, does not exist for lesser forms of aggression that do not depend upon border-crossing military attacks by the armed forces of one nation upon another. In fact, intrastate violence is governed by diametrically opposed considerations, whether approached from the perspective of law, morality, or national interest. It remains quite rational in the contemporary world to pursue national and ideological objectives by a selective use of the instruments of intrastate violence.

Internal wars present expanding nations and blocs with opportunities for strategic expansion that do not involve the high risks of reaching those self-destructive levels of conflict that are likely to attend major armed attacks across international boundaries. This political characteristic places heavy pressure upon nonintervention norms that are designed to restrain partisan foreign participation in domestic strife. This pressure is accentuated by the moral commitments that are held currently by many important international actors. Both the Communist and the Afro-Asian states endorse, with missionary zeal, the

[5] For a discussion that highlights the destructive gap that often separates the *perception* of self-interest from the *facts* of self-interest, cf. Myres S. McDougal and William T. Burke, "Crisis in the Law of the Sea: Community Perspectives versus National Egoism," in McDougal and Associates, *Studies in World Public Order* (New Haven: Yale University Press, 1960), pp. 844–911. The argument in the context of the use of the seas is transferable to any assertion of a national competence that infringes the welfare of other nations.

importance of achieving certain radical changes in some domestic societies—such as the elimination of colonialism or constitutional racism. Ordinarily the governing elites of these target societies will not permit radical change to come about by peaceful means. This breeds recourse to illegal protest movements and insurgent violence, stimulated and supported by friendly nations abroad.

This congeries of capability, risk, goal, and necessity places great emphasis upon the strategic manipulation of intrastate violence by groupings of nations contending for dominance in the world today. If empire once depended primarily upon the extent of colonial occupation, it now increasingly depends upon the capacity to influence the outcome of important internal wars.

Thus the Afro-Asian and Communist states appear pledged to repudiate the norms of nonintervention as a general principle of restraint. In such an international atmosphere, the continuing existence of formal commitments based on the doctrine of nonintervention seem to give the West, and especially the United States, the debilitating alternatives of cold-war frustration and international lawlessness.

Can there be any relevance of international law to internal war in such a situation? There is a dynamic element that must be fed into the analysis of a response. It is necessary to consider where we want to go as well as what we want done with events as things now stand. This requires policy preferences as well as a confrontation of the apparent dilemma posed by the need to choose between law-complying political defeat and law-violating political effectiveness. To build a safer international system we should take advantage of the potentialities for improving the present system of world order. Prospects for this improvement are almost always seriously diminished when leading national actors, especially those possessing revered domestic traditions of compliance with law, behave as if their duty to obey international law were confined to matters of postal regulation and maritime safety. Our challenge to these patterns of conduct requires a persuasive demonstration that national sovereignty will be best served by the progressive submission of states to common norms of restraint even in those situations involving risks to vital national interests. This demonstration can no longer be dismissed as a utopian project; it is a matter of immediate self-interest for all major nations. This is especially obvious with regard to all violent conflict. Peace exists only when the world is free from unauthorized patterns of sustained violence everywhere. A crucial variable is increasingly the magnitude of the violence; and this expands the traditional concern with whether or not the violence constitutes a military struggle between nations that brings to bear the law of war. It is thus necessary to examine the maintenance of peace in the light of the legal status of various foreign involvements in internal wars.

This concern leads to undertaking a critique of prevailing interpretations of rules of international law. In this respect, also, it seems useful to blur deliberately the line that is supposed, according to hallowed juristic tradition, to separate commentary on the state of the *lex lata* from speculations *de lege ferenda*. In an age of system transition on the international level [6] it is necessary to identify the expanding competencies of new institutions and to accord provisional legal status to emerging patterns of stable restraint.[7] Otherwise one misses the main contribution of law to the rational control of behavior and

[6] This view of system transition pervades the recent literature of international relations. It has been most comprehensively developed by Morton A. Kaplan in *System and Process in International Politics* (New York: John Wiley & Sons, 1957).

[7] This has been done in a creative fashion from a legal perspective by C. Wilfred Jenks in the series of essays that comprise *The Common Law of Mankind* (New York: Frederick A. Praeger, 1958); cf. also Richard A. Falk and Saul H. Mendlovitz, "Some Criticisms of C. Wilfred Jenks' Approach to International Law," *Rutgers Law Review*, XIV (Fall 1959), pp. 1–36.

neglects the capacity of global and regional organizations to act in legislative and constabulary roles. This period of transition and legal creativity is especially relevant to an understanding of the role of intrastate violence as the main instrument of coercion in the cold war. The characterization of a pattern of restraint as "law" itself adds obligatory force, since respect for law is itself a factor in the growth and effectiveness of a restraint. The scholar's perception and his supporting rationale operate in a primitive legal order as a subsidiary way to specify the province of law, and thereby to curtail the dangerous tendency to deny that there exists a national self-interest in world order, a tendency that unfortunately reflects popular attitudes about the national pursuit of power, wealth, and respect.

Although the traditional system of international law is seriously inadequate, many of the traditional rules remain helpfully relevant in setting reciprocal standards of behavior. This is true, for instance, of the rules that give individual combatants in major internal wars the protection of rules of land warfare, mainly as they have been incorporated into the Geneva Conventions of 1949. In our haste to reform the major prescriptions that govern national participation in internal wars, we should not be oblivious to the achievement of an earlier international law, especially at the margins of the subject. It is not our desire to promote an abandonment of older rules until we find the basis either for agreement or for tacit coordination that will support the reliable formation of more adequate new rules. In this interim it is often better to abide by unsatisfactory norms of guidance than to be without any guidance at all.

It seems useful to begin with a brief account of the conception of international law that will be used to analyze the problems of internal war. This is followed by a description of the basic approach taken by the traditional system. The descriptive account is then criticized for its failure to deal adequately with some extralegal developments: cold war, nuclear weapons, Communist strategy, the United Nations, regional organizations. After this critique, a final section argues in favor of certain shifts of competence from national to supranational decision-makers. Perhaps, here, an early warning will reduce confusion and misunderstanding. The criticisms directed at national policies of intervention and the argument for supranational legislative competence are not considered to provide a *solution* to the problems posed by internal war, but are presented as an optimum response in *certain circumstances* to a dangerous and difficult situation, however handled. For so long as domestic instability is widespread and intense, so long as there is an international Communist movement that participates in national politics with the benefit of external guidance, so long as there is a cold war and an arms race, the problems of responding to intrastate violence will remain serious and controversial both for United States policy-makers and for architects of an improving world order. This essay tries only to shorten the distance between these two perspectives and to make suggestions for improvement. Such a purpose falls far short of claiming that one's ideas, if accepted, could overcome the torments of the day.

There are many current and obvious restrictions upon the capacities of supranational institutions to act effectively or justly. Some of these restrictions will be discussed at the end of the essay after the argument for their strengthening has been strongly stated, perhaps overstated; to favor a gradual substitution of supranational for national participation in internal wars involves creating difficulties not present heretofore. Perhaps a few salient caveats will serve to qualify, at the outset, my own endorsement of the position urged.

First of all, there is little hope that dominant nations are presently prepared to transfer increased authority and power now and forever to emerging international institutions. Second, this essay adopts an instrumental perspective—how should we act to maximize our values?—which is quite disconnected from patterns of national behavior that are formed, as might be expected, by the irrationalities of imperial competition.

In a sense, one seeks for an unavailable prince in an age when events have rendered Machiavelli's cynical prescription obsolete.[8] There is a need, that is, for a new cynicism that turns out to look curiously like idealism. The egoist and the altruist share an increasingly common interest. To proclaim this is not to demonstrate it and to demonstrate it is not to change settled habits of thought. Part of the resistance to this style of argument arises from hardened habits of "political intelligence" that have assimilated too deeply the willingness to trust only egocentric pursuits of power in world affairs. It is itself an occasion for lament that, should he present himself, a contemporary Machiavelli, perceiving this novel necessity for a community of mankind, might be dismissed by the best minds as recklessly utopian. One danger arises from precisely this inability and unwillingness to reform our perception of what is practical politics. I hope that this reform will come about by the evolution of a new awareness forced upon us by a perspicuous response to the gathering facts, rather than by awaiting that other kind of compulsion—the corpse-littered rubble of our cities.

Mankind solicits the destiny of the dinosaur if it responds to these urgencies with complacent trust in present patterns of thought and conduct.

II. *A Framework for a Contemporary System of International Law*

Three series of distinctions help to identify the conception of international law that is used here to clarify the relations between law and internal war: the functions of international law,

[8] It is intriguing to note, as Lucian Pye has pointed out ("Lessons from the Malayan Struggle Against Communism," MIT Center of International Studies, C/57–15), that Machiavelli was also trying to formulate a strategy that would enable nation-building to overcome insurrectionary harassment.

the actors in the international legal system, and the types of norms and processes that claim to assert legal control. It is necessary also to appreciate that this presentation accepts implicitly a controversial interpretation of the province of law in international affairs that is considerably more fluid than the one authorized by the Austin-Kelsen tradition.

First, then, let us describe the *functions* assigned to the international legal system at the current stage of its development. We are interested only in the performance of functions that influence the extent and quality of the legal control of the international impacts of internal war:

(1) International law provides a process for designating the degree of formal *acknowledgment* by third states of the claims made on behalf of the anti-government faction; this allows the internal war to remain fully domesticated ("rebellion"), partially internationalized on an *ad hoc* basis ("insurgency"), and fully internationalized on an *a priori* basis ("belligerency").

(2) International law contributes a rhetoric for claiming and contesting various forms of external *participation* in internal wars; support for "just wars of national liberation" or "national self-determination" can thus confront various allegations of "intervention" or "indirect aggression and subversion."

(3) International law establishes a system for regulating the *scope* of hostilities by the application of the rules of war to the conflicting factions, provided that the internal war attains sufficient magnitude to receive international status.

(4) International law facilitates the exercise of limited control over the *outcome* of internal wars whenever the community consensus can be effectively mobilized in support of one faction; this control arises especially in response to nascent claims of legislative competence that have been made recently by regional and universal institutions in response to internal violence that is deemed to threaten external peace and security.

Second, there are various kinds of actors, the identity of

which is an important ingredient of the legal status of claims to assert control over internal wars:

(1) Nations. The classical level of national interaction remains paramount; there is, then, in international law a primary emphasis upon the rights and duties of a nation vis-à-vis the factions involved in an internal war.

(2) Individuals, corporations, political parties. There is an increasing significance given to infranational participation. Individuals, private groups, transnational political associations instigate, participate in, and use intrastate violence to achieve political objectives abroad; this emphasizes the extent of the legal duty assumed by a domestic government to forbid the use of its territory to carry out hostile expeditions abroad.

(3) Regional organizations. Regional actors are beginning to claim and assert competence with respect to internal wars and threats to the peace within its region.

(4) The United Nations Organization. Universal actors, the principal organs of the United Nations, claim and assert an increasing competence to control the dimensions of and to influence the outcome of internal wars that constitute a threat to the maintenance of international peace.[9]

Third, there are various types of norms that have relevance to the legal control of internal war:

(1) There are norms that express decentralized grants of semi-discretionary authority; for example, each nation has discretion, within broad limits, to confer on or withhold provi-

[9] It is also exceedingly important to clarify the various spheres of competence given to each set of actors, especially in view of the likelihood of overlapping, incompatible claims to assert control. The hierarchy of actors is not necessarily a guide to their relative competence. For instance, nations have retained some vague claim to supremacy by virtue of the domestic jurisdiction concept, at least with respect to some subject matter. Regional actors may operate on the basis of very restricted grants of competence from their membership in relation to universal actors. Article 53(1) of the Charter seems to require a regional actor to await Security Council approval for any undertaking that is properly classified as an "enforcement action."

sional legitimacy from an insurgent by its control over the recognition ceremony; the discretion is restricted, since a nation that recognizes an insufficient insurgent is guilty of a form of illegal intervention that is often described as "premature recognition."

(2) There are norms which involve decentralized grants of fully discretionary authority; for example, a state is at liberty to grant or refuse asylum to foreign political fugitives.

(3) There are centralized norms of restraint; these concern the various international codifications of the rules of war, including especially the rights and duties of belligerents and third states on the high seas and the so-called humanitarian rules of warfare (care for the sick and wounded, treatment of prisoners).

(4) There are norms that involve centralized claims of authority and control; as when, for instance, the United Nations invokes its authority to manage an internal war (the Congo operation).

(5) There are decentralized tacit norms of restraint; for example, the nonuse of nuclear weapons as a mode of external participation in internal wars; nonparticipation in internal wars carried on within a cold war bloc: Hungary (1956), Cuba (1958–1959).

(6) There are decentralized norms arising from the effective assertion of novel claims to act; for example, the prudent use of the high seas or the atmosphere to test nuclear weapons or the extension of notions of pacific blockade to cover the "quarantine" proclaimed by the United States to preclude the shipment of offensive weaponry to Cuba in October 1962 or the use of outer space to orbit intelligence-gathering satellites over other nations.

(7) There are intermediate norms arising from the claims of regional actors; for example, the determination of Punta del Este to exclude Castro's Cuba from the Inter-American System because of the incompatibility of Marxism-Leninism with hemispheric ideals.

This differentiation of perspective based on functions, actors, and norms underlies the description of the traditional system that follows. This system arose in a simpler international environment in which most interaction was between nations, and especially between a few dominant nations centered in a rather small part of the world.

III. *The Old International Law of Internal War*

The rights and duties of nations are governed, first of all, by the status accorded to the factions in conflict. Traditional international law provides three relevant statuses: (1) rebellion, (2) insurgency, (3) belligerency. These characterizations of a challenge to the authority of an incumbent regime are designed to distinguish among conflicts along a continuum of ascending intensity.[10] Rebellion is supposed to be invoked in response to a sporadic challenge to the legitimate government, whereas insurgency and belligerency are intended to apply to situations of sustained conflict, a serious challenge carried on through a considerable period of time over a wide space and involving large numbers of people within the society.

If the faction seeking to seize the power of the state seems susceptible to rapid suppression by normal procedures of internal security, then it is supposed to be treated as a "rebellion." For instance, Kotzsch indicates that "domestic violence is called rebellion or upheaval so long as there is sufficient evidence that the police force of the parent state will reduce [*sic;* induce] the seditious party to respect the municipal legal order." [11] If the status of rebellion is given to an occasion of "internal war,"

[10] This standard view is expressed in relation to grants of recognition: ". . . it is believed to be the nature and extent of the insurrectionary achievement, rather than any other consideration, that afford the test of the propriety of recognition." Charles Cheney Hyde, *International Law Chiefly as Interpreted and Applied by the United States I,* 2nd rev. edn., (Boston: Little, Brown and Company, 1945), p. 202.

[11] Lothar Kotzsch, *The Concept of War in Contemporary History and International Law* (Geneva: Librairie E. Droz, 1956), p. 230.

then external help to the rebels constitutes illegal [12] intervention.[13] Furthermore, the incumbent government can demand that foreign states accept the inconvenience of domestic regulations designed to suppress the rebellion, such as the closing of ports or interference with normal commerce. Foreign states have no duty to remain aloof (as nonparticipants) or neutral, and therefore are free to render affirmative assistance to the incumbent as requested. There is also the duty to prevent domestic territory from being used as an organizing base for hostile activities overseas.[14] This duty is imposed upon foreign states regardless of the scope of the internal war, but it seems to be especially applicable in a situation that precedes recourse by rebels to the instruments of violence. Thus if an internal war is a "rebellion," foreign states are forbidden to help the rebels and are permitted to help the incumbent, whereas the incumbent is entitled to impose domestic restrictions upon commerce and normal alien activity in order to suppress the rebellion.

International law thus purports to give no protection to participants in a rebellion.[15] Rebellion usefully covers minor in-

[12] The United States tends to avoid challenging a particular rule of restraint. Instead it bases noncompliance upon special political circumstances that overcome the relevance of law. This makes legal restraint avoidable whenever it turns out to be inconvenient. The U-2 incident and the Bay of Pigs invasion of Cuba both suggest this kind of denigration of the legal order in situations in which more candid challenges of particular rules would have been both more convincing as an explanation and less destabilizing as "illegal" conduct.

[13] The basic norms of noninvolvement were adopted by the Institute of International Law in 1900. For texts, see James Brown Scott, ed., *Resolutions of the Institute of International Law Dealing with the Law of Nations* (New York: Oxford University Press, 1916), pp. 157–61.

[14] Cf. note 48 below. See generally Hersh Lauterpacht, "Revolutionary Activities by Private Persons Against Foreign States," *American Journal of International Law*, XXII (January 1928), pp. 105–30; Manuel R. Garcia-Mora, *International Responsibility for Hostile Acts of Private Persons Against Foreign States* (The Hague: Martinus Nijhoff, 1962).

[15] Kotzsch, *op.cit.*, p. 230. See also Ambrose Light Case 25 F. 408 (1855); Emmerich de Vattel, *The Law of Nations, or the Principles of Natural Law Applied to the Conduct and to the Affairs of Nations and Sovereigns*, trans. of 1758 edn. by Charles G. Fenwick (Washington: Carnegie Institution of Washington, 1916).

stances of internal war of a wide variety: violent protest involving a single issue (Indian language riots, Soviet food riots) or an uprising that is so rapidly suppressed as to warrant no acknowledgment of its existence on an extranational level (East European rebellions against Soviet dominion in 1953 and 1956). These norms of identification are, however, vague and seldom serve *expressis verbis* to adjust the relation between the rebellion as a state of affairs and international actors affected in various ways by its existence.

It is even more significant, however, to suggest the separation between the *facts* of strife and the *decisional process* by which national officials invoke norms to explain and justify a national response. The self-determination of norms identifying the legal status of civil strife severely restricts any role of law connected with the establishment of an objective status binding on all actors uniformly through the system. A decree of marriage or divorce usually generates a status for the parties that is given universal respect. International law is not generally able to fulfill this role of status creation for internal strife on a system level, although it does so bilaterally, and occasionally on a regional or bloc basis. The existence of international institutions provides a structural basis for further centralization of procedures of status creation in this sensitive area.

"Insurgency" is a catch-all designation provided by international law to allow states to determine the quantum of legal relations to be established with the insurgents. It is an international acknowledgment of the existence of an internal war but it leaves each state substantially free to control the consequences of this acknowledgment. This contrasts with "belligerency," which establishes a common regime of rights and duties that exist independent of the will of a particular state. On a factual level, almost all that can be said about insurgency is that it is supposed to constitute more sustained and substantial intrastate violence than is encountered if the internal war is treated as a "rebellion." It also serves as a partial internationalization of the conflict, without bringing the state of belligerency into being. This permits third states to participate in an internal war without finding themselves "at war," which would be the consequence of intervention on either side once the internal war had been identified as a state of belligerency. Interventionary participation in an insurgency may arouse protest and hostile response, but it does not involve the hazards and inconveniences that arise if a state of war is established with one or the other factions.

Hersh Lauterpacht suggests the relative vagueness of the legal concept of insurgency by observing that "[t]he difference between the status of belligerency and that of insurgency in relation to foreign States may best be expressed in the form of the proposition that belligerency is a relation giving rise to definite rights and obligations, while insurgency is not." [16] The unreliability of the factual test becomes evident if one realizes that such major internal wars as the Cuban independence wars in the late nineteenth century and the Spanish Civil War of 1936–1939 were both treated by many principal nations as instances of insurgency. The insurgent is often given extensive rights by foreign states and is usually assumed to have the duty to conform to applicable rules of international law. Thus, for instance, British courts respected, as valid, Falangist legislation enacted to apply to territory under the control of the insurgency and accepted an insurgent claim of immunity for a public vessel under insurgent control.[17] These decisions had the consequence of treating the Franco faction as equivalent to a foreign sovereign state with respect to activity carried on within its orbit of effective administration. Such deferential treatment is a flagrant disregard of the incumbent government's normal claim

[16] Hersh Lauterpacht, *Recognition in International Law* (Cambridge: Cambridge University Press, 1947), p. 270; hereinafter cited as *Recognition*.

[17] The leading case came before the House of Lords in Great Britain: The Arantzazu Mendi, [1939] A.C. 256; cf. also Banco de Bilbao v. Rey, [1938] 2 K.B. 176.

to be the exclusive agent of the state for all matters within *national* jurisdiction. However, it represents a characteristic attempt by international law and national actors to use law to reconcile the claims of formal right with the facts of effective control; to maintain trade with a port under insurgent control it is essential to heed the administration of it by insurgent institutions even if this requires a disregard of the regime of law created by the government acknowledged in world affairs as the sole and legitimate seat of national authority. Actually, foreign states are rather free, given limitations of capability, to determine their own relations with insurgent and incumbent. Ordinarily insurgents are permitted to use the high seas for naval and air operations against the incumbent, provided that there is no interference with the shipping of third states. Thus, although third states have no duty to respect insurgent rights and no duty to subject themselves to the obligations of neutrality, there is a characteristic tendency to regard insurgent operations on the high seas as non-piratical and to give some domestic deference to the governmental nature of an insurgent regime for territory under its control (for example, insurgent legislation and official acts are often validated to the extent relevant to the outcome of a domestic legal controversy).[18]

For humanitarian reasons, there is an increasing willingness to regard the laws of war as applicable to protracted conflict if it is carried on in a form that entitles it to the status of an insurgency. The acceptance of this viewpoint by the incumbent is conclusive. Third states cannot treat an internal war as a "rebellion" once it has been identified as an "insurgency" by the parent government.

In general, the status of insurgency is a flexible instrument

---

[18] See Kotzsch, *op.cit.*, pp. 232f. However, in the context of intense political conflict, the presence of executive hostility to the insurgent faction may determine the judicial outcome. Cf. Salimoff and Co. v. Standard Oil of New York, 262 N.Y. 220, 186 N.E. 679 (1933), and Bank of China v. Wells Fargo Bank & Union Trust Co., 104 F. Supp. 59 (N.D. Cal. 1952).

for the formulation of claims and tolerances by third states. If it is used to protect the economic and private interests of nationals and to acknowledge political facts arising from partial successes by the insurgents in an internal war, then it can adjust relative rights and duties without amounting to a mode of illegal intervention in internal affairs. Trouble arises, however, when third states use the status of insurgency to influence the outcome of an internal war. Political objectives distort the connection between the status of insurgency and the existence of the facts warranting it; such a distortion is often disguised, however, by the decentralized grant of competence that authorizes the third state to characterize an internal war and to proceed as it sees fit.

A special application of insurgent status involves the occasional claim of third states to treat certain actions on the high seas as piratical. Thus, for instance, the Nyon Agreement concluded by several states during the Spanish Civil War provided for collective measures to destroy submarines that attacked third-power shipping on the high seas if they attacked in a manner forbidden by Part IV of the London Treaty of 1930, governing submarine attacks on merchant shipping.[19] The characterization of insurgents as "pirates" by the incumbent is not binding on third states.[20] Nevertheless, it is generally conceded that unrecognized insurgent operations on the high seas can be treated by third parties as piratical, provided that the factual conditions of belligerency do not exist.[21] Even when this is done, it is, as Lauterpacht observes, infrequent that the notion of piracy is extended to the officers and crews of insurgent ships seized for piratical operations.[22]

---

[19] Lauterpacht, *Recognition*, pp. 295–96.
[20] For a discussion of the relation between piracy and claims of governmental status in the contemporary world, see Ferenc A. Vali, "The Santa Maria Case," *Northwestern University Law Review*, LVI (March-April 1961), pp. 168–75.
[21] For discussion of belligerency, see pp. 199–200 above.
[22] Lauterpacht, *Recognition*, p. 304.

Belligerency, as distinct from insurgency, is a formalization of the relative rights and duties of all actors vis-à-vis an internal war. Kotzsch puts it simply: ". . . the recognition of belligerency gives rise to definite rights and obligations under international law, insurgency does not." [23] Usually the conferral of belligerent status is achieved by indirect means rather than by explicit statement. Commonly, acknowledgment of belligerent rights on the high seas to either faction establishes a state of belligerency. International law treats an internal war with the status of belligerency as essentially identical to a war between sovereign states. This also means that an interventionary participation on behalf of either the incumbent or the insurgent is an act of war against the other. That is, as with a truly international war, a state is given the formal option of joining with one of the belligerents against the other or of remaining impartial.[24] Of course, the sharpness of the choice is belied by the history of international relations, which abounds in instances of partiality and participation that are treated as fully compatible with neutral status.

Belligerent status, if objectively determined by the community, would enable supranational actors to have a technique to justify treatment of serious internal wars as international wars. That is, rebellions and insurgencies could be treated as remaining within the scope of domestic jurisdiction, subject to the traditional distribution of claims and duties between in-

[23] Kotzsch, op.cit., p. 233.
[24] The compatibility of this option with the United Nations system is open to serious question [even for non-Members; see Article 2(6)]. Certainly, once a determination of aggression has been made authoritatively by a principal organ of the Organization, then other states are not "at liberty" to help the state or states characterized as the aggressor nor are states free to remain neutral [see Article 2(5)]. The formal claims of the Charter must, however, be regarded as no more than *potential* norms of restraint in view of *actual* patterns of practice. Practice continues to affirm the option of states to decide for themselves, and so the textual statement possesses a continuing validity, despite the presence of a formal agreement (Charter) pledging Members of the United Nations to renounce discretion in this area of national behavior.

ternal factions and external actors. But belligerencies should be internationalized, thereby vindicating the claims of regional or global institutions to restore internal peace either by reference to constitutional (incumbent) or normative (insurgent; human rights) legitimacy. This new notion of belligerency requires an explicit assumption of competence by the relevant institutions first to confer the status, then to act in view of it. Traditions of sovereignty and the split associated with the cold war are formidable obstacles to this recommended centralization of supranational authority over *serious* internal wars. The status of belligerency would be equivalent to determination of the seriousness of the internal war; that is, it would be a flexible and formal way for the regional or global organization to convey its claim of competence to the actors in the community. Criteria of seriousness could be formulated to restrict somewhat the judgment of belligerency by the organization, or at least to give the judgment a greater appearance of restriction.[25]

The degree to which incumbent and third states have discretion over the decision to recognize belligerent status is virtually unrestricted; diplomatic practice also seems to waver between the duty of third states to allow insurgents to claim belligerent rights if certain factual conditions are present and the discretionary nature of the insurgent claim. If the incumbent claims belligerent rights on the high seas, then it operates to confer the status of belligerency upon the entire conflict. Third states are expected thereafter to regulate their relations in a way that accords each faction formal parity; partiality shown to either faction is regarded as an act of war, or at least as a violation of neutral rights. The insurgent faction, for in-

[25] Appearances of principled behavior are especially needed in an emerging legal order. The early success of English common law can be attributed, in part, to its clever insistence upon pomp, ritual, and technicalities. These attributes of law, now degraded as "mystique," help to gain habitual respect for law by members of the community. The development of such a habit continues to be a desideratum in international affairs.

stance, must then also be able to assert belligerent rights on the high seas. The humanitarian laws of warfare become fully applicable to all hostilities.[26] Among the specific claims authorized by acquiring belligerent status, the following are quite prominent: the right to obtain credit abroad, to enter foreign ports, to maintain blockades, to engage in visit and search procedures, and to confiscate contraband.[27]

The incumbent government cannot oblige third states to accept its claim to exercise belligerent rights unless certain factual conditions are satisfied.[28] Hersh Lauterpacht summarizes these conditions in the following way: ". . . first, there must exist within the State an armed conflict of a general (as distinguished from a purely local) character; second, the insurgents must occupy and administer a substantial portion of national territory; third, they must conduct the hostilities in accordance with the rules of war and through organized armed forces acting under a responsible authority; fourthly, there must exist circumstances which make it necessary for outside States to define their attitude by means of recognition of bel-

[26] It is significant that Article 3 of the Geneva Conventions of 1949, regulating aspects of the conduct of international war, makes the humanitarian norms applicable "in the case of armed conflict not of an international character occurring in the territory of one of the High Contracting Parties." Also Article 4 of the Prisoners of War Convention and Article 13 of the Wounded and Sick Convention extend coverage to "members of regular armed forces who profess allegiance to a Government or an authority not recognized by the Detaining Power"; this presumably applied to any factual *or* legal state of prolonged insurgency. However, if the insurgency is conducted by unconventional military techniques, then it is unclear under what conditions the personnel qualify as members of "regular armed forces." For a discussion of when various rules of the law of war (especially the Geneva Conventions of 1949) apply to guerrilla warfare, see Morris Greenspan, "International Law and Its Protection for Participants in Unconventional Warfare," *The Annals,* Vol. 341 (May 1962), pp. 30–41.

[27] Cf. Ann Van Wynen Thomas and A. J. Thomas, Jr., *Non-Intervention: The Law and Its Import in the Americas* (Dallas: Southern Methodist University Press, 1956), p. 219.

[28] This is important with regard to the right of internal war factions to subject neutral shipping on the high seas to various interferences.

ligerency." [29] These conditions are supposed to govern the propriety of attaching the status of belligerency. If these conditions are not satisfied, then it is premature to grant belligerent rights to either warring faction. Once they are met, however, then it is arguable that it is intervention to refuse recognition of the insurgency as belligerency. As there is no objective way to meet the test of belligerency, attention is often given to the conduct of the incumbent that discloses a willingness to negotiate with the insurgent elite on the level of equality. Such a demonstration often forms part of an argument that there can arise a duty for third nations to treat a given internal war as an instance of belligerency.[30]

The status accorded to an internal war is designed primarily to reconcile its character as violent conflict with the orderly maintenance of the interests of third states. A presumption in favor of stability in the world allows foreign states to intervene on behalf of the incumbent in the situation of mere rebellion. However, if the intrastate conflict is sustained in time and place, it becomes interventionary, according to the traditional theory, to help either faction. Therefore, the notions of insurgency and belligerency are designed to allow third states to remain neutral and yet to have some control over interferences with their normal activities that result from strife between internal factions.

There are several difficulties with this form of response by international law to the phenomenon of internal war. First, the tendency of nations to avoid express bestowals of status makes it hard to establish the precise nature of claims by third states; the functional role attributed to the distinctions between rebellion, insurgency, and belligerency is more an invention of commentators than a description of state behavior. Second, the

[29] Lauterpacht, *Recognition,* p. 176.

[30] This argument is urged with respect to the Algerian War of Independence by Mohammed Bedjaoui, *Law and the Algerian Revolution* (Brussels: Publications of the International Association of Democratic Lawyers, 1961).

decentralized assertion of claims to treat an internal war as rebellion, insurgency, or belligerency makes it impossible to standardize what is permitted and what is forbidden with sufficient clarity to enable a protesting party to identify a violation; thus international law cannot do much to promote community policies favoring nonintervention, self-determination, and the rights of peoples to resort to revolution by distinguishing among various types of internal wars.[31] The basic duty of third states to maintain impartiality is difficult to implement. Third, the goals of noninterference are incompatible with the revolutionary ideology of China and the Soviet bloc and the anti-colonial commitments of the Afro-Asian nations. Notions of support for wars of national liberation and anti-colonial wars are direct repudiations of the duty to refrain from evaluating the contending claims of the factions in an internal war. The old international law based its regime upon the factual character of the conflict and not upon the justice of certain insurgent causes. If major national actors reject in practice and doctrine the policies of impartiality in the traditional system, then adherence to the rules becomes self-destructive for the remainder of the community.[32] Although it sounds paradoxical, offsetting participation by nations in internal wars may often be more compatible with the notions of nonintervention than is an asymmetrical refusal to participate.[33] Therefore, the decline of

[31] At best, *norms of relationship* are established by the *specific* responses of individual states. The status distinctions may help to clarify and identify the character of a specific response, thereby fulfilling the role of international law to provide national actors with a medium of communication. There are no norms generated that set system-wide standards of response. Participation by the United Nations or a regional organization may qualify this assertion somewhat.

[32] And yet the violation of clear norms by law-oriented societies leads to confused behavior that disappoints the conscience of the community, both within the society of the actor and without. The United States' response to Castro's Marxism-Leninism illustrates the difficulties of either ignoring or adhering to applicable legal restraints.

[33] Such a conclusion is a central tenet of Manfred Halpern's stimulating essay, "The Morality and Politics of Intervention," originally pub-

mutuality makes the idea of nonintervention obsolete, even dangerous, if mechanically applied by the non-Communist and nonmodernizing nations in the world.[34]

As a consequence, several desiderata exist. First, objective tests and centralized interpretations of the factual character of an internal war are necessary. Second, a rule of mutuality is needed to act as a basis for applying policies of nonparticipation in sustained instances of civil conflict. Third, it would be helpful to have procedures to enable an expression of community approval, most probably through the agency of supranational institutions, for certain instances of insurgency; approval would thereby serve to authorize some forms of outside participation. The Congo Operation suggests the growth of a community willingness to remove internal wars from the sanctuary of "domestic jurisdiction," especially if the magnitude of the conflict is considerable and if the alternative is likely to be interventionary participation by the big powers.

Traditional international law bases its response to civil war upon the factual characteristics of the conflict and its material effect upon externally situated international actors. Thus a third state with shipping interests subject to harassment on the high seas was regarded as more entitled to accord recognition of rights to an insurgent faction than was a state unaffected by the internal war.[35] Today, however, the interdependence of domestic and international conflict, the special attitude of Com-

---

lished as a pamphlet by the Council on Religion and International Affairs and reprinted below, Chapter 9.

[34] Cf. also George Modelski's "International Settlement of Internal War," Chapter 5 in this volume.

[35] "The right of a state to recognize the belligerent character of insurgent subjects of another state must then, for the purposes of international law, be based solely upon a possibility that its interests may be so affected by the existence of hostilities in which one party is not in the enjoyment of belligerent privileges as to make recognition a reasonable measure of self-protection." William E. Hall, A Treatise on International Law, 8th edn., ed. by A. Pearce Higgins (Oxford: Clarendon Press, 1924), p. 39.

munists and newly independent states toward the outcome of
internal wars fought for political objectives, and the dangers of
nuclear war escalating from internal war create new requirements of minimum order.[36] The rules and processes of law must
be revised to take appropriate account of these extralegal
developments. We need, first of all, to discriminate between
internal wars that it is safe to treat as domestic so as to pro-
scribe participation by nations or supranational institutions, and
those that it is not because the internal arena of conflict is the
scene of indirect aggression or because it represents a struggle
for certain minimum domestic rights that the world as an
emerging and limited community is coming to recognize as
mandatory.[37] Once this discrimination seems to have been
made, then, as has been indicated, it is important to develop
processes for regional and universal management of internal
wars with an important strategic impact on patterns of international conflict or upon firm and overwhelming crystallizations
of international morality. If community institutions fail to
perform in a situation where an internal war is an arena within
which third powers seek to extend their national domain of
political influence, then it is essential to authorize neutralizing
participation by others. The rules of nonparticipation would
thus be made subject to suspension whenever any major international actor violates them; this premise of mutuality must be
introduced into the legal process so as to reconcile interests of
collective self-defense with notions of respect for applicable
legal rules.[38]

[36] For an exciting exposition of the relations between legal order and
the maintenance of peace in the contemporary world, see Myres S.
McDougal and Florentino P. Feliciano, *Law and Minimum World Public
Order: The Legal Regulation of International Coercion* (New Haven:
Yale University Press, 1961), especially chaps. 1–4.

[37] For a fuller development of this theme, see Richard A. Falk, *Law,
Morality, and War in the Contemporary World* (New York: Frederick
A. Praeger, 1963).

[38] Cf. the opening pages of this essay and note 32. It is essential to
find a way to act that avoids embarrassment or opportunism. To be com-

IV. *Toward a New International Law of Internal War*

It is essential to approach this exposition with an awareness of the significance of the decentralized quality of the international system, for this encourages an appreciation of the broad discretion that exists on a national level. This discretion is complicated by the presence of complementary patterns of norms and explicit grants of competence that allow nations to confer authoritative legal status by their own characterization of the contested facts. Recognition practice serves as a paradigm instance of the formation of legal status by reliance upon decentralized processes. Each state is free to accord or withhold recognition from a new state or government as it sees fit.[39]

Acknowledgment of this decentralized pattern underlying the establishment of legal rules should make one somewhat skeptical about the value of international legal restraints; it is quite proper to be dubious about the degree to which the rules described as regulative do, in fact, restrain the behavior of national and other international actors. But such a caveat is not, as is so often supposed, reason to denigrate the role of international law in relation to the control of internal war. It is an oddly shared mistake of idealists and cynics to evaluate the success or failure of a legal system by examining the extent to which national behavior conforms to international rules. The restraint of behavior is only one of several functions performed by law in any social order. It is a function in international affairs that can be best appraised by reference to the characteristic of a

---

pelled to choose between such alternatives disowns our heritage and violates the fundamental basis of international order. See J. C. MacGibbon, "Some Observations on the Part of Protest in International Law," *British Year Book of International Law, 1953* (London: Oxford University Press, 1954), pp. 293–319.

[39] For an explanation of the rule against premature recognition, see Lauterpacht, *Recognition*, pp. 94–96, 283–84. Cf. the argument of Mohammed Bedjaoui in favor of early recognition of the anti-French Algerian insurgency as a matter of policy *and* duty (*op.cit.*, pp. 110–38).

horizontal legal order.[40] A central function of international law, especially with regard to the use of force, is to provide participants with an orderly process for identifying, asserting, and communicating claims to engage in controverted conduct.[41] That is, law provides a medium for precise communication between international actors. This is itself an indirect restraining influence. It expresses the basic nature of horizontal law: a process of claim and counterclaim that can be vindicated or repudiated in any particular instance, depending upon (1) the extent to which it can be established as reasonable or unreasonable in the context of assertion, (2) the degree to which its application is accompanied by community approval and participation, and (3) the degree of effectiveness achieved in the assertion of the claim.[42] Such a medium of communication

[40] The character of rules for a legal order must reflect the functions assignable to law by a given social order. The horizontality of the international legal order implies a range of interpretative discretion by nations that impedes the growth of highly specific rules of restraint. This is simply an attribute of the system. It is not an occasion for lament. It does not inform us at all about the success or failure of various rules of international law as measured in terms of their distinctive ordering functions. There is an ironic tendency for people to expect law in international affairs to do more for the order and welfare of the community than it does in domestic affairs. Perhaps law is given special duties in world affairs to compensate for the weak international social structure; when these extravagant expectations are disappointed, the contributions actually made by law to world order are extravagantly neglected. Neither extremes of expectation nor extremes of disappointment are conducive to an awareness of reality.

[41] The relation between national assertions of claims to engage in controversial conduct and the development of world order is examined in Richard A. Falk, "Space Espionage and the World Order: A Consideration of the Samos-Midas Program," in R. J. Stanger (ed.), *Essays on Espionage and International Law* (Columbus: Ohio State University Press, 1962).

[42] This approach to the validation of a unilateral claim permits a sophisticated legal argument to be made in support of the imposition by the United States of its 1962 "quarantine" upon shipping bound for Cuba that was carrying as cargo components of "offensive" military equipment. Reference should be made to the narrowness of the claim, to the minimum threat of force consistent with the attainment of the security objective, to regional support and participation, to the degree of acquiescence to the claim by shippers subject to its interference, to

inhibits the tendency of nations to overrespond to perceived crises, and it establishes a matrix and rhetoric that facilitate diplomatic negotiation. This puts international law in a position to contribute significantly to the supranational management of the dangers to international peace that arise from those patterns of intrastate violence which highlight the conflict between cold war rivals in a nuclear age. It is in this spirit that the limits and opportunities of legal order should be conceived for the contemporary world.

However, the reality of normative indeterminacy [43] requires a sharp sense of the distinction between the facts *as impartially perceived* and *as characterized by national officials* holding heavy stakes in the outcome of a particular internal war.[44] A state eager for a successful overthrow of an incumbent govern-

---

the willingness of the United States to negotiate, and to the Soviet compliance with the demand. As an adversary process is implicit in the legal system of settlement, a contrary set of considerations can be advanced to oppose the legality of the claim: a failure to attempt prior negotiations, an unwarranted threat to use force in violation of Charter norms, an impermissible interference with shipping on the high seas, an intervention in the domestic affairs of Cuba, an asymmetrical claim to defend national security in view of United States "offensive" missile bases along the Soviet periphery, an unreasonable assertion of competence vis-à-vis the shipping of third states, and so on.

International law often comes into being through the gradual acceptance of behavior first perceived and condemned by casual observers as "illegal." The doctrine of pacific blockade was itself established by the effective assertion of limited unilateral claims by dominant national actors. This poses difficult problems concerning the distinction between a violation of an existing rule and a claim to establish a new or revised rule and between illegality and legislative enactment. For stimulating discussion, see Lauterpacht, *Recognition*, pp. 426–30.

[43] That is, the same set of facts is capable of two or more plausible contradictory legal characterizations. This is a characteristic of all law, not just international law. However, the absence of centralized and objective international decision-making often makes it impossible to eliminate indeterminacy. Cf. note 60 below.

[44] This distinction is made sharply by William T. Burke in "The Legal Regulation of Minor Coercion: A Framework of Inquiry," in *Essays on Intervention and International Law,* to be published by the Ohio State University Press. Cf. also McDougal and Feliciano, *op.cit.* (note 36 above), p. 10.

ment is much more inclined to characterize the facts in a manner that is favorable to the insurgent cause.[45] A proper awareness of the success of international law in its role as a restrainer of national conduct depends upon measuring the distance between the facts and the doctrinal response.

It is very important to maintain the distinction between the rights and duties of international actors and their implementation by domestic societies. For example, the discretionary nature of recognition permits the executive, by virtue of his primary responsibility for foreign affairs, to influence the way in which the judiciary treats the legal claims of an insurgent faction either during or after an internal war.[46] This may have an important influence on the fiscal position of a revolutionary society, affecting its access to foreign assets and exchange. It is often very important to obtain respect abroad for controversial economic acts at home; it influences the international capital position of a government, especially if it is a newcomer to the international stage, as is the case after a successful revolution. Very often the dramatic controversies surround the interna-

---

[45] The divergent images of reality held by participants with varying perspectives constitute one of the most profound themes in human experience; this insight achieved consummation in the evocative Japanese tale, *Rashomon*. For a more pertinent illustration, one might compare a standard positivistic international law text—say, that of Lauterpacht and Oppenheim—with representative writing from the newly independent or socialist states—say, J. J. G. Syatauw, *Some Newly Established Asian States and the Development of International Law* (The Hague: Martinus Nijhoff, 1961), or Bedjaoui, *op.cit.* (note 30 above).

[46] A British case acknowledges this influence: A. M. Luther v. James Sagor & Co., [1921] 3 K.B. 532; cf. also 1 K.B. 456. American practice is very complicated. Cf. the affirmative internal effect that is supposed to be achieved by recognition (United States v. Pink, 315 U.S. 203 [1942]) with the negative effects of nonrecognition (Latvian State Cargo & Passenger S.S. Line v. McGrath, 188 F. 2d 1000 [D.C. Cir. 1951]). For discussions of executive-judicial relations with respect to the influence of the foreign policy of the forum upon the outcome of a legal controversy, cf. Bernstein v. N.V. Nederlandsche-Amerikaansche, 173 F. 2d 71 (2d Cir. 1949), with Banco Nacional de Cuba v. Sabbatino, 193 F. Supp. 375 (S.D.N.Y. 1961), aff'd 307 F. 2d 845 (2d Cir. 1962), and Rich v. Naviera Vacuba, S.A., 295 F. 2d 24 (4th Cir. 1961).

tional validity of expropriation laws and decrees. There is a connection here with foreign policy, for a refusal to recognize a new government or its radical economic program alienates it and tends to encourage it to adopt the orientation of those nations that acknowledge the validity of its existence and show respect for its governmental undertakings.[47] This is a very crucial aspect of the way in which the international system reacts to internal war, as it subtly accentuates the discretion of national actors to regulate their participation or nonparticipation without contradicting the formal obligation to treat an internal war as if it were a matter within domestic jurisdiction of the strife-torn state. The difficulty of conceiving of international law as a common regulative regime is also disclosed. For if each nation is free to determine the internal effects of "nonrecognition" and is free to refuse recognition, then it is clear that there is no common set of duties that arises from the *factual* circumstances in the course of or at the end of an internal war. The techniques used by judicial institutions of third states to adjudge the competing claims of insurgent and incumbent are beyond the scope of this paper, although they are relevant to full appreciation of the limits of traditional notions such as nonintervention and the duty of impartiality. For it is obvious that the court must be able to identify the legal interests of the state in the midst of an internal war in order to settle disputes about ownership, immunity, and obligation that come before it.

Somewhat related to the impact of internal war on the operation of domestic courts is the degree to which nations are

[47] For instance, an expropriating state cannot compete in international commercial markets without reasonable assurance that it can pass secure title. In fact, even the prospect of litigation would dissuade most purchasers unless the offering price was a real bargain. This means that often socialist states are alone available as traders willing to pay fair value for expropriated property. Apart from possible unfairness to investors, it is clear that asymmetrical responses by third states to nationalization has an important influence on the capacity of a state to benefit from its program of capital centralization.

permitted to tolerate or encourage activity within their territory that is related to the pursuit of an internal war abroad.[48] Here the range of activity includes hostile propaganda, asylum, governments-in-exile, and the financing, training, equipping, and transporting of insurgent expeditions. To what extent are these activities subjects essentially within the domestic jurisdiction of the state in which the constituent acts take place? If the concern is with political stability, then it is desirable to assert some supranational control over conduct taking place in A that is designed to change the political *status quo* in B. The willingness of the Republic of the Congo to advertise its support of training bases for Angolese rebels on its territory is an illustration of flagrant disregard for the traditional assumption that one state has a duty to prevent its territory from being used to endanger the political independence of another state. Tolerance by the United States of anti-Castro exiles and the Soviet training programs for insurrection, guerrilla warfare, and subversion further illustrate a tendency to immunize aggressive designs by acting behind the walls of territorial sovereignty. Does the target state have any recourse in the absence of express treaty commitments? And even if target states can invoke obligations to enforce neutrality abroad, is there any way to enforce com-

[48] See, e.g., Draft Code of Offenses Against the Peace and Security of Mankind, Adopted by the International Law Commission, 28 July 1954, GAOR, IX, Supp. 9 (A/2693), pp. 11–12, Article 2, which designates "offenses against the peace and security of mankind" in paragraph (4): "The organization, or the encouragement of the organization, by the authorities of a State, of armed bands within its territory or any other territory for incursions into the territory of another State, or the toleration of the organization of such bands in its own territory . . . as well as direct participation in or support of such incursions," and paragraphs (5) [encouragement of civil strife by acts or their toleration] and (6) [*ibid.*, use of terror]. To like effect, see Convention on the Rights and Duties of States in the Event of Civil Strife, to which the United States is a ratifying party; *American Journal of International Law*, XXII, Documents Supplement (July 1928), p. 159. The United States has been implementing domestic legislation that makes it a crime to plan, organize, or participate in a hostile expedition against a state with which the United States is at peace. Cf. 18 U.S.C.A. § 960 (1948).

pliance? Behavior in states other than the state that is the scene of the internal war may be highly interventionary; yet given the fundamental territorial distribution of authority that persists in the world, it may be difficult to stigmatize or control. Thus the policies of nonparticipation inherited from the traditional image of the posture of international law toward internal war give way to the realities of participation. These realities are dramatically important in the modern world in which mass communication, rapid transportation, economic interdependence, ideological fervor, and transnational revolutionary parties are significant characteristics. The traditional system shields activity by spatial criteria (jurisdictional formulae) although function and space increasingly diverge; that is, the policies of nonparticipation cannot be protected by rules against explicit participation in the internal war itself. For instance, it would be strained to contend that the overt participation of the United States in the internal wars throughout Southeast Asia is more interventionary than the covert participation of the Soviet Union in the People's Republic of China. We witness, then, the inadequacy of traditional norms of territorial allocation of authority to uphold the world community policy—the insulation of internal war from external participation. To overcome this inadequacy requires either centralized procedures to assure the domestic suppression of insurrectional activities or a candid abandonment of nonintervention obligations on the grounds of nonmutuality of adherence and of the failure of self-restraint to serve as a sufficient ordering technique. It is better explicitly to discard particular rules of international law that have become obsolete than to make the entire legal system appear obsolete by disregard of rules in practice.

It is today properly commonplace for experts to criticize the traditional system of international law as inadequate to meet certain specific needs of modern life. The problematic relevance of the traditional norms of international law to the various contemporary phenomena of sustained intrastate violence, collectively identified throughout this essay as "internal war," [49] is as yet strangely exempt from this line of criticism, perhaps because the subject has been inexplicitly absent from recent scholarly concern.[50]

The term "internal war" is consciously selected as a substitute for the usual designation: civil war. This is done to facilitate an accurate perception of the modern phenomena of intrastate political violence. It is especially important to appreciate the extent to which external actors participate in internal wars so as to distract the mind from a predisposition to view internal war as a domestic matter. The spatial matrix of conflict does

[49] Cf. James N. Rosenau's "Internal War as an International Event" (Chapter 3 in this volume) for a useful differentiation of internal wars based on struggles concerning personnel, authority, and structure. Recent definitions of internal war have been based upon the identification of different kinds of violent struggles carried on within national territory. For example, Harry Eckstein defines internal war as "any resort to violence within a political order to change its constitution, government, or policies" (mimeographed report on "Internal War: The Problem of Anticipation," p. 1, submitted to the Research Group in Psychology and the Social Sciences at the Smithsonian Institution on January 15, 1962). To emphasize the disparateness of internal war raises the important question of whether variables other than the extent of internal violence and of external participation (intervention) and impact (e.g., threat to international peace) should be taken into account in recommending an adequate international legal response to contemporary phenomena of internal war. To fail to add such variables is to neglect the objective of an insurgency in the study of the relevance of supranational legal norms to the control of internal wars. This corresponds more closely to the definitional emphasis suggested by Andrew C. Janos: "For purposes of systematic inquiry, internal war has been defined as a violent conflict between the parties subject to a common authority, and of such dimensions that its incidence will affect the exercise or structure of authority in society" ("Unconventional Warfare: Framework and Analysis," *World Politics,* xv [July 1963], pp. 636–46). The issue is quite significant. For if one treats the objective of a particular insurgency as crucial to its status as an internal war, then it is probably important to develop a parallel series of normative responses. This essay raises this fundamental question only implicitly. The explicit focus adheres to the traditional concerns of international law with the coercive impact within and without the afflicted society. It might be very illuminating to develop the international law of internal war on the basis of Rosenau's three types of internal wars.

[50] See note 2 above.

not always adequately reveal the necessary boundaries of significance. It is certainly true that instances of internal war such as the 1962 food riots in the Soviet Union or the Bombay language riots are accurately considered afflictions of a single society. But the dominant examples of internal war in the post-World War II era possess a different character. In fact, warfare *between* states now most frequently takes place *within* a single national society. The emergence of the shift in the role of intrastate violence in world political processes first became evident in the Spanish Civil War, although there had been a much earlier emphasis on internal war during the period of struggle between democratic liberalism and monarchial legitimacy, in the decades following the French Revolution and then in the period following the Congress of Vienna (1815). It is important to distinguish between the extranational consequences of civil strife that arise as an inevitable result of social, economic, and political *interdependence* and the distinctively modern *participation* of rival nations in domestic arenas of violence. Significant multinational participation transforms an internal war into a species of international war.[51] And, in fact, as a result of the inhibiting impact of nuclear weaponry upon recourse to direct forms of aggression, it becomes increasingly evident that the

[51] Even without multinational participation, the outcome of an internal war may have an unsettling impact upon international affairs. This is illustrated by the Batista-Castro struggle, which seemed to be as domestic as we can expect conflict to remain in the modern world. The course taken by Castroism subsequent to its victory would suggest to many Western observers that an early intervention would have improved the quality of world order; that is, even with mutual adherence to the norms of nonparticipation, occasions may arise where considerations of world order or the maintenance of human rights might prompt intervention on either side. Who would look back critically upon a successful insurgency in Nazi Germany that had depended heavily for success upon the interventionary participation of third powers? Our search is for more than the discovery of norms and institutions that establish an effective formula of nonparticipation, and thereby allow the balance of domestic forces to decide the political destiny of each society. We seek, as well, a process for facilitating the elimination of intolerable domestic social orders, because they are intolerable and because their existence threatens world peace.

politics of expansion are now mainly concerned with the struggle to help sympathetic elites gain control of the apparatus of government in foreign societies.[52] This concern is coincidental with and reinforced by the mounting pressures for radical social change throughout the portions of the world engaged in the modernization process. For these pressures produce a climate hospitable to revolution and domestic violence.[53] Thus the external ambitions of imperial dynamism combine with domestic conditions of instability to give an unprecedented prominence to internal wars in contemporary patterns of world politics.

Such an extralegal environment places new strains upon the traditional system of international law. In the course of examining international law in the light of these developments, we discover the need for reinterpreting part of the traditional approach, discarding another part, and retaining, almost unaltered, a third part. We are led at the outset to question the adequacy of the *apparently* rigid separation between civil strife and international war, itself derivative from the overarching distinction between war and peace.[54] Standard legal commentary regards recourse to intrastate violence as a normal process of domestic political life; such an insulation of civil strife from international legal concern has as its normative justification the attempt to reconcile the rights of revolution

[52] This line of analysis is strongly developed by Samuel P. Huntington in two essays: "Instability at the Non-strategic Level of Conflict," Study Memorandum No. 2, Special Studies Group (Washington: Institute for Defense Analyses, October 6, 1961), and "Patterns of Violence in World Politics," in *Changing Patterns of Military Politics* (New York: Free Press of Glencoe, 1962), pp. 17–50. This pattern is studied from the perspectives of law and morality in Falk, *op.cit.* (note 37 above).

[53] This domestic receptivity to social and political violence results from a combination of factors: rising expectations, inadequacy of constitutional methods of achieving domestic change, absence of democratic capability or tradition, oppressive and privileged governing elites.

[54] See Philip C. Jessup, "Should International Law Recognize an Intermediate Status Between Peace and War?" *American Journal of International Law*, XLVIII (January 1954), p. 98; McDougal and Feliciano, *op.cit.*, pp. 97–120; Fritz Grob, *The Relativity of War and Peace* (New Haven: Yale University Press, 1949).

with the authority of an incumbent government to establish order within its territory. Thus tolerance of revolutionary activity expresses the traditional reliance upon the territorial ordering capacity of governments as a principle designed to stabilize international transactions and to promote a climate hospitable to the activity of nationals abroad. From the exclusive perspective of protecting the political *status quo*, it would make more sense to use the power of third states, on a mutual basis, to secure the stability of governments in the face of domestic protest and rebellion. It is rather surprising that the incumbent regimes of sovereign states did not perceive a common interest and react in concert to the threat of international revolution. For in an international society lacking ideological levels of conflict, there was less tendency to appraise foreign governments as good or bad. Nevertheless, despite this mutuality of interest in the security of governmental tenure, international law developed a stronger emphasis upon anti-intervention doctrine than upon doctrine favoring constitutional legitimacy. This produced a tradition of deference to the natural outcome of a violent struggle between hostile factions for domestic control as the fundamental response of international law to internal war.

This deferential pattern rested upon a factual assumption: that an internal war possessed a truly domestic character. But, as we have tried to indicate, many instances of internal war now operate primarily as a restricted arena of international conflict. It seems inappropriate for international law to refuse a response to internal wars that attain major magnitude or that include the substantial participation of third powers. This is especially true whenever an internal war grows out of or into the cold war rivalry, as was the case in the violent conflicts taking place since World War II in Greece, Malaya, Laos, South Vietnam. This variety of civil strife is more realistically characterized as a form of "international war" despite the confinement of military operations to the territory of a single nation and despite the absence of an armed attack across an international boundary.[55] Internal wars of this dimension increase the risks of escalation into nuclear war and intrinsically disrupt international peace and security.

But international law, even in its traditional formulation, is capable of a more complicated relationship to internal war than is indicated by the basic policy of noninterference. In fact, much of the superficial inadequacy of traditional international law arising from this apparent unconcern gives way upon closer scrutiny to residual concern that supports a perception of potential adequacy. For the ascription of belligerent status to the insurgent group by word or deed can lead to the treatment of the factions of an internal war almost as separate states. This, in turn, subjects the conflict to the regulatory claims of international law.[56] Over a century ago, Emmerich de Vattel made the

[55] Despite this "recognition," it is crucial to retain the distinction for *military* purposes between intrastate and interstate violence. This distinction is quite consistent with the hypothesis of this essay that internal war provides the main arena for contemporary forms of violent international conflict. But the facts of political, social, and economic interdependence that tend increasingly to ignore national boundaries and thus to depreciate their objective significance do not lessen the usefulness of national boundaries as conflict-retaining limits in intrastate military campaigns. The antagonistic perspectives of General MacArthur and President Truman in the Korean War illustrate the nature of the problem. Within their respective roles both men seem to have been correct, but fortunately the principles of military necessity gave way to the principles of minimum international order. A decentralized legal order must seek to preserve respect for the few objective limits that exist; a limit is objective if its nature is easily discerned independent of the perspective of the actor—for example, a well-defined boundary or recourse to nuclear weaponry. This reliance upon limits to restrain conflict is especially important for international affairs as the hostility and distrust prevailing between principal actors inhibit explicit agreement and direct communication of mutually acceptable self-restraining standards of behavior. The role of tacit limits upon international actors is sharply perceived by Thomas C. Schelling in *The Strategy of Conflict* (Cambridge: Harvard University Press, 1960), pp. 81–118.

[56] The concept of "belligerency" as a transforming norm is discussed later in detail. To the extent that actors have discretion (a type 1 norm, cf. pp. 195–96 above), nations have authority to change the status of an internal war from a matter of domestic jurisdiction to one of international concern.

authoritative observation that "Civil war breaks the bonds of society and government . . . it gives rise, within the Nation, to two independent parties, who regard each other as enemies and acknowledge no common judge. Of necessity, therefore, these two parties must be regarded as forming, for a time at least, two distinct Nations." [57] This allowed nations to assimilate an internal war into the normative framework applicable to international war even before the League Covenant or the United Nations Charter came into existence.[58] It is not without interest to observe that leading treatises of international law discuss problems of belligerent status for insurgents under the rubric of "War" rather than "Peace." A more accurate description of the traditional system, then, includes acknowledgment of a basic normative disposition to defer to intrastate strife as a domestic matter, but couples this with reference to residual norms that enable other nations to internationalize its legal significance if this should be found necessary.

Even this initial vindication of the traditional system must be qualified by four serious criticisms. First, the law of war never made extensive claims to restrain the significant elements of national discretion with regard to war. In fact, with the collapse of the just-war doctrine in the nineteenth century, international law allowed states to decide for themselves, as a matter of sovereign prerogative, when to wage war. The role of law was restricted to the avoidance of unnecessary suffering and inconvenience arising from the pursuit of belligerent objectives. Such matters as neutral rights, the protection of civilians, the treatment of prisoners, and the rules of belligerent occupation

[57] Emmerich de Vattel, *op.cit.* (note 15 above).

[58] This has importance in refuting the argument that participation by the United Nations in an internal war is an unwarranted intrusion upon domestic jurisdiction. For it is evident that an internal war, if sustained, is from a functional point of view a breach of international peace. This does not, however, lessen the need to emphasize the factual internalness of violence in order to assure the applicability of the restraining rules associated with intrastate warfare—a need that goes back to the stabilizing relevance of objective limits in a decentralized order (cf. note 55 above).

were developed to reduce the impact of evil side-effects (to counter tendencies toward brutality) and to confine the scope of belligerency (to avoid the involvement of neutrals). Thus the traditional law of war must be considered as an essentially modest attempt to impose legal restraints upon national discretion to use force, and even if applicable to an internal war it does not contribute much regulation.

Second, the traditional criteria used to support the recognition of belligerent status are insufficient for modern needs. The old rules allowed belligerency to be proclaimed when the insurgents controlled territory, established an administering government that appeared effective, displayed a willingness to be bound by the laws of war, and impinged upon maritime or other interests of world-wide concern.[59] Today, however, it is essential that substantial participation in the internal war by private or public groups external to the society experiencing violence serve as a basis for internationalizing civil strife. The facts of external participation are more important than the extent or character of insurgent aspirations as the basis for invoking transformation rules designed to swing control from the normative matrix of "domestic jurisdiction" to the normative matrix of "international concern." [60] There is a need, therefore,

[59] From a legal perspective, many complications arise from the decision to treat an insurgent as a belligerent. Among other consequences, it changes rights and duties on the high seas and influences the treatment of domestic controversies involving property of the state that is the scene of the war. For a general survey of problems, see Lauterpacht, *Recognition*, pp. 175–328.

[60] A legal system provides contradictory and complementary norms that permit antagonistic actors to express their preferred outcome in the rhetoric of a legal claim. This facilitates the use of the adversary process and expresses the nonmechanical quality of legal decision-making. The legality of behavior, then, is not a logical exercise of finding the rule that fits the facts. It is rather a balancing of a variety of considerations, including past treatment (precedent), community expectations, the promotion of community policies, acquiescence of the state subject to the claim. See Myres S. McDougal, "The Ethics of Applying Systems of Authority: The Balanced Opposites of a Legal System," in Harold D. Lasswell and Harlan Cleveland, *The Ethic of Power* (New York: Harper & Bros., 1962), pp. 221–40. The classic statement of this characteristic

to develop criteria for the recognition of belligerency that takes account of internal war as the most prevalent and threatening form of international violence, involving both the principal pathway of aggression and a dangerous breeding-ground for a provocative initiation of an escalatory spiral that has a thermonuclear catastrophe as its upper limit.

A third flaw in the traditional system is its allocation of authority on the basis of a world composed of sovereign states. International law arose to permit rising nation-states to accommodate their relations by the acceptance of common standards to serve the bilateral or multilateral convenience and interests of the states concerned. Throughout this period of growth between the Reformation and World War I, the notion of national sovereignty played a dominant ordering role in international relations and law, expressing its importance by the rule that required national consent to act as a basis of all international obligations and by the tendency to confer maximum discretion upon states to specify unilaterally their attitude toward new political developments in the world. This discretion is most familiarly present with respect to the recognition of new states and governments, but pervades the relevance of law to the response of a nation to an internal war elsewhere in the world. Thus, for instance, the recognition of belligerency is itself a discretionary act by a foreign state.[61] Hall states the prevailing view as follows: "As a belligerent community is not itself a legal person, a society claiming to be belligerent, and not to have permanently established its independence, can have no rights under that law. It cannot therefore demand to be recognized,

complementarity of the legal order is found in Benjamin N. Cardozo, *The Paradoxes of Legal Science* (New York: Columbia University Press, 1928).

[61] That is, there is no duty to recognize once a certain set of facts exists. This tolerance of decentralized authority processes allows status to depart radically from role. This is most obvious in the post-internal war situation in which recognition is withheld; for instance, United States recognition of the Soviet Union was deferred until 1933 and the People's Republic of China remains unrecognized today.

and recognition, when it takes place . . . is from the legal point of view a concession of pure grace." [62]

In a world of intense rivalry for political influence, it is not surprising that the granting and refusal of recognition are dominated by political considerations.[63] If the transformation rules of international law remain politicized, then the flexibility of the traditional system is almost without value for the problems of today. It brings neither stability nor control to the phenomenon of internal war if nations of the world are free to manipulate the legal status of intrastate violence to express their preferences with regard to the outcome of the particular conflict.[64] National discretion is formally restricted by certain minimal duties owed by foreign states to established governments; thus there are norms that prohibit "premature recognition" of an insurgent elite. However, it is difficult to apply any norms consistently once behavior becomes as conditioned to political manipulation as recognition practice has become. The dangers of unregulated internal wars are great in a world community that is increasingly riven; this makes it imperative

[62] A. Pearce Higgins (ed.), *Hall's International Law*, 8th edn. (London: Oxford University Press, 1924), p. 39.

[63] Even in 1947, Lauterpacht wrote in his Preface that ". . . there is probably no other subject in the field of international relations in which law and politics appear to be more closely interwoven [than recognition]. As a result, there has grown up a tendency to maintain that the crucial question of granting or refusing recognition is not one of international law" (*op.cit.*, p. v).

[64] The result is that the same constitutent acts possess a different legal character depending upon the national setting in which the determination is made. Thus, title to property conveyed by insurgents may give good title in some places, but not in others. It is an expression of the totalness of modern political conflict that there is an increasing tendency to govern private transactions involving a society undergoing internal war by reference to national policy about the preferred outcome. Cf. especially Bank of China v. Wells Fargo Bank & Union Trust Co., 104 F. Supp. 59 (N.D. Cal. 1952); Latvian State Cargo & Passenger SS Line v. McGrath, 188 F. 2d 1000 (D.C. Cir. 1951), cert. denied, 342 U.S. 816 (1951); Stanley Lubman, "The Unrecognized Government in American Courts: Upright v. Mercury Business Machines," *Columbia Law Review*, LXII (February 1962), p. 275.

to discover an objective method to transfer an internal war into the realm of official international concern. Preliminary to this, however, is the need for a reformed doctrine of recognition, imposing upon foreign states a duty to recognize, once certain uniform criteria set down in advance as ground rules are satisfied. Ideally, this would lead to the development of a nonpolitical procedure of collective recognition in which the more impartial judgment of the community was used to answer certain factual questions about the conditions of governmental tenure in the society in question.[65] The legal status of an internal war is thus objectified and centralized. This would produce a more uniform treatment of an instance of insurgency; the traditional system allows various states to overindividualize their relationship to an internal war. One consequence of this is to allow the same set of facts to give rise to several inconsistent patterns of rights and duties.[66]

A fourth difficulty with traditional international law results from the changed dimensions of internal war. The old types of civil strife were either a spasm of insurgent activity that succeeded or failed in a very short time or a protracted war between regular military forces using conventional tactics. Now, however, several varieties of irregular warfare have developed that enable an insurgency to continue for a considerable period without establishing a clear belligerent or political identity. This new phenomenon of prolonged insurgency requires a special international status that enables third states to adjust their relations, but there is no assured way to achieve this on a noninterventionary basis. Nations can neither deal with the insurgent and incumbent elites on the basis of impartiality nor can they ignore the existence of insurgency. This tends to eliminate neutrality and to polarize participation in internal wars

[65] Lauterpacht, *Recognition,* § 54, pp. 165–69; Thomas and Thomas, *op.cit.* (note 27 above), pp. 250–72.

[66] John Fisher Williams, *Aspects of Modern International Law* (London: Oxford University Press, 1939), pp. 109–10. See also note 58 above.

in the factional manner that dominates international politics. United States neutrality in the Castro-Batista struggle for control of Cuba illustrates the kind of difficulty, for intervention on either side at some early stage would have reached more stable results, requiring less internal polarization to attain or to renounce the proclaimed goals of the revolution.

The emergence of supranational institutions on a regional and quasi-universal basis provides the apparatus to permit the recommended changes in the locus of competence. However, hostility and distrust militate against the acceptance of mandatory political responses by the leading cold-war antagonists. The political atmosphere and the state of national consciousness in powerful nations lag seriously behind existing institutional growth and even further behind the minimum needs of world order. And yet there is no doubt that any serious move to create a warless world by implementing a disarmament arrangement must include a grant of comprehensive authority to supranational actors to exercise decisive control over internal wars that threaten the strategic stability of the system. Already there is some movement toward the supranational management of internal violence when the situation is acknowledged by major states to threaten international peace. In the Congo operation, the United Nations shifted its justification for action from the duty to repel Belgian aggression to the duty to restore and maintain internal order; to a lesser extent, the earlier presence of the United Nations in Lebanon and Jordan also rested upon the competence of the Organization to preserve internal order in a situation where the consequences of civil strife are perceived by dominant actors as a serious threat to international peace.[67] To some extent this development was anticipated, or —more accurately—not foreclosed, by the language of the Charter, which qualified the deference in Article 2(7) to "mat-

[67] For a thorough narrative, see Arthur Lee Burns and Nina Heathcote, *Peace-Keeping by U.N. Forces from Suez to the Congo* (New York: Frederick A. Praeger, 1963).

ters which are essentially within domestic jurisdiction" by a clear assertion that "this principle shall not prejudice the application of enforcement measures under Chapter VII." [68]

This centralization of authority might come to jeopardize ideals of national self-determination, especially as they are dependent upon revolutionary activity. The need for peace overrides an optimal preference to allow the natural outcome [69] of a violent domestic clash to resolve questions of challenged national destiny. Quincy Wright attempts to balance the competing claims in the following way: "Since international law recognizes the right of revolution, it cannot permit other states to intervene to prevent it. The United Nations itself cannot intervene to stop civil strife, unless it concludes that such strife threatens international peace and security or violates an internationally recognized cease-fire line." [70] This way of perceiving

---

[68] The architects of the design for the United Nations evidently did not understand that the central peace-keeping tasks of the post-World War II world would require gradually expanding competence to restrain the scale and scope of intrastate violence.

[69] Earlier views of national self-determination assumed the hermetic reality of the national unit. This expresses the spatial approach to international relations that underlies the traditional conception of international law and gives rise to such fundamental doctrines as territorial jurisdiction, nonintervention, domestic jurisdiction, and sovereign equality. It is no longer possible to speak rigorously of a natural outcome for the domestic clash of forces, as extranational influence has necessarily been decisive in so many of the recent instances of internal war. It is now very dangerous for major states to remain aloof from civil strife by adhering to a doctrinaire faith in the acceptability of outcomes generated by the supposedly free play of internal processes of self-determination. Participation or nonparticipation by third states has become a crucial part of policies of aggression and collective self-defense pursued by expanding and containing states. We need a new vocabulary that can justify the legal competence that is developing to take the action needed to prevent internal wars from becoming the domestic scene of major international violence.

[70] Quincy Wright, "Subversive Intervention," *American Journal of International Law*, LIV (July 1960), pp. 521, 529. Wright's approach assumed a more legalistic deference of supranational actors toward the domesticity of internal war than does this essay. See, generally, Quincy Wright, *The Role of International Law in the Elimination of War* (New York: Oceana Publications, 1961).

traditional international law suffers from its tendency to repress a recognition of the possible contradictions between rigid adherence to ideals of self-determination, self-defense, domestic jurisdiction, nonintervention, and the maintenance of peace. A particular phenomenon—say, internal war—must be perceived in relation to the over-all normative climate; the traditional system, relying on the dominance of national power and authority perspectives, does not indicate a univocal normative response. It permits nations wide discretion and generates a spectrum of norms that enable nations to form a clear statement of national response. Without central institutions and assurances of enforcement, international law, in relation to coercion, was more concerned with the development of a rhetoric for the self-respecting resolution of disputes by diplomacy than with the imposition of common standards of restraint. This essay accepts a conception of international law that is wide enough to include the processes of claim and counterclaim that make use of normative rhetoric; it seems imperative to liberate the understanding of international law from a habitual perception of its role in domestic life.[71] The form of every legal order depends upon the distinctive structural and cultural characteristics of the social order within which it performs.[72] This assertion,

[71] This should enable nonlawyers to perceive the relevance of international law to matters of vital national interest and convince lawyers that international law cannot be understood when it is torn from its socio-political context. In a sense, both kinds of audience share a provincialism about the nature and function of international law. Of course, this position assumes a basic jurisprudential stance for the purpose of deepening the comprehension of a single substantive problem: law and internal war.

[72] Law does not operate as an autonomous force. Its rules on crucial matters gain effectiveness as their claims overlay perceptions of self-interest. The convergence of law and self-interest is not, as is so frequently suggested, a weakness of a legal system; it is a central constituent of law's effectiveness in *any* social order. However, until the actor perceives the convergence, even if it should exist in the objective situation, the restraining impact of law is likely to remain minimal, especially in planning crisis responses. Thus the growth of effective law depends greatly upon a reorientation of the perceptions of self-interest

which may seem like a digression, applies to the relevance of international law to internal war. For the diverse perspectives of national actors lead to a wide variety of behavioral postures. This does not mean that there is no legal order, but it does require us to comprehend legal order as something other than the effective establishment of behavioral regularities.[73] This "some-

---

by officials acting on behalf of nations. International law, especially, would benefit from an improved perception of the role of processes of spontaneous adherence. In like manner, instances of violation do not reveal lawlessness, but suggest the identity of the limit transcended. The dominance of patterns of conformity permits us to take note of the non-conforming instance. Perfect compliance suggests the triviality of a rule, for significant rules are those designed to restrain or suppress tendencies to act in a manner that has been forbidden by the rule. If there is no pressure on the rule, there would be no social function for it. Thus one would expect every significant rule of law to be subject to violations and to be challenged by conduct that has an ambiguous legal status. The legal process only gradually crystallizes a consensus in order to identify with assurance instances of illegality through the development of procedures of authoritative decision-making. These characteristics are now taken for granted in domestic affairs. One would not challenge the validity of domestic law after reading about unsolved homicides in the newspaper or even after discovering the disappointing ratio that exists between crime and enforcement in the United States. Why, then, does a successful violation of international law tend to put the whole system in doubt? It is a totally false expectation to seek nations to comply 100 per cent with legal restraints that seem to forbid the satisfaction of their interests on certain occasions. A compliance of 97 per cent may not be enough to prevent a system breakdown—for instance, if the 3 per cent includes a nuclear war—but it remains an achievement of law to secure that level of compliance. At least, one should realize what one is denying when one denies the contribution of international law to world order, as well as appreciate the loss of stability that would follow from its nonexistence.

[73] I have attempted a depiction of the special character of international law in a series of articles: Falk, "International Jurisdiction: Horizontal and Vertical Conceptions of Legal Order," *Temple Law Quarterly*, XXXII (Spring 1959), pp. 295–320; Falk, "Jurisdiction, Immunities, and Act of State: Suggestions for a Modified Approach," in Falk *et al.*, *Essays on International Jurisdiction* (Columbus: Ohio State University Press, 1961), pp. 1–20; Falk, "Toward a Theory of Participation of Domestic Courts in the International Legal Order: A Critique of Banco Nacional de Cuba v. Sabbatino," *Rutgers Law Review*, XVI (Fall 1961), pp. 1–41. It is important to appreciate that horizontal law implies decentralized decision-making. This entails tolerance for a range of discretion exercised by those charged with the application of common standards in international

thing other" is mainly a formulation of claim to inform actors of behavioral intentions and to create a basis for further claim, counterclaim, explanation, and resolution.

It is important also to consider the special role of legitimacy in the application of international law to internal war. The term "legitimacy" itself was first used by international law to express the propriety of claims to dynastic succession in monarchial systems of government throughout Europe until after the French Revolution. The legitimate government was not, then, necessarily the government in effective or constitutional control of the national community. However, the rise of nonmonarchial societies to international prominence and the desirability of conferring legal status upon the operative governments of national societies led to an identification of legitimacy with the incumbent government, especially if its power was stabilized and constitutionalized over time and its authority acknowledged by widespread diplomatic recognition. The frequency of revolutionary challenges to established government in Latin America led to the Tobar Doctrine, which expressed a policy of refusing recognition to any government that had attained power by unconstitutional means.[74] This policy seeks permanently to deprive insurgents of the means to achieve legitimacy in the international legal order. The Tobar Doctrine never did attract

---

law. Such discretionary latitude would disturb us in domestic law. Thus, for instance, there is wide agreement about the status of activity that takes place in "territorial waters," but considerable disagreement persists on matters affecting their width, effective claims varying from 3 to 12 miles. Again, states are free to fix the diverse conditions attaching their nationality to ships, but now this freedom can be exercised only if a "genuine link" connects the ship to the flag.

[74] The Tobar Doctrine was incorporated into Central American treaties in 1907 and 1923 and followed in practice by the United States on several occasions. (See Lauterpacht, *Recognition*, p. 129.) It is interesting that subsequent Latin American concern with the interventionary impacts of nonrecognition produced the Estrada Doctrine, which stood for the opposite principle: recognition is automatically conferred upon the government in control, regardless of whether it attained power by constitutional means. Cf. *The Foreign Relations Law of the United States* (Philadelphia: American Law Institute, 1962), pp. 361–62.

much of a following, although it illustrates a recurring temptation to identify legitimacy with the established social order and to repudiate the right of revolution. It also tries to develop as a role of law the expression of national policy in a form that helps the world community to render judgment and make a response. For the rejection of the Tobar Doctrine requires an explicit appreciation of the dependence of legal status in international affairs upon the effective facts of political control. It is generally inadvisable for a decentralized legal order to use criteria other than effective control to qualify a status as "legitimate." For this reason, practices of prolonged nonrecognition violate the integrity of the international legal system. Only a strongly hierarchical legal order can shape the facts to express the commitments to justice that prevail in the community.

In recent decades, however, legitimacy has been tied to a policy of justifiable intervention by powerful states. Notable illustrations include Western counter-revolutionary intervention in Russia after World War I, Fascist and Communist interventions in the Spanish Civil War, and successful resistance of the Western Hemisphere to Fascist encroachment in South America—especially in Bolivia, where collective and consultative nonrecognition led to the fall of a pro-Fascist government.[75] That is, legitimacy has reacquired a normative quality in contemporary world politics. There is less interest in stability *per se* than in a stability that extends and defends the sphere of influence of one of the major groupings of nations that exist: Afro-Asians oppose stability for South Africa, favor it for the Congo; the Soviet Union opposes stability for most of Asia and Latin America, favors it for East Europe; the United States opposes stability throughout the Sino-Soviet sphere of influence, favors it elsewhere.[76] We are concerned here with the quality

[75] Thomas and Thomas, *op.cit.* (note 27 above).
[76] This analysis is carried out in Falk, "Historical Tendencies, Modernizing and Revolutionary Nations, and the International Legal Order," *Howard Law Review*, VIII (Spring 1962), pp. 128–51.

of the connection between certain dominant attitudes toward normative legitimacy and the pursuit of a policy of active participation in intrastate violence by nations acting individually or in concert.

It is thus relevant to mention the pledge to support "wars of national liberation" that has been taken by Communist states.[77] The official Soviet textbook on international law revives the classical distinction between just and unjust wars, explicitly including wars of national liberation in the category of just wars.[78] If the idea of "liberation" extends eventually to any movement directed against a non-socialist order, as it apparently does,[79] then this is a far-reaching justification for active participation in internal wars. The Yugoslav theorist, Edvard Kardelj, denounces international warfare as being destructive and as acting as "a brake on internal progressive social processes"; nevertheless, with evident pride he writes that "socialist Yugoslavia has within the limits of her capabilities always offered the oppressed peoples consistent all-round support in their struggle for liberation." [80] Kardelj—following the Soviet doctrinal lead—considers defensive war and "people's liberation and internal revolutionary wars" as the only types of "progressive, justified war." [81] From a legal and political viewpoint, the

[77] It is important to distinguish among various Communist interpretations of the "pledge." A main difference among Soviet, Chinese, and Yugoslav foreign policies arises from the extent of support that is appropriate. For to give sympathy, guidance, and asylum to the supporters of a foreign insurgency is probably an illustration of permissible coercion that does not violate the duty of nonintervention. This contrasts with clandestine shipments of arms and ammunition, the establishment of rebel training bases, or the direction of a revolutionary movement.

[78] *International Law: A Textbook for Use in Law Schools* (Moscow: Foreign Languages Publishing House, n.d.), p. 402.

[79] Cf., e.g., "Declaration of Representatives of the Eighty-one Communist Parties Meeting in Moscow, November-December 1960," in Dan N. Jacobs (ed.), *The New Communist Manifesto*, 2d edn. (New York: Harper Torchbooks, 1962), pp. 27–29.

[80] Edvard Kardelj, *Socialism and War: A Survey of Chinese Criticism of the Policy of Coexistence* (London: Methuen and Co., 1960), pp. 32, 99, 107; cf. generally, pp. 30–109, 178–94.

[81] *Ibid.*, p. 194.

most discouraging aspect of this policy of giving support to certain forms of insurgency is the apparent autonomy of the claim. For there is no willingness to entrust supranational institutions with competence to implement wars of national liberation on behalf of the community of nations. So long as participation in internal wars is left a matter of national policy, it is profoundly inconsistent with a serious quest for workable and acceptable disarmament.[82] The only apparent way to balance social progress with enduring peace is to entrust regional and universal institutions with a gradually increasing competence and responsibility for social change.[83] From this perspective the Congo operation and the resolutions of the General Assembly concerning Rhodesia, South Africa, and Angola are encouraging. It is also well to appreciate the significance of the distinction between United States sponsorship of the invasion of the Bay of Pigs in 1961 and United States leadership at the Foreign Ministers' Conference at Punta del Este, which excluded Castro's government from participation in the inter-American system because its Marxist-Leninism was considered incompatible with the objectives and principles of the Organization of American States.[84] The point is that the future of international legal order depends upon the emergence of effective supranational management on a regional and universal basis of external participation in internal wars. Normative

[82] Disarmament cannot proceed safely or significantly without an accompanying assurance that a political rival is unable to use force to achieve aggressive political objectives. This requires the development of techniques to prevent third powers from the pursuit of policies based on the exploitation of domestic instability. In view of Soviet and Chinese doctrines, capabilities, and practice with respect to the exploitation of domestic discontent, this assumes a peculiar urgency as an essential input in current disarmament thinking.

[83] For a preliminary formulation, see Falk, "The Legitimacy of Legislative Intervention by the United Nations," in the forthcoming volume, *Essays on Intervention and International Law* (note 44 above).

[84] There exists a full and provocative discussion of the general problems: A. J. Thomas, Jr., and Ann Van Wynen Thomas, "Democracy and the Organization of American States," *Minnesota Law Review*, XLVI (December 1961), pp. 337–82.

legitimacy, if codified, objectified, and centralized, would provide a suitable basis for guiding the conduct of supranational agencies of social change. However, so long as participation in internal wars is left to national discretion and capability, the rhetoric of normative legitimacy merely confers a semblance of respectability upon policies fraught with danger and instability. It should be stressed, perhaps, that there is a need to promote certain social changes by organizing and encouraging external participation in anti-governmental insurgencies, but that this participation must itself be legitimized by a centralized process of decision and implementation. So far as this problem is a consequence of the broad discretion given to nations by traditional law, it suggests the need for, but hardly the probability of, a fundamental reallocation of authority between national and supranational communities. Ideological rivalry, nuclear weapons, pressures for rapid social change bid us heed with new seriousness T. A. Walker's comment in 1893: "Men do not always distinguish easily between the impelling power of conscience and the attractive force of interest." [85] Dependence upon self-restraint and a regime of self-construed reasonableness does not produce a reliable legal order, especially when the atmosphere is made tense by fear, hostility, and a sense of vital concern. These conditions curtail the ordering potentiality of decentralized systems of law.

The facts of participation contradict the norms of nonintervention. Behavior does not conform to the claims of the traditional legal order. Major nations identify their vital interests with the outcome of internal wars. This stimulates substantial participation in internal wars that is moderated only by dangers of escalation, cost-benefit analyses, and considerations of resource utilization. Restraining rules are undercut by notions of normative legitimacy that are available to vindicate participation by characterizations of "anti-colonial war," "war of national

[85] T. A. Walker, *The Science of International Law* (London: C. J. Clay and Sons, 1893), p. 148.

liberation," or "anti-Communist war." In addition to this, there is a widespread acceptance of the propriety of counter-interventions designed to neutralize a prior intervention; the participation of the United States in the wars in Laos and South Vietnam [86] seems to depend primarily upon this justification.[87] Also, there is a continuing acceptance of participation in internal wars on behalf of and in response to a request for help by the established government; the entry of United States troops into Lebanon in 1958 illustrates this type of participation.[88] This allows unpopular and oppressive regimes to suppress insurgents indefinitely; if this became an operative principle in a disarming world, it would prolong indefinitely the life of a government premised upon the abuse of fundamental human rights. In contrast, societies subject to external pressure and internal subversion are quite vulnerable to skillfully exercised takeovers. The engineering of the Communist *coup d'état* in Czechoslovakia illustrates this method of extending political influence—as the Communist Party acted within, Soviet troops massed along the borders.[89]

[86] See, e.g., "A Threat of the Peace—North Viet-Nam's Effort to Conquer South Viet-Nam," Parts I & II, U.S. Department of State Publication 7308, December 1961. Cf. also Roger Hilsman, "A Report on South Viet-Nam," *U.S. State Department Bulletin,* XLVII (October 8, 1962), pp. 526–33.

[87] After the Spanish Civil War, prevailing United States *practice* has assumed the privilege of counter-revolution. However, no accompanying revision of *doctrine* has been attempted to diminish the validity or extent of the claims of strict nonintervention commitments. For a comprehensive critique of United States policy toward intervention, see Manfred Halpern, "The Morality and Politics of Intervention" (Chapter 9 below). Cf. also Karl Loewenstein, *Political Reconstruction* (New York: Macmillan Company, 1946).

[88] This occasions sharp criticism from the perspective of positive international law; it is a result of the failure of traditional rules to be responsive to the changed social function of intrastate violence in world affairs. See Quincy Wright, "United States Intervention in Lebanon," *American Journal of International Law,* LIII (January 1959), pp. 112–25.

[89] See Morton A. Kaplan, *The Communist Coup in Czechoslovakia* (Princeton: Center of International Studies, Research Monograph No. 5, 1960).

Several conclusions seem to follow. First, there is the adoption of an interventionary approach to political expansion by China and the Soviet Union. Second, there is the development of a counter-interventionary approach to political containment by the West. Third, there is the vulnerability of small states to the power rifts of the great states. Despite these characteristics of contemporary international relations, there is no disposition to challenge foreign participation in an internal war by threat or recourse to an old-fashioned armed attack by one state upon another.

In effect, then, these several varieties of foreign participation in internal wars are more or less tolerated by the legal system, except for an occasional interposition of supranational authority as in the Congo. If substantial participation on behalf of the insurgent is identified by the incumbent, then it provokes notes of protest and perhaps a proportionate response, especially an appeal for help to third states in order to neutralize the insurgent strength that is claimed to be attributable to external sources. This continuing tolerance by the legal system of participation on the side of one's choice in an internal war gradually assumes a place in the horizontal, self-delimiting portion of international law. A horizontal norm is a rule derived from patterns of national behavior, adherence to which is widely perceived by actors as obligatory and violation of which is understood to be destabilizing.[90] A horizontal norm may be inferred that prohibits the use of nuclear weapons in the course of participating in an internal war. Another horizontal norm prohibits significant assistance to an insurgency that challenges the incumbent government in the central spheres of influence of either nuclear bloc leader; for example, the West remained aloof from the uprising of 1956 in East Europe and the Soviet

[90] For development of this view, see references cited in note 73 above; an application to the control of force is attempted in Falk, *op.cit.* (note 37 above).

bloc did not render support to Castro until well after he was acknowledged and formally recognized as the leader of the incumbent government of Cuba.

The argument made here is that these horizontal norms convey the impact of law upon behavior with far greater accuracy than do the norms of the traditional system of international law. First, the rigidity of nonintervention is inappropriate for a world of growing interdependence, where the welfare of nations often depends upon foreign aid, technical assistance programs, guaranteed prices, and military alliances; whatever a nation does or doesn't do, once it possesses the capacity to influence the outcome of an internal war, is bound to be "interventionary" unless powerful nations participate or refrain from participation on a symmetrical basis. Symmetry neutralizes external participation far more than does unilateral adherence to a policy of strict nonintervention. Second, the tactics, ideology, and organization of the Communist Party give the Sino-Soviet bloc a big comparative advantage under the traditional system. Participation, at least as a potentiality, is assured by the ability of the Communist Party to breed sturdy, indigenous Trojan horses throughout the world. The West, in contrast, must adopt explicitly interventionary policies to neutralize implicit intervention that follows from the presence of a revolutionary party trained and managed from Moscow or Peiping. Third, the widespread refusal to honor norms of nonintervention tends to make Western nations appear as lawbreakers, thereby impairing the dignity of international law and adding weight to the claim that considerations of power are the only important influence upon international relations. It seems preferable to repudiate the traditional norms in the face of these challenges and to substitute instead a group of emerging horizontal norms. Such conduct would disclose more accurately the role of law in relation to internal war, and would at the same time refuse to qualify as "law" rules which have lost their effectiveness in the course of changed conditions and persistent violation.[91]

It could be argued that complementary norms introduce adequate flexibility in the traditional system. Thus participation on behalf of an incumbent can be justified by stressing arguments of legitimacy, whereas help to insurgents can be justified as self-defense. This strains the accepted usage of norms by insisting upon novel applications, as when the United States asserts that a Communist government in Cuba is a threat to our national security sufficient to legalize the use of force within the scope of self-defense. It also encourages reciprocal extensions of restraining norms: if Cuba is a threat to the United States, then Turkey or Pakistan is a threat to the Soviet Union. And, finally, complementary norms, self-interpreted and self-applied on a national level, lead to a weakening of the entire normative structure by generating self-serving invocations of norms to rationalize and vindicate behavior that we would expect impartial observers to assess as impermissible. The relation between national claims of self-defense and the Charter norm in Article 51 makes this plain. Article 51 limits the right of self-defense to action taken in response to prior armed attacks across international boundaries. This is quite different from invoking self-defense to justify forcible intervention in another nation because it has adopted a hostile form of government.[92]

[91] A critical intellectual task is to conceive more fully the problems of overcoming obsolete norms in a legal order that lacks a legislature. An interesting, if oblique, treatment of the problem of transforming rules of international law is found in two articles by I. C. MacGibbon: "Some Observations on the Part of Protest in International Law" (note 38 above), and "The Scope of Acquiescence in International Law," *British Year Book of International Law, 1954* (London: Oxford University Press, 1956), pp. 143–86.

[92] The scope of self-defense continues to be subject to various interpretations. In view of the precarious condition of contemporary peace, this is especially unfortunate, as it leads actors to arrive self-righteously at contradictory interpretations of the same event. This may inflame international relations and even produce armed conflict. For instance,

For all these reasons, there is an urgent need to reformulate the relevance of international law to internal war. This reformulation is guided by the need to centralize authority and control with respect to internal war, to substitute community management for domestic autonomy, and to entrust supranational actors with gradually increasing competence and responsibility for the regulation of an internal war.[93]

V. *Problems, Self-criticisms, and Conclusions*

Considerable difficulties beset this recommended approach. To what extent is the test of participation to be self-determined on the national level? Does the international character of the Communist Party make "domestic" Communist participation in an internal war equivalent to explicit Sino-Soviet participation? Does the obligation of nonparticipation preclude large-scale external military and nonmilitary support for an incumbent regime confronted by the prospect of a radical protest movement? Or should there be a provisional tolerance for nonmilitary participation by third powers in support of the legitimate aspirant to domestic power? Is it desirable to consider alternatives to constitutional legitimacy as the basis for permissible third-state participation?

These questions touch upon fundamental issues that cannot be discussed in this essay. Besides, satisfactory answers do not exist; these questions are troublesome because they identify attempts to fulfill contradictory policies: the maintenance of international order and the promotion of domestic social and

---

both the stationing of missiles in Cuba by the Soviet Union and the United States' demand for their removal could be plausibly included in the wider conception of self-defense that has been urged by Julius Stone in *Aggression and World Order* (Berkeley and Los Angeles: University of California Press, 1958) and McDougal and Feliciano, *op.cit.* (note 36 above), pp. 121–260.

[93] This orientation is anticipated under very different international conditions by Hans Wehberg, "Civil War and International Law," in *The World Crisis* (New York: Longmans, Green and Co., 1938), pp. 160–99.

political progress. Certain tentative directions of response can be suggested. An adequate line of response must begin by recognizing that decentralized patterns of control will continue to dominate international behavior whenever cold war issues and participation lie at the explicit center of intrastate violence. It is equally important to identify an emerging centralism in the response of the community to intrastate conflict involving colonialism and institutionalized racism.[94] Here, vertical processes and institutions for registering and implementing community consensus appear to be growing increasingly significant.[95]

These two opposing trends cast doubt upon any unified attempt to describe or prevision appropriate regulation for the treatment of internal wars by the international legal order. Thus, for instance, a treaty that attempted to centralize all participation in internal wars would overlook political realities by neglecting the doctrine and practices of revolutionary and Afro-Asian nations; this would make attempts to achieve centralized legal control futile. Even if a set of ground rules prohibiting indirect aggression and subversion could be incorporated into a mutually acceptable treaty, it would probably turn out to be ineffective in practice and neglected in controversy. This reflects the general ineffectiveness of legal claims that are extended too far beyond the disposition of powerful governing elites. Whenever this happens, law will suffer from noncompliance and fall into disrepute as an instrument of community welfare.

At the same time, it is desirable to make explicit the centralizing tendencies that result from a consensus about the disposition of the colonial and racist issues. The establishment of

[94] That is, racist policies endorsed by the prevailing governmental elite and incorporated into the constitutional structure of public administration.
[95] Peter Calvocoressi, in *World Order and New States* (note 1 above), uses this line of analysis to emphasize the disappearing capability of major states to carry out peace-keeping and law-maintaining roles.

community competence for the coercive settlement of domestic conflicts in a manner that opposes the prevailing government's policy is a radical contradiction of traditional notions of national sovereignty, domestic jurisdiction, and supranational authority. As such, it is an important area of developing law that needs appreciation. It bears closely upon the opportunities for international law to regulate the *outcome* of a certain class of internal wars. The assertion of a claim to affect outcome is itself a radical innovation if we remember that the guiding policy of traditional international law was nonparticipation in internal wars.

Regional claims to control the outcome of domestic conflict rest upon more problematic grounds. For example, should a nation that disappoints regional ideals but is acceptable to the universal order be made a victim of regional coercion or be the beneficiary of universal protection? This problem is posed by the current quality of relations between Castro's Cuba and the Organization of American States.[96] For the alleged "incompatibility" of Castro's Marxism-Leninism with the inter-American system contrasts with its evident compatibility with the United Nations Organization.[97] The coercive implementation of regional ideals of social order does improve the quality of international stability by reducing the points of hostile contact in world politics. However, the human costs of homogeneity are high, especially if premised upon the general primacy of regional ideals over competing universal standards. It is difficult, for instance, to endorse an international system that would tolerate an Arab movement to eliminate Israel by the use of force. But the "incompatibility" of Israeli society with the rest of the Middle East is at least as persuasive as is that of Castroist Cuba with the Western Hemisphere. If one seeks international order,

[96] Israel and Formosa also exist in a hostile regional atmosphere.

[97] This point is vividly raised by the decision of the Special Fund of the United Nations in February 1963 to go ahead with the construction of an experimental center in Cuba to help increase agricultural productivity.

not *ad hoc* opportunism, then it is difficult to distinguish between the relative validity of these two regional claims.[98]

This point can be sharpened by a contrast. If African regional groupings sought to apply pressure upon Angola or the Republic of South Africa on the basis of "incompatibility," then this would be acceptable from the perspective of world order. For the conditions identified as incompatible are also unacceptable when viewed from the perspective of universal order. Therefore, the bases for regional coercion are consistent with wider ideals and the target states are not victims of regional provincialism. If the regional coercion is intense, then it would seem to require Security Council authorization under Article 53(1) of the United Nations Charter.[99] In any event, there is a basic difference between regional coercion that contradicts and that which fulfills universal conceptions of minimum conditions for an acceptable form of domestic order.

Notions of legitimacy, however, should enable a preliminary principle for orderly standards of national and supranational participation in internal wars to emerge. A guiding presumption of legitimate status might be given to the incumbent government. This presumption could be overcome if the incumbent regime premises its social order upon colonial subordination or upon principles of elite racial supremacy (a white minority ruling a black majority); that is, the legal rules about nonintervention are suspended in those instances in which the community is confronted with an "illegitimate" incumbent regime. To avoid instability, this certification of illegitimacy must be formally expressed by the United Nations resolutions

---

[98] A persuasive argument for distinguishing Cuba and Israel could stress Cuba's insistence upon pursuing external ambitions, including using its territory as a base for Communist expansion in the hemisphere.

[99] Article 53(1): "The Security Council shall, where appropriate, utilize such regional arrangements or agencies for enforcement action under its authority. *But no enforcement action* shall be taken under regional arrangements or by agencies *without the authorization of the Security Council* . . ." (emphasis supplied). There is need, of course, to interpret the meaning of what is an "enforcement action."

of censure that achieve support from the overwhelming majority of Members, including leaders of both cold war blocs. If an internal war assumes the form of a major civil war between two rivals who each govern a portion of the disputed state (the factual conception of belligerency), then a situation of dual legitimacy exists with the participation of third powers governed by rules of mutuality. The most orderly disposition is to refrain from participation, but this no longer binds if hard evidence exists of intervention by third nations.

The notion of dual legitimacy is an inappropriate basis for determining standing in supranational institutions. For as long as an internal war continues, the incumbent should be allowed to operate as the exclusive representative of the state. However, if the outcome of an internal war is clear and violence has ceased, then the results should be expressed by the accreditation of the party in control. This is a factual approach based on a conception [100] of international institutions as organizations that represent the wielders of the power that is distributed throughout the world and most prominently held by national actors.[101] It thus should make legitimacy depend upon effectiveness, not normative legitimacy. This matter of *standing* in the organization, however, is radically different from the response of an institution to an internal war. The presence of the incumbent in the institution is not compatible with participation in favor of the insurgent. If the outcome of an internal war is a permanent division of the old state into two or more

---

[100] An alternative conception would admit to international organizations only those states that satisfied certain minimum moral conditions in their administration of government and practice of foreign policy.

[101] The *statement* in Article 4(1) of qualifications for membership in the Organization is somewhat difficult to reconcile with the recommendations made here. In fact, the *practice* of the United Nations indicates much greater fidelity to the criteria of factual effectiveness than to normative compliance. And the *meaning* of the Charter is more reliably ascertained by an examination of practice than by a dissection of the statement. However, the refusal to admit the Republic of China does provide a most important pattern of practice pointing back to the relevance of criteria other than factual control.

separate units, then this, too, deserves institutional acknowl-edgment without prejudice to the refusal of the factions to accept such an outcome. Here, again, the prime consideration is to confer standing upon the effective agents of political power in a neutral manner with relatively little concern about the constitutional or moral propriety of relative claims.

Can regional institutions withdraw legitimate status from an incumbent regime in a state that is a member of the region? Does this withdrawal entitle coercive participation on the side of insurgent groups seeking to reestablish a social order that is acceptable to the regional consensus? These questions suggest the central issues raised by the determination at Punta del Este in 1962 that the Castro government, having identified itself with the principles of Marxism-Leninism, is thereby "incom-patible with the principles and objectives of the inter-American system" and further "[t]hat this incompatibility excludes the present Government of Cuba from participation in the inter-American system." [102] It is possible to regard this action as a progressive step toward the centralization of authority as it claims for regional institutions a competence to withdraw legitimacy from states within its domain and thereby enables third powers to adopt a quasi-legal basis for participating in anti-governmental insurgencies. The contrary position would maintain that the Communist character of a domestic social order is irrelevant to its legitimacy in international affairs. The overwhelming majority of states, and especially the nonaligned nations, favor an international order based on mutual tolerance of Communist and capitalist systems of government.[103] It is difficult to reconcile the contradictory claims of bloc politics in the cold war, the ordering role of regional institutions, and the

[102] Final Act, Second Punta del Este Conference, January 1962 (Eighth Meeting of Consultation of Foreign Ministers Serving as Organ of Consultation in Application of Inter-American Treaty of Reciprocal Assistance).
[103] See, e.g., Declaration of the Heads of State or Government, Bel-grade Conference of Nonaligned Nations, 1961.

overseeing competency of universal consensus vis-à-vis the status of incumbent and insurgent factions as legitimate and illegitimate.

If the resolutions of censure passed in the United Nations to condemn the incumbent regimes of the Republic of South Africa or Angola manifest a centralized abandonment of deference to constitutional legitimacy as a basis for world order, then the practice of according diplomatic recognition to governments-in-exile is a decentralized equivalent. For instance, prior to the Evian Accords of 1962, establishing the independence of Algeria, at least twenty-five states accorded *de facto* or *de jure* recognition to the Algerian Provisional Government as the legitimate political representative of the "state" of Algeria.[104] The community is placing certain restrictions upon the capacity of an incumbent government to retain exclusive legitimacy for itself.

There are several conclusions that seem supported by this analysis of the application of international law to internal war. First, traditional decentralization can be overcome to the extent that regional and universal institutions assume competence to interpret and act in relation to the factions fighting against one another in an internal war. The presence of supranational institutions provides the basis for standardizing community responses through the development of community procedures of recognition. Second, deference to an overriding community policy to allow the internal war to reach an outcome that expresses the domestic balance of power is only adequate as a first approximation to determine proper national responses to internal war. The cold war, the politics of expansion practiced by the revolutionary nations, and the global character of the Communist Party undermines the international basis for adherence to the norms of nonparticipation, as these norms have been summarized in the doctrine and practice of nonintervention. Thus

[104] For a table indicating states extending recognition to the insurgent faction, see Bedjaoui, *op.cit.* (note 30 above), p. 138.

the applicability of traditional norms must be made subject to a condition of mutual adherence. Third, dangers to peace in a nuclear age make it desirable to promote the community management of those forms of intrastate violence that threaten to emphasize the cold war rivalry, even if this management may destroy the normal outcome of an internal war. Fourth, community coercion to achieve outcomes in accord with a universally held consensus is an emerging form of legislative competence for supranational organizations. If the community actor has the support of a regional consensus, then it is important to require an expression of approval by universal institutions prior to intervention in favor of the anti-incumbent faction in an internal war. Fifth, nations can significantly participate passively in internal wars by allowing exiles the use of their territory to form and organize expeditions. Such a pattern of activity is detrimental to peaceful relations and is inconsistent with the maintenance of order in a horizontal system of law. On the other hand, it expresses the unwillingness of states to accept the autonomy of domestic social order as an unqualified basis of restraint. Sixth, legitimacy as a prime criterion for distinguishing between justifiable and unjustifiable participation in internal wars is not usefully restricted to an identification of the incumbent regime. In fact, a supranational consensus can overcome a presumption of deference to the constitutional sovereign. Furthermore, the Communist states as a matter of doctrine and belief tend to confer effective legitimacy upon the insurgent whenever internal wars take place in nonsocialist societies.[105]

It is important to preserve the aptitude of the traditional system for drawing fine distinctions. In this sense, the threats to the policies of nonparticipation implicit in revolutionary ideology and the increasing significance of international actors

[105] However, one should not neglect the refusal of socialist states to grant any legitimacy to successful right-wing insurgencies—e.g., Franco's Spain.

other than nations call attention to the dominant function of international law in the context of intrastate violence: the provision of an instrument for the communication of precise claims by various actors concerned with the conduct and outcome of an internal war. Restraints upon behavior depend upon the distributions of value preferences and power potentials within the community more than upon the formulation of rules. Especially with respect to internal war, as a result of the various interpretations of the morality of participation, the notion of restraint based on formal rules of substance ignores the *actual* restraining role of law as a restrictive claiming and negotiating process. In this respect, the refinement of the traditional distinctions among piracy, rebellion, insurgency, and belligerency continue to be useful to describe national and supranational responses to internal wars, although dangers to the peace and order of the world in the nuclear age make it necessary to objectify the status of internal wars, to the extent possible, by the substitution of regional and universal recognition for unilateral recognition practice. Such centralization is also needed to confer the status of legitimacy and to determine by collective methods the proper quantum of coercive participation on the side of the legitimate faction. Thus the rhetoric and doctrine of traditional international law remain useful, especially if they can be adapted to the new roles of supranational actors and responsive to the realities of the cold war. The future of world order depends heavily upon the improvement of our capacity to use supranational community mechanisms to control the course and outcome of internal wars. It also depends upon the perception and acceptance of tacit norms of self-restraint by dominant national actors.[106]

106 This is especially true for tacit rules about the instruments of participation—for example, the nonuse of nuclear weapons in internal wars. The point is more fully developed in Falk, *op.cit.* (note 37 above).

CHAPTER 9

The Morality and Politics
of Intervention

BY MANFRED HALPERN[*]

I. *Intervention Redefined*

It is not inevitable that men should ask whether it is moral to
intervene in the internal affairs of other nations. To some, it has
obviously become a mere question of posture—how to keep a
straight face while intervening, how to smile piously when discovered, and how to win converts during the moral upsurge
that should accompany the exposure of others in the great game
of intervention. Some are convinced that the Communist world
represents a menace so evil that any action against this threat,
as long as it is successful, is by definition moral, or else merely
a problem of techniques.

If the question of morality is evaded by the technicians of
power and the secular crusaders, the meaning of intervention

* This essay has been reprinted, in somewhat revised form, from a
pamphlet of the same title originally published by the Council on Religion and International Affairs (New York, 1963). Its permission is
gratefully acknowledged.

I am deeply indebted to Ernest W. Lefever, Washington consultant
to the Council on Religion and International Affairs, for first inviting
me to explore these ideas under the intellectually hospitable and rewarding auspices of the Council; to Robert E. Osgood, Robert C. Good,
John Courtney Murray, S.J., Robert C. Tucker, Arthur Hertzberg, Robert
Gordis, William A. Lybrand, Samuel P. Huntington, Kenneth W. Thomp-
son, and William Lee Miller, who served as chairman or first discussants
during Council consultations; and to the board of trustees and the staff
of the Council, and to more than fifty government officials, men of religion, and scholars who joined for several intensive hours in Washington
and New York to discuss an earlier draft; and to Gregory Massell, Thomas
P. Thornton, and Betsy Steele Halpern, who read this paper at various
stages. The ideas offered here owe much to their criticism and suggestions
even if, at times, these revisions may only have served to clarify and
sharpen differences of opinion. Needless to say, I speak for no one in
this essay but myself.

is often obscured by traditional preconceptions. Only at first glance does "intervention" seem an obviously identifiable act carrying obvious consequences. In a world built upon national sovereignties and jurisdictions and the equality of independent states, any state that intervenes in the internal affairs of another undermines the institutional and legal foundations on which its own existence rests. This is a truth of great consequence to which we shall have to return. But it is not the only truth. Intervention, which by its nature subverts the foundations of the existing international system, takes place in a system which is by its nature fundamentally unstable. States in fact are not equal: nations can exploit the rules and opportunities of the present international system to enlarge their power over others and so risk death on a vast scale. We live at a time when intervention, by subverting the sovereignty of national independence, may further undermine the only rules of the game that now maintain order, yet when intervention alone may be able to restore the free operation of these rules, save freedom in a nation or, indeed, help to create a more secure and more freely interdependent world order. In our world, intervention can be moral or immoral, or simultaneously illegal and justifiable. The morality of intervention is determined both by the principles it creates or destroys and by the contingencies of circumstances. Intervention therefore involves a realm of morality in which a discussion of principles is essential but in which no discussion of principles has relevance for the next act of intervention or nonintervention until the circumstances surrounding that act have also been discussed.

It is an illustration of the unstable character of the present international system that there is no agreement on the definition of the two acts most likely to destroy the sovereignty, independence, and equality of any participant in the system, or perhaps even the system itself—namely, aggression and intervention. That is not to say that there is no agreement whatever. There is enough agreement to make the system endure; not sufficient agreement to make it stable. Nonetheless, to say that intervention is interference (falling short of aggressively crossing the frontiers with military force) in the internal affairs of another sovereign state is almost to obscure the question. We live, more now than ever, in an interdependent world. Almost everything that a powerful nation does (or almost everything that a weak nation, like the Congo, is powerless to do) vitally affects the internal affairs of many other nations.

A Great Power intervenes in the domestic realm of other states when it says "yes" and when it says "no"; indeed, by its sheer existence. By our very model of life we set an example for the Russians which stings Khrushchev to competition and not a few of his citizens to an emulation subversive of the official ideal of Bolshevik Man, even if not directly of the Soviet government. We intervene when we say "no" to the Aswan Dam, without which Egypt's standard of poverty would further deteriorate; we intervene correspondingly when we say "yes" to the Volta Dam in Ghana.[1]

It has been said that if the American economy sneezes, the world's economy, and especially countries depending on the export of a single raw material, catch pneumonia. A socialist is entitled to say that deliberate nonintervention by governments in their own richer and more powerful domestic economies may cause as much suffering, not only at home but abroad, as the deliberate exploitation of poorer and weaker foreign economies. The capitalist recognizes the potency of such economic intervention in the affairs of other sovereign

[1] Robert Batchelder has raised the question of what responsibilities the American government ought to accept when a private U.S. corporation establishes a plant abroad which, by virtue of the scope of its activities in an otherwise underdeveloped country, not only dominates that economy but sets in motion a social and political transformation which the local government is too weak to guide into channels conducive to domestic welfare and national independence. On the more limited question of the rights of private companies abroad, the U.S. government has for several decades now adhered to the policy that each nation has the right to nationalize foreign property, provided it pays fair compensation.

states both when he opposes and when he supports selective domestic subsidies and foreign aid. Intentions alone do not keep actions from being interventionist. The Western democracies' intention not to intervene in the Spanish Civil War was one of the crucial factors intervening in favor of General Franco's victory.

Intervention may include propaganda, espionage, discriminatory economic policies, assistance to legitimate governments in their domestic tasks [2] no less than aid to subversive movements, and support or denial of support to governments or opposition parties in domestic crises where such foreign support might prove to be decisive. There is no validity in confining the term only to those actions which the *legitimate* government of the country considers to be intervention. In an age of social and colonial revolutions, any prudent government will be as sensitive to the reactions of the future rulers of Angola or Iran to intervention and its consequences as to the reactions of the present ruling regimes. In trying to distinguish intervention from other actions that have consequences across frontiers, one can only set outer limits: intervention is any action, beginning with deliberate or remediable interaction among nations, that significantly affects the public internal realm of another sovereign state and which stops short of aggressive crossing of international frontiers.[3] Intervention is action along

[2] For example, agreeing to the holding of a summit conference because, among other reasons, it may benefit the British Conservatives in a forthcoming election, or training the Iranian police in more effective techniques of coping with anti-government activities.

[3] It may be argued that the threat of aggression, and even aggression itself, may constitute intervention. The United States has repeatedly moved military forces into Caribbean states for the sake of altering their internal policies without, however, staying long or taking sovereign title to the countries involved. The question is difficult to decide. The British army "intervened" in Egypt in 1882 and stayed for seventy-four years without taking title to the country. Is that therefore merely to be called "intervention"? This ambiguity illustrates the difficulties of defining the most desperate encounters nations may have, and how readily intervention can shade into the ultimate kind of force.

a continuum of possible choices. The range of alternative courses once men have decided to intervene (or indeed, not to intervene) is far greater than is usually thought of when men debate intervention. Our political and moral responsibility in the realm of intervention is therefore far greater than we usually assume.

Several objections may be raised against so broad a definition of intervention. Certainly it would not be helpful for USIA to speak of such constructive American policies as the application of the Truman Doctrine in Greece and Turkey, or our successful efforts to deter the French from deposing in 1951 the nationalist-minded King of the then French Protectorate of Morocco, as a policy of intervention. To refer to American policy publicly as a "diplomacy of involvement" may be no less accurate, but more agreeable—reserving the harder word "intervention" to describe the actions of unfriendly nations. In the present clinical discussion, however, a single term is more fitting for describing this singular form of national behavior.

A more profound and substantive objection may be raised —namely, that giving such wide compass to the meaning of intervention will tend to undermine precious distinctions between coercion and persuasion in international diplomacy. These distinctions are vital, but they do not take the simple form often ascribed to them. No serious Great Power tries to persuade another nation unless it means to convince. Whether it wins its case or strikes a bargain depends not only on the soundness of its arguments but also on the coercive weight of power that each interested nation has experienced or wishes to avoid experiencing. In international affairs, coercion begins at the moment of persuasion. There is only one important exception—namely, where two nations have agreed on overlapping national interests in a situation in which one nation is not invidiously dependent on the other. In all other cases, the crucial distinction in international relations does not lie in the separation of power and persuasion, but in the difference among the means and ends of power and persuasion—or among types of intervention (discussed below). It still makes a considerable difference whether the coercive component in intervention is assassination and terror or whether it is a deliberate reduction in economic aid. Men who in the present world order are inclined to draw a fundamental contrast between persuasion and coercion in international affairs tend to become either impotent idealists or else seeming realists who hand over to the technicians of power any problem not yet solved by discussion. Those who know that persuasion and coercion are inseparable in the uses of authority may require experts in covert activities and armed combat, but they have no need for men who specialize solely in power, or else in morality.

II. *The Relevance of Morality to Intervention*

At this point, some may be ready to respond to the complex interrelationship of power and morality by relaxing into moral ambiguities or, what is the same thing, platitudes. Others may be content to trust instead to individual moral leadership, forgetting that the same man who rightly would not read another man's mail must find standards by which he would enthusiastically break another nation's code. A man who would not hesitate physically and immediately to avenge an insult to his wife's honor may not act with similar assurance when a hundred million dead become the price of avenging a nation's honor.

Complexity must not deter us. The need for wisdom has grown: intervention is likely to become more common than ever before precisely as we succeed, through military technology, in making gains through outright aggression less probable, even while the conflict between ourselves and expansionist communism remains unresolved. Under these terms also, the danger of uncontrolled intervention escalating into unintended but destructive aggression rises—but so also rises the price of nonintervention whenever Communist nations are already intervening. The greater our power and our responsibility, the greater the need also to find a valid and moral code for our actions in history.

There is no obvious synthesis between morality and intervention. It is a cruel simplicity that makes a virtue of necessity or a necessity of virtue. To balance the demands of morality against the demands of victory in order to strike a mere compromise is almost bound to frustrate action and damage morality. Nor is morality merely an added decoration or only an ultimate grace: morality, especially when it serves to strengthen lawful stability or stabilizing change, has obvious practical consequences. These we ignore at our peril whenever we are tempted to gain only the practical results of power, and imitate the tactics of conflict management developed by Communists or sometimes attributed to them by our own secular crusaders, who compliment Communists beyond reason by believing them to be omnipotent and omnipresent in conspiracy and subversion. Surely the problem deserves to be resolved in terms of choices based on our own values of world order.

Nothing is easier than to state the solution in abstract terms: we must choose the right means for the right ends, and then apply our full force to achieve our goals. But what can this mean in practice? I would attach myself to a view voiced for about two and a half millennia: morality is not the highest value, and neither is power or knowledge. What matters is the best and most relevant relationship among these three—a union which in its contemplative aspect may be called wisdom, and, in its active phase, justice. Nothing is more difficult, or more necessary, to achieve in practice.[4]

Let us see just how difficult it can be. On July 14, 1958, the State Department in Washington received a telegram from the President of Lebanon requesting the landing of American

---

[4] Rabbi Robert Gordis has suggested that morality is the highest good, since, unless it includes honesty and intelligence, it is simply moralism. I do not put it this way because I want to make sure that we explore anew the power and knowledge that have become part of our morality.

forces within twenty-four hours in order to save that country's political integrity and independence. The issues seemed clear enough. The President of Lebanon had been the only Middle Eastern leader to endorse the Eisenhower Doctrine, which committed the United States to come to the aid of any Middle Eastern country which requested assistance "against armed aggression from any country controlled by international communism." Here, explained President Eisenhower, was a government that had been democratically elected, and that was now threatened by subversion armed and encouraged from outside. Here, as the State Department briefed the press, appeared to be a clear-cut case: we must demonstrate that we are ready to support our allies when they need us. American inaction, especially at a moment when pro-Western leaders had just been overthrown in Iraq, could result in the dominance of the Middle East by Soviet or Nasser imperialism, "assuming," as American officials expressed it at that time, "that these are or could remain separate." In a recent prize-winning series of articles on communism, *Life* recalled our Lebanese intervention as a major demonstration that we could stop communism in its tracks.

The real story, however, did not begin in July 1958. Early in 1957, Lebanese President Chamoun faced the bitter truth that during the preceding decade, the birth rate had shifted the balance of power in his country. In 1943, when Christian Arabs were still the majority in the country, the Moslem Arabs and the other minorities had agreed that Christians would always assume the position of President, Foreign Minister, and Commander-in-Chief of the Army, while Moslems would always assume the office of the Prime Minister and the Speaker of Parliament. All other positions in the state were similarly frozen on the basis of sectarian strength. By 1957 it had become clear to everyone that Moslems were turning into a majority, and that most Moslems and an appreciable number of Christians were being attracted to Nasser's neutralist, socialist, and authoritarian Arab nationalism.

Chamoun was unwilling, in a state founded upon ten Christian sects, three Moslem sects, and several "others," and hence viable, if at all, only by compromise, to strive for a new bargain consonant with the changing situation. He might have eased the transition to a system in which Moslems would have gained more responsibility or to a secular state in which all jobs were indiscriminately open to all men of talent and in which Lebanese Christians, thanks to their superior education and prosperity, would have remained at least equal in influence for a long time to come. Instead, in order to make up in foreign backing for what he had lost in domestic support, he agreed to the Eisenhower Doctrine. Then, in order to perpetuate the *status quo,* Chamoun rigged the 1957 election enough to give himself that two-thirds parliamentary majority required to amend the constitution so that Parliament could reelect him for a second six-year term.[5]

When the majority had thus been deprived of the effective use of the ballot while the country, hitherto neutral in intra-Arab conflicts, was being transformed into a pro-Western bulwark against the spread of neutralist Arab nationalism, the opposition resorted to bullets and the civil war began. Into this civil war, Nasser soon sent arms, money, and men, and we, after several months, our own armed forces.

One other fact has to be mentioned. Most politically active Lebanese believe that there is conclusive evidence that the Lebanese President and Foreign Minister, though they failed to consult other members of their government, had from the start acted in concert with CIA. The American intervention in Lebanon seemed to them, as to most other observers, to be part of American efforts after the Suez crisis of late 1956 to stem the growing influence of Nasser's neutralist nationalism. This nat-

---

[5] Oddly enough, Chamoun had become President in 1952 after helping to overthrow President Khuri—a man who had greatly increased the number of his enemies by his attempt to amend the Constitution so that he might serve an additional six-year term.

urally raises a major question to which we shall have to return: does our knowledge of Middle Eastern forces and trends suggest that it is a moral or necessary use of American power to intervene against neutralist nationalism?

By July 14, 1958, however, there were some additional issues at stake. By the day the telegram arrived, U.N. observers had already contributed materially to the reduction of the level of UAR intervention in Lebanon. The Commander-in-Chief of the Lebanese army, who had used his Christian-officered, but Moslem-and-Christian-manned army to umpire the civil war rather than to fight the opposition, was already laying the groundwork for the compromise that would end the war and make him President. It had also become evident that we were progressively less eager to have Chamoun cash the blank check we had given him —calling for the intervention of American troops. On the other hand, the telegram was sent a few hours after a coup in Iraq overthrew the only Arab government bound to the West by a defense pact. Since no one in Beirut or Washington had anticipated this coup at this moment, nor knew much about its main actors, ignorance conjured up fears and fears led some to think about being close enough, if necessary, to intervene in Iraq.

In addition to seeming new dangers, those who had to answer the telegram now also had to face fundamental and conflicting moral issues only distantly related to their original intentions. Could they, seeing the Lebanese situation itself now closer to solution, afford to say "no," and so let it be said by our allies in NATO and elsewhere that when it comes to a showdown, the United States is likely to have second thoughts? How reliable would that make us as an ally? Who would trust our pledge in the future? Yet should the United States now add a larger, more dramatic commitment to support a *status quo* that had already been undermined by the kind of forces against which Marines lack adequate weapons—birth rates and nationalism? What would have been a wise and just decision?

We chose to land troops. The troops fired on no one; the

American mediator who entered in their wake strengthened and secured the compromise that had already been in the making. But our landing of 10,000 troops in a country half the size of New Jersey also had various other consequences. The compromise brought about the departure from his country of the all too pro-Western Foreign Minister, Charles Malik, and gave the rebels the Premiership, but under the firm neutral leadership of the new President, General Chehab. The compromise has also led to a new, yet deeply frustrating, deadlock among Lebanese factions. As a result, little has been done since 1958 to resolve the imbalance between political structure and political reality which helped to produce the civil war.

The case must be summed up in paradoxes. We concluded that our international status demanded our intervention at a time when we were beginning to feel that the situation in Lebanon itself no longer required it. We demonstrated to the world the solidity of our commitment to our friends by intervening with immediate, well-coordinated, and major force, but we also exposed to the world our incapacity to airlift more than 10,000 troops to more than one trouble-spot at one time.[6] The compromise solution we helped to fashion left our closest friends without further power, so that other Middle Eastern governments could draw various valid lessons: the United States, whether in a right or wrong cause, will not deny itself the use of force and therefore must always be reckoned with; it will employ its horses and its men in its own national interests, and not necessarily in trying to put even an apparently pro-Western Humpty Dumpty together again. Even so, the Humpty Dumptys on our side may still take comfort: we do not use our strength to make structural changes; we merely put others on top of the wall. A U.N. resolution propounded with remarkable unanimity by all Arab states (presumably the kind of unity which we had earlier viewed with reserve) provided the basis on which our forces agreed to leave Lebanon. And

[6] Our military mobility has much improved since that time.

contemporary Lebanese governments find it more difficult to act on our advice for dealing with their still searing problems of social change than the pre-1958 government with whom we so eagerly agreed to repress the problems of change.

I have dealt with the Lebanese intervention in such detail because no wise and just action is ever hypothetical. Unlike our interventions in Cuba or Laos, the Lebanese case also is neither familiar nor (oddly enough) controversial, and hence may most easily lead to fresh insights. For from this one example (with suitable footnotes to other similar actions), we shall be able to raise most of the relevant questions and, possibly, conclusions for the general problem we are considering.

Needless to say, I consider most aspects of our intervention in Lebanon as an unhappy demonstration of American power, morality, and knowledge. Our difficulties stem from failures in each of these three realms and from the faulty connections we fashioned among them.

III. *The Relevance of Knowledge to Moral Intervention*

To begin with knowledge, we have scarcely begun to develop theories of social change that would allow us to understand the fundamental revolutions now in progress in the world, and hence to develop doctrines of intervention relevant to the politics of modernization.[7] Khrushchev has a theory. It is a dogmatic one, and it has led him into error as often as not. But he has a theory which sensitizes him to the great fact of rapid historical transformation that constitutes the modern age. It makes him more aware than we are to the probability that govern-

[7] I have dealt with this issue specifically in relation to "Perspectives on U.S. Policy in Iran," published in the SAIS *Review* (Washington), April 1962. This and the next two paragraphs are largely drawn from that article. A more extended analysis of the politics involved in the revolution of modernization may be found in my studies, *The Politics of Social Change in the Middle East and North Africa* (Princeton: Princeton University Press, 1963), and "The Social Revolution," in *The Developmental Revolution in the Middle East*, ed. by William Polk (Washington: The Middle East Institute, 1963).

ments owing their power to deadlocked sectarian parochialism or to absentee landlords are not long for this world. Communists are not responsible for having started the revolution of modernization and Khrushchev is dogmatically wrong about the inevitability of the next stage of social development. But if we compete against his partially correct theory about social change with no theory at all, he may well turn out to be right about the next stage as well, not because of his theory but because of our errors and omissions.

Lacking a theory that would help us understand the transformation of societies, we have tended to play for possible lucky breaks in history, though the breaks have not always come or do not always linger. Or else we have tended to be hardheadedly manipulative, but without a sense of theory or ideology. We are the inventors of a new kind of revolution—the hit-and-run revolution. We help make it and go home and leave the politics of social change, which alone can justify and fulfill a revolution, almost entirely to others who have even less appreciation of the problems of social transformation than we do.

We are not entirely without knowledge. If we do not yet possess a major theory about social change as broad in its concerns and as related to action as Marx's but a hundred years younger and less dogmatic (for it would lead to mischief merely to look for a countercreed), we still have available a number of insights that would form part of any such theory. One such proposition, for example, is that improved administrative efficiency, economic amelioration, and political concessions offered by a regime that is morally and politically isolated from the most important newly emergent classes cannot preserve political stability. When a social structure is radically changing and the political consensus has broken down, the price of political stability in modern times is to overcome the moral and political isolation between ruler and ruled. This certainly requires, among other things, economic and administrative progress, but these cannot substitute for political enterprise that goes to the root of the matter. Another proposition is that the longer repression succeeds in postponing the political adjustments to the transformation of a society's structure and values, the more likely it is that the more extreme and violent elements will gain leadership of the opposition. From these propositions alone it would follow that you can, if you must, use Marines to intervene in a rebellion affecting a change in top personnel. You cannot, even if you try, use Marines effectively to intervene in a revolution that is transforming what men believe, how they live, and how they relate to each other.

The revolution of the peoples of the underdeveloped areas to build institutions that would put them in command rather than at the mercy of the forces of modernization is more searing than any that ever confronted the West. It takes place, for the most part, in the face of fewer resources and skills, greater poverty and population pressure, and in societies that were, until a few decades ago, sure of their ancient truths and traditions. They are now driven by the pressure of sheer needs and new aspirations and the pain of backwardness and powerlessness in the presence of the industrialized nations to pass through their revolution in telescoped time.

If we have failed to understand the dimensions of the forces now transforming Asia, Africa, and Latin America, and viewed them frequently from the shallower perspective of cliques and personalities struggling for power, the fault has not only been in the inadequate state of our intellectual knowledge. The experience that would make us receptive to such knowledge has until recently been lacking. Our own society has been in the midst of constant change, but we have always, barring one civil war, been able to maintain a consensus on our basic social, economic, moral, and political values and institutions. We have been able to pay so much attention to the individual because we could afford to take our institutions for granted. We are only now beginning to experience the pain of bafflement and frustration that comes from living in a world changing both hopefully and dangerously, and certainly quickly and seemingly beyond control. We are coming to recognize that our institutions are not yet adequate to maintain peace, eliminate ignorance, bigotry, and poverty, deal with the sheer growth of the number of people, facts, and institutions, master technology, and preserve and spread beauty. We are only gradually becoming interested in the theory and practice of social change.

We cannot yet effectively capitalize on our knowledge in this field because we have so far invested much more in power than in the knowledge on which the prudent and effective exercise of power must be based. We intervene about as often in the internal affairs of other nations as the USSR, but the world is (and we ourselves ought to be) harder on us when we do. Since intervention when it involves duress is normally neither a legal nor a democratic exercise, we must when we intervene have better reasons, founded on better values and sounder knowledge, than are offered by Communist dogma.

One reason for our intervention is, of course, partly beyond our control: we cannot be secure in a world where domestic political life is in turmoil or guided by dogmatic or cynical adventurers. Within limits, the USSR can prosper from such instability. But not all burdens which this invidious problem imposes on us are inescapable. Had we really explored the roots and implications of neutralism when we intervened against it in Lebanon and Laos? Have we explored all mechanisms by which internal conflicts can be insulated from the cold war?

Our lack of knowledge and foresight about problems of Asian, African, and Latin American stability in which we have an intrinsically greater stake than the USSR also often forces us into intervention against our expectations. We often fail to anticipate crises. Yet there is a world of difference between the range of choices and the decisions one can make when one is aware of the forces and trends of history and the decision at a moment of crisis—when you are no longer free to pick the issue but when you must say yea or nay. On July 14, 1958, we were no longer free to say nay in Lebanon and break our word, yet many were the options we had before that day.

The position of the United States in world affairs, for the sake of power and morality alike, puts a premium on adequate knowledge. Yet the institutional barriers remain high against overcoming our historical ignorance and preconceptions about our rapidly changing world. Until very recently, we were governed by a generation whose education did not include knowledge about that majority of the world which lives in Asia, Africa, and Latin America. A large number of our policy-makers are lawyers, and many lawyers tend to see history as moving from case to case, instead of as a ceaseless trial that can sometimes be made to move in one direction rather than another but that has no final solutions. We are also, as a people, so action-minded that many of our best and most devoted policy-makers are seldom tempted enough, and therefore seldom find time enough, after their intense preoccupation with the evils that are sufficient unto the day, to think about the relevance of their actions to the long-term forces and trends of history. The machinery they have built over the years reflects their predilections. It swarms with facts; it seethes (if not always productively) with action; but few sections of the State Department or CIA are smaller than those whose task it is to devote themselves, full time, to long-range analysis and estimates.

Knowledge, however, bears an effective relationship not only to power but also to morality. One major reason why there is not yet a controlling international sense of morality is that the world does not yet share a single structure of knowledge, values, and sanctions. This moral deficiency in turn demands and perpetuates a hierarchical inequality of knowledge in each nation. This is an issue of intrinsic and not altogether avoidable danger. Precisely on the most vital questions of power, where emotions most require the discipline of knowledge and life itself may be at stake, knowledge can least of all be prudently shared with others who will certainly experience the consequences of action. Just prior to intervention and war, security is likely to dictate the greatest restrictions, even within the government itself, on men's "need to know."

Granting all this, I believe nonetheless that we have let secrecy hinder the application of knowledge and advice so far that both morality and power have suffered. This is worth saying, especially since all the pressures are still moving in the direction of narrowing the spread of knowledge and the range of debate: witness President Kennedy's pleas for voluntary press censorship after the Cuban intervention. As long as rivalries among independent sovereignties force citizens to accept an inequality of knowledge about questions of security, it remains all the more essential to insist that the leaders of our nation persist in constant exchange with the moral and political consensus of their community. Yet their isolation from that consensus is proceeding apace. We are, as a nation, approaching the moral disability of the international system as a whole. Differences in power positions are leading to growing differences in knowledge, values, and sanctions available to different segments of our community.

The fact that the community can no longer arrive at a sense of wisdom and justice because it lacks adequate knowledge and power in the crucial fields of subversion, weapons technology, and social change in strange civilizations makes its notions about the morality of intervention often impractical or else seemingly relevant only because its maxims survived from an earlier age when our institutions were being created, and knowledge, power, and morality were still more closely entwined with each other. Compensations for this weakness are possible, but they are seldom brought into play. Our leaders do not, on the basis of their own special knowledge, take much more time to lead the discussion that could clarify our national purpose than they now take for clarifying the historical and moral context of their acts of intervention. On the contrary, they sometimes feel impelled right up to the moment of intervention to speak enthusiastically against it.[8] Congress seems to have yielded its legislative and educational power on fundamental national issues to the Supreme Court, but the Supreme Court will not be able to guide us with equal strength on foreign affairs. Congress has a watchdog committee over the Atomic Energy Commission, which can transform matter, but it still neglects to appoint a similar committee over CIA, which can transform men and history.

Most of the press west of the Potomac is of little help in discussing and clarifying issues that could lead to intervention. Bipartisanship among our political leaders helped to turn the failure of our 1961 intervention in Cuba into a numbing celebration of national unity before the discussion had scarcely begun, and it inhibits debate on Laos or Vietnam. In contrast to democratic Britain, we also suffer from a peculiar form of patriotism. While the British Parliament sharply debated the merits of the Suez invasion of 1956 while it was in progress, and similarly argued about British troop landings in Jordan contemporary with American landings in Lebanon in 1958, the Speaker of the House of Representatives, Mr. Rayburn, effectively stopped debate in Congress during the Lebanese intervention by saying that "in times like these we had better allow matters to develop rather than make remarks about them." Though our national interest had become deeply involved, our survival as a nation was not at stake in Lebanon. Why then should the noble sentiment of patriotism turn into a crippling disease of eye, ear, nose, and throat? Is a congressional, instead of a parliamentary, system doomed to either irrelevance or irresponsibility in the conduct of today's foreign affairs?

The top decision-makers are thus usually left to pursue the

[8] Mr. Nixon, one of the earliest and strongest advocates of intervention in Cuba, in retrospect perceives only the electoral ironies that arose from his having declared on TV in August 1960, while preparations for the invasion were under way: "We would lose all of our friends in Latin America, we would probably be condemned in the United Nations, and we would not accomplish our objectives."

national interest, especially in the field of intervention, without any lively, free, or constant touch with the moral and intellectual consensus of the nation or its most representative institutions. What is more, this relative isolation of the decision-makers from the community's consensus, rendered painless by the community's widespread stereotyped acquiescence, persists in institutionalized form almost to the pinnacles of power. Few are the experts in government who are consulted prior to an intervention. What is publicly known about our intervention in Cuba in 1961 illustrates this. Considerations of security, curbing the security-cleared government official's access to information, may well at times have harmed our security.

It is my impression that there are very few among our experts at intervention who are not hard-working, intelligent, imaginative, and courageous far above the average of men. It is also my impression, however (and this one is more likely to be erroneous than the first), that just as the Office of War Information during World War II tended to attract an unusually large number of men who responded to the grandly heroic, hopefully liberal, and victory-promising aspects of the war, so CIA has attracted a core of men similarly attuned to one aspect of their task and their age. They know they are engaged in a cold war without foreseeable end, in an institution which reflects America's recent reaction against its long infatuation with idealistic legalism and its tough-minded discovery of the morality of power. They are involved in a task that must avoid publicity as much as possible, engaged in acts they would not countenance as citizens in their own country, blocked from discussing their problems with anyone but their immediate colleagues, under attack more often from the liberal moralist than the rightist actionist. They have rejected the ideological historicism of their enemy, but they have not yet developed a systematic understanding of their own concerning the forces of history. It is not surprising, therefore, that CIA should have attracted to its ranks of expert interventionists especially the technician of power and the energetic but doctrineless conservative. They are not the only kind of person working at CIA, but their presence inhibits that concern with the linking of knowledge, morality, and power that ensures, as far as it can be ensured by man, wise and just intervention.[9]

We have been fortunate so far that at the very top of power, in the Presidency, and often close to it, the country has been blessed ever since our final initiation as a world power—during the months preceding our entrance into World War II—with leadership of intelligence and morality. If the actions and interventions of this leadership have not always lived up to expectations, it is in part because our leaders are human and not omnipotent. It is in part also because they have been most intimately in touch with two, not entirely helpful, collections of men. On issues of intervention, the broad American constituency acquiesces in any seeming success against communism and is most erratic in the interpretation and punishment of what it, or some segment of the public, considers failures. (Compare the public's reaction to China, Cuba, Lebanon, and the Congo.) The other group, the President's most immediate advisers on intervention, have labored under the limitations which we have been describing, affecting the state of the art and constituting a profession more skilled in surgery than in the

[9] Readers of the *New York Times* and *Time* before, during, and after the Cuban intervention should have no difficulty recalling evidence for this view. We seemed to have lacked adequate knowledge about a country 90 miles from home, or at least failed to utilize knowledge that was available; we ruthlessly manipulated men and groups among Cuban exiles; we gave unconcerned support (or showed pragmatic and instinctive favoritism) to ex-Batista or pre-Batista men, rather than men willing to deal with the discontent that Castro had exploited. Had we insisted on the military success of this particularly ill-conceived venture, it would have been a moral and political tragedy.

There are also outstanding men at CIA who have produced major and imaginative projects in what will be defined below as constructive precautionary intervention. Their successes, by nature, evolve slowly and lack the drama of failure. It is my impression, however, based on inadequate knowledge, that the failures at intervention deserve the greater weight of attention.

problems of disease. The final responsibilities of the President cannot be lessened, but under present circumstances the handicaps under which any President must decide on intervention are dangerously high. A wiser American consensus on the merit and uses of intervention has become a necessity for clarifying and sustaining that final decision which only one man can make in each concrete case. Informed public discussion of at least the fundamental issues and types of intervention is essential to this end. But discussion is no longer a simple task. It could easily make intervention of any kind more difficult to carry out. It could arouse public pressure for crusades in behalf of moralism. Practice and passion have outrun discussion. Whatever the perils, there is no way of creating a relevant consensus except by discussion.

IV. *Types and Uses of Intervention*

As one contribution to such a discussion, I should like to examine several types of intervention and ask to what degree each might be wise or just.

Counter-intervention: No other kind of intervention is as easy to justify. It is an action designed to help free a country from the interventionist manipulations of another power and so enable it to regain its sovereign integrity and independence —that is, to stand free again of all interventions. It is coercion intended to create options rather than, as in the Soviet interventions in Hungary, to foreclose them.

Easy to justify, it is not at all easy to do well. For while it is not unreasonably difficult to define the point at which intervention becomes imperative, it is most difficult to help create that degree of internal stability which makes it prudent again to end intervention. Intervention involves, clearly, not merely a manipulation of power, but a sharing in the historical trials of others.

Intervention through indirect imperialist rule: Though its advocates may wish to call it "preventive intervention," it closely resembles that form of colonialism known as "indirect rule." We intervene to impose rulers who promise to be resolutely anti-Communist, but we leave them otherwise free to pursue any domestic policy they please. This indirect imperialist form of intervention has caused the United States more harm than any other kind of initiative we have undertaken, in particular because—for a number of good reasons—it can usually be counted upon to produce the very dangers we most feared when we first embarked on such adventures.

The initial argument raised in favor of indirect imperialist intervention is normally not confined to the reasonable proposition that if the USSR or its agents are about to intervene, why let the USSR gain the initiative—why wait until the legal government can no longer seek our aid and we are forced to embark on the more difficult path of helping to organize a counter-revolution? Such clear and present danger would justify *pre-emptive intervention.* (And the final justification of such a pre-emptive purchase of time is, of course, what constructive use we make of it.) The argument for indirect imperialist intervention goes further. It does not trust the existing government —one composed, say, of Laotian neutralists—to invite our aid *if* pressed by the USSR or its agents. It does not trust Mosadeq of Iran or Kassim of Iraq to know when or how to stop short of opportunistic collaboration with local Communists. Or, in the form of an Anglo-French argument, it does not trust Nasser to keep the Suez Canal open or run it efficiently. One could readily list more examples: it has been our favorite form of forceful intervention, and it has almost invariably backfired. Why?

It was founded, in part, on insufficient knowledge. In an Asia, Africa, and Latin America that have a highly sensitive pride in their new nationalism, the danger that neutralist nationalists might willingly yield to Soviet control has usually been less than we have feared. On the other hand, the danger that "pro-

Western" regimes, by stifling popular nationalist and reformist impulses, would sap their internal support has been far greater than we have usually anticipated. We have also tended to underestimate the readiness and effectiveness, as in the Congo, or in Syria between 1954 and 1958, with which nationalists will turn to whichever Great Power did not intervene first for countervailing force against the original transgressor. The results might have been much worse had it not been possible to mobilize U.N. intervention to counter national interventions which the United States did not support, as at Suez, or about which it had second thoughts, as in the Congo.

Indirect imperialist intervention has been pernicious morally because it has invariably been invoked against nationalist neutralists instead of Communists, apparently on the devil-ridden notion, happily on the decline since about 1960, that those who are not with us are against us. It has thus obscured the moral distinction between our sense of world order and that of the Communists—all the more so since the USSR has, from about 1951, based its foreign policy on the premise that those who were not against it were potentially for it.

In the realm of power, indirect imperialist intervention has therefore alienated rather than won people. It has never been truly preventive. In no instance—neither in Iran nor Lebanon nor Laos nor in other places not to be mentioned—was power first devoted to the creation of that dynamic stability that might produce a resilience and immunization to subversion by extremist forces. In the future, indirect imperialist intervention may prove even less pertinent as an exercise in power than before. Given the state of the international Communist movement, not every local Communist coup may be automatically interpreted as a Moscow initiative. It may be a new thorn in Moscow's (or Peking's) side. Yugoslavia may not be the only Communist nation we can afford to live with.

Precautionary intervention: This involves a kind of action which our government and our people have least discussed. Let me, therefore, for the moment merely outline some of the pros and cons of such intervention.

Among the most significant examples of how we failed to intervene in time are Hitler's Germany three decades ago and Algeria, where French colonial policy had reached a dead end more than a decade ago. Today the most foreboding case is probably the Republic of South Africa. Our own moderate Southerner need not fear: there is an obvious distinction between a policy intent upon achieving rapid equality, with deliberate speed, and a policy bent on perpetuating and deepening racial inequality. There is a technical strategic question (there usually is): can we defend ourselves successfully against missiles looped around the South Pole without the cooperation of the Republic of South Africa? But there is also one obvious estimate to be made: within the next few years, the Republic of South Africa is going to be a bloodier battleground within the free world than Algeria, because the Republic has no imperial overlord that can act as final arbiter, because the white settlers do not have an obvious place to which to return (though there are available areas for emigration), and the grievances of the non-Europeans are obviously worse than in Algeria. Do we intervene now or after the bloodbath starts? Do we insist on a solution now, or after the Communists gain greater influence among the Africans, and other African nations also covertly intervene?

The objections to such intervention can be phrased in terms applicable to both the Republic of South Africa and other similar areas. Is the United States to intervene in the domestic affairs of countries with which we have satisfactory foreign relations? Are we to intervene wherever men are oppressed and exploited? Do we not establish a mischievous breach in international law if we proclaim our right to overthrow tyrants who, however brutal at home, trespass on none of their neighbors? After all, we do not intervene against Communism because it is tyrannous, but because it is expansionist and threatening us. If precautionary intervention from outside seems prudent, should it not be reserved for the collective action of the states of the region or, when that appears infeasible, the United Nations?

The contrary position is not destroyed by these arguments, however. The various regions of the world suffer from various limitations in handling precautionary intervention by agreement among their constituent states. Neither Asia as such, nor any important subregion within it, possesses the requisite unity for this kind of joint positive action. Africa might be able to act in unison, but only against European, not African, leadership on that continent. The Americas cannot act without us, and might not act with us. U.N. action, affected by these differences among and within regions, therefore depends powerfully on the response of the United States. What do we stand for in the world? We no longer, to be sure, intervene to collect our debts. Some of our best friends are now our debtors. But shall we only intervene against tyranny which expands abroad, and take obviously milder measures against other evils, so that we seem to become champions of the *status quo* while the USSR makes itself the champion of racial equality and the abolition of poverty and exploitation?

I am not yet sure how to resolve all these questions, in principle. When it comes to practice, however, I am certain that the gassing of millions of human beings, or the official suppression of elemental human rights for millions of others because of the color of their skin, must not be placed beyond remedy as a "domestic issue." I must confess that I liked very much the last paragraph of President Kennedy's letter answering Chairman Khrushchev's protest against our 1961 Cuban intervention: "I believe, Mr. Chairman, that you should recognize that free people in all parts of the world do not accept the claim of historical inevitability for Communist revolution. What your government believes is its business; what it does in the world is the world's business. The great revolution in the history of man, past, present and future, is the revolution of those determined to be free." [10] But the letter ends at that point, and the operating clause that would show how this statement could be made effective is missing, just as it was from the Cuban intervention in the Bay of Pigs.

I think it may be possible, however, to distinguish among (1) countries which, despite tyranny (or its obverse, instability), are yet some distance from internal warfare involving extremists, or foreign adventurism inviting aggression; (2) countries which, like Ataturk's Turkey, have chosen an authoritarian road that is intended to lead to democracy; and (3) countries which, like the Republic of South Africa, are clearly heading for the kind of catastrophic internal or external explosion that will make intervention by outside powers unavoidable. In the first two categories, the United States might well undertake the kind of joint precautionary and constructive diplomatic and economic measures that constitute *intervention in partnership*,[11] even though the disparity of power and needs between the collaborating parties seldom permits this kind of partnership to proceed without friction. In this sense, the "Alliance for Progress" with Latin America is an agreement giving the United States and other participating states the right to create effective pressures for altering the social, economic, and political structure of Latin American states for the sake of ultimately putting an end to tyranny, instability, and poverty. In the third category of countries, is not the real choice between precautionary intervention and subsequent intervention under much more unfavorable terms? Our little-publicized but morally and politically sound intervention against the Trujillo dictatorship in the Dominican Republic soon after our Cuban

[10] *New York Herald Tribune*, April 9, 1961.

[11] In the pamphlet published as an earlier version of this essay, I had designated this kind of action more cumbersomely as "positively accepted intervention."

fiasco demonstrates our ability to act prudently despite encumbrances in the realm of precautionary intervention.

There are other forms of intervention. One is equivalent to bearbaiting without invitation in other people's gardens—as when, for a time, we subsidized Chinese Nationalist troops on Burmese soil—but it would not be rewarding to explore further in that direction. Another is constructive, though it seldom earns credit in the short run, as when we inject ourselves powerfully as arbiters in disputes that touch us only because they divide two countries friendly with us. Espionage is also a form of intervention when it involves entering without permission into areas, on the ground or in the air, that fall under the national jurisdiction of other states. This kind of intervention, having the commendable purpose of expanding the world's knowledge, is based upon rules of the game implicitly agreed upon among nations. As an activity, it damages the international system less than adultery damages the institution of marriage. Like adultery, it damages the formal system of intercourse whenever the culprit is caught or insists on publicly championing his right to adultery. That was our compounded sin in the U-2 incident. Unlike adultery, which can damage most by the act itself—that is, by betraying love and trust—no love or trust is present to be undermined in the international system, a vital point to which we shall return in our conclusion.

V. *Toward the Limitation of Intervention*

Surely it is a symptom of the aberrant state of the world that the preceding section might well have been entitled, "Toward a Wise and Just American Intervention in the Internal Affairs of Other Nations." I submit that such a discussion is necessary, but I cannot bring myself to suppose that it would be wise or just to stop here. No state has the sovereign right to intervene in the internal affairs of another sovereign state. Such a "right" is not merely a contradiction in terms but an attack on the very system on which the freedom of every nation rests. It cannot be dismissed as a "mere" breach of international law. It undermines the very structure of a world order which is most imperfect, but in whose survival we have a far greater stake than does the USSR; for, unlike the intended Communist international system, the present international order contains the actuality of national freedom and the potentiality of voluntary collaboration.

We have two choices especially worth discussing. We can accept the world as a jungle in which right and wrong do not apply but only survival matters, and we concentrate on improving the skill and thrust of our power. Since we are still in a jungle, it would be foolish not to do so. But since we do not want to remain where we are, since our very lingering is likely to spell our doom, we must also act to limit the terms of the competition and enlarge the effective power of law.

At the moment we are doing badly. We accept as inescapable the proposition that the challenge posed by the USSR gives us the right and duty to intervene, and that we can deny the same right of intervention to the USSR by threatening to escalate the kind of forces we shall enlist in the fray.[12] To ease the burden

[12] The following quotations illustrate our position. On our right to counter Soviet interventions: "Let the record show that our restraint is not inexhaustible. . . . This Government will not hesitate in meeting its primary obligations, which are to the security of our Nation." (President Kennedy, "The Lesson of Cuba," *Department of State Bulletin*, xliv [May 8, 1961], p. 659.) On the USSR's claiming the same rights: "If you consider yourself to be in the right to implement such measures against Cuba which have been lately taken by the United States of America, you must admit that other countries, also, do not have lesser reason to act in a similar manner in relation to states on whose territories preparations are actually being made which represent a threat against the security of the Soviet Union. If you do not wish to sin against elementary logic, you evidently must admit such a right to other states." (Mr. Khrushchev's Message to President Kennedy, *ibid.*, p. 665.) On escalation: "We are resolved," said Secretary of Defense Robert S. McNamara, "to continue the struggle in all its forms," coping with Soviet long-range ballistic missiles armed with nuclear warheads as well as subversion and indirect warfare, "until such a time as the Communist leaders, both Soviet and Chinese, are convinced that their aggressive policies, motivated by their drive to communize the world, endanger their security as well as ours." (*New York Times*, January 20, 1962.)

and danger of our vigilante activities in a lawless world, we have tried several methods. We have tried to explain to the world the superior justice of our cause. Most people might well grant that ours is a better country to live in than the USSR, but the appreciation of the justice of our cause has often been marred by the kind of interventions by which we have tried to translate justice into practice and by our declarations—perhaps justifiable on other grounds but certainly far more frightening than any uttered by the USSR—about the risks we would take in behalf of justice. And though some are tempted, there is one attitude toward the justice of our cause which we cannot afford to adopt. "Intimidation," Trotsky wrote, "is a powerful weapon of policy, both internationally and internally. . . . The revolution works the same way: it kills individuals, and intimidates thousands. . . . 'But, in that case, in what do your tactics differ from the tactics of Tsarism?' we are asked by the high priests of Liberalism. . . . You do not understand this, holy men? We shall explain it to you. The terror of Tsarism was directed against the proletariat. . . . Our Extraordinary Commissions shoot landlords, capitalists, and generals who are striving to restore the capitalist order. Do you grasp this—distinction? Yes? For us Communists it is quite sufficient. . . ." [13] Should means no longer matter to us, justice will become a remote question.

We have also tried to ease our burden by emphasizing order above social change, taking care to improve the repressive machinery of other governments, and employing economic aid to diminish the political violence which often topples rulers in rapid succession in Asia, Africa, and Latin America. We have often neglected, however, to develop the political enterprise by which they and we might limit the international consequences of such internal warfare. By giving priority to order, we found it more difficult to seize such political initiative, for

[13] Trotsky, *Terrorism and Communism, 1920;* English translation, *Dictatorship vs. Democracy: A Reply to Karl Kautsky* (New York: Workers' Party of America, 1922), pp. 54, 57–59.

while it is true that control of rapid social change itself requires strong, stable authority, such resilient stability is unlikely to arise in most underdeveloped areas until many more fundamental changes have taken place.

In a similar vein, we have championed world law without adequate study of how law might play a constructive role in a rapidly and fundamentally changing world. Our concept of law is fit largely for a world in which political conflicts no longer touch the very purpose and character of life. We have, moreover, failed to live up to international law which we have helped to shape.[14] For example, we agreed in Article 15 of the Charter of Bogotá (1948) that "no state or group of states has the right to intervene directly or indirectly, for any reason whatever, in the internal or external affairs of any other state. The foregoing principle prohibits not only armed attack but also any other form of interference or attempted threat against the personality of the state or against the political, economic and cultural elements." In Article 16, we agreed that "no state may use or encourage the use of coercive measures of an economic or political character in order to force the sovereign will of another state or obtain from it advantages of any kind."

It is true that in subsequent treaties we and the Latin Americans agreed on collective intervention against the encroachments of communism in this hemisphere, that we and they could not agree on effective action against Guatemala and Cuba, and that we therefore had no alternative, as our government saw it, but to proceed unilaterally against a danger condemned in principle by collective agreement. I would not

[14] I am greatly indebted for insights into the relationship of international law to the politics and morality of intervention, and for information, to three contributions by Professor Richard A. Falk: "The United States and the Doctrine of Non-Intervention in the Internal Affairs of Independent States," *Howard Law Journal*, v (June 1959), pp. 163–89; "American Intervention in Cuba and the Rule of Law," *Ohio State Law Journal*, xxii (Summer 1961), pp. 546–85; and *Law, Morality, and War in the Contemporary World* (New York: Frederick A. Praeger, 1963).

worry so much about such a few, somewhat ambiguous breaches of law—hope, patience, and fortitude have sustained the international system as much as law, and these are not as gravely damaged yet by such actions as is the law—except that I foresee no end to such breaches, and it is this which makes me fearful. We have already reached a dangerous point. After our Lebanese intervention, our Secretary of State, forgetful of the origins of our travail, thought of asking for a U.N. resolution against "indirect aggression," but relented when he remembered how vulnerable we would be both in the debate and through the intended law.

One may sympathize with those who would judge our record in this field with some forbearance, pointing out that our nation has only recently arrived fully as a world power. (Our interventions prior to World War II had an impact only on our immediate region and only an indirect effect on the world order.) But one must not sympathize too long, for we shall not be given much time to learn our lessons. It is imperative to move on, if not yet to world government, at least to a system based on self-restraint, constructive forms of intervention, and a broader overlap of national interests.

I do not think such a movement is impossible. Self-restraint would mean, for example, rejecting Edmond Taylor's recent proposal in *The Reporter* for "encouraging and explicitly accepting responsibility for the revolutionary forces behind the Iron Curtain. . . . We should oppose only premature and uncoordinated insurrections." [15] It would mean curing ourselves of the anxious and dogmatic aggressiveness that has caused us to intervene against neutralists and authoritarian socialists in usually unjustified fear of the next stage in their development. It would require us not to treat every Communist challenge—as in 1961 in Cuba—as an issue of survival, and not to turn any confrontation that could affect survival into alternatives that must lead either to complete victory or complete defeat.

[15] *The Reporter,* September 14, 1961.

Such a strategy would also involve forbearance when non-Communists challenge the *status quo*. Imposing the high standards of American political comfort on the rest of the world, we have scarcely paused to be surprised by how the passing of traditional society has been accompanied by far less violence in most of Asia, Africa, and Latin America than during a similar period in Western Europe. But we must not expect this historical transformation to be an entirely peaceful event, nor prepare to intervene whenever it is not.

We shall have to be more tolerant of violence connected with the end of the system of colonial domination than with violence threatening the system which governs the relationship among independent states. (India's usually justifiably high ideals have often fallen short of India's sometimes justifiable and sometimes unjustifiable practices. Our reaction to Goa, however, was an idealistic exaggeration, unmindful of the distinction I have suggested.) I believe we should insist that the arbitrary and artificial frontiers drawn by Europeans for African and Middle Eastern states must not be altered by direct aggression, but forbearance of a kind unjustified in Europe may also be in order when such kindred peoples intervene, short of aggression, in each other's affairs. We need neither become involved in their rivalries nor protect them from such excesses in their attempts to achieve unity. Counter-intervention would be justified, however, to keep other Great Powers from exploiting such rearrangements.

Above all, we need to rid ourselves of the erroneous notion that whenever a privileged Western position in Asia, Africa, or Latin America is lost, the USSR correspondingly gains. The conversion of a pro-Western nation like Iraq to neutralism is not a loss to the West. On the contrary, it usually rids the West of a discreditable relationship and, in bringing about a neutralist state, creates a situation with which we, by virtue of our sense of world order, can live but which the USSR is pledged to alter. Whether our subsequent relationship with a former client state is satisfactory or not depends on our mutual ability to transform our relationship by cementing overlapping national interests and enhancing such a country's internal stability.

That brings us to the second major task in moving toward a more lawful world—namely, finding more constructive forms of intervention. Self-restraint may be helpful in reducing instability and tension within the international system as a whole, but it cannot prevent or cure the internal conflicts within countries of the non-Communist world that incite the interventions of the Great Powers. We also need to develop wiser and more just forms of precautionary intervention and counter-intervention.

A number of possibilities may be suggested. Diplomacy and, at worst, the threat of unilateral intervention may be employed for the specific purpose of persuading the reluctant smaller nations of a region to act or even intervene collectively themselves in order to avoid the intervention of a Great Power. This, after much waste motion, was the final outcome in Lebanon when all the usually disunited Arab states agreed not to intervene, and was achieved even more effectively and with greater dispatch in Kuwait when the Arab states agreed collectively to protect that country against Iraqi intervention. Increasingly it may be possible to parlay the threat of Great Power intervention, as in the Congo, or earlier in Lebanon, into U.N. intervention.[16] Since Great Power intervention is initially masked in most instances, and there is no international law-enforcement agency that can investigate and act in time, the counter-intervention may have to be initiated by the United States. But such action should from the first moment be accompanied by a pledge to withdraw as soon as a U.N. or regional peace force can take its place, while those employing force under the duress

[16] What cannot be used as an effective threat, however, is collective intervention by NATO in the non-European and non-Communist areas of the world. Those who would neglect the U.N. in favor of NATO do not appreciate the limited usefulness of common action by the white partners of a military alliance in the rest of the world.

or discipline of a great foreign power withdraw their threat.[17] An international police force should therefore be organized so as to be in constant readiness.

Precautionary intervention could also be internationalized to a considerable degree. Societies that are already deeply split politically and therefore are unwilling to become dependent on a single Great Power should be helped in larger (and not merely technical) measure through the U.N.[18] Aid from the USSR should also be welcomed, even for joint projects, for what counts is not the source of the money and not even the prestige it earns for a foreign power, but the constructive use to which it is put inside the country.

Neither our self-restraint nor more constructive forms of intervention will help, however, unless the USSR reciprocates in like fashion. Is there any hope that the two powers might develop and enlarge an overlap of national interests in the realm of intervention? It is just such reciprocity that finally creates international law. Fortunately, such an overlap already exists to a significant degree, though amid the sound and fury we have paid little attention to it.

We are now operating on implicit rules that keep the USSR from intervening in sufficient measure within the Western community and the Western Hemisphere to make it the decisive force in placing its local men in power and protecting them there. We have accepted the same restrictions within the Soviet satellite area. This does not mean that the Soviets or the

[17] It will be noted that I speak only of intervention against elements employing *force* under the duress or discipline of a *great* foreign power. Threats from smaller nations can surely be handled in less spectacular ways. In restricting counter-intervention to a reply against force, I should like to reject the other alternative with entire clarity. If, as a result of an inadequate performance by democratic forces in India and the West, for example, Indians turn to communism in a free election, I would not for a moment regard the forceful reconversion of India into a Western colony as a morally justifiable or politically prudent alternative.

[18] For a discussion of problems of political therapy involved in U.N. intervention, see Manfred Halpern, "The U.N. in the Congo," *worldview*, Vol. 6 (October 1963), pp. 4–8.

West refrain from intervening in each other's realm in a great many other ways. But Hungary and Cuba indicate the limits of the game with precision. In October 1962, it had clearly become necessary to take bold measures to remind the USSR of these tacit rules as they affect Cuba. Moscow agreed with no resistance and little delay. We, however, offered only to pledge ourselves not to undertake an outright invasion.

In the uncommitted but hitherto non-Communist areas of the world, the USSR is willing to take risks, but not as many as we do in intervening. We have never been deterred from intervention in these areas by fear of the Soviet reaction. By contrast, in several instances where the USSR had excellent opportunities for assisting Communists in seizing control (as in Iran in 1953, Syria in 1955–1958, and Iraq in 1958–1960),[19] the USSR restrained itself for fear of the international consequences. It is also noteworthy that the USSR no less than the smaller states in the U.N. agreed that it would be better, even after the murder of the undoubtedly popular Lumumba, to let Congolese fight each other as Congolese rather than as Great Power puppets. Nor are these instances accidental. One of the chief conflicts between the USSR and China concerns the risks the USSR does not think it prudent to take in assisting "national wars of liberation."

What can we do to harden and to multiply the number of these restricting rules of the game? The first (there is no avoiding it) must be to keep ourselves strong enough to convince the USSR, and increasingly also China, that the risks of intervention on their part remain too high to allow them to take chances. Secondly, we must take diplomatic initiatives to reduce the incitements to intervention. It might be useful to explore, for example, whether it would help to agree to neu-

[19] For detailed documentation of this point, see my essay on "The Middle East and North Africa," in Cyril E. Black and Thomas P. Thornton (eds.), *Communism and Revolution* (Princeton: Princeton University Press, 1964).

tralize the Middle East—outlawing all foreign military alliances and foreign bases, agreeing on limitations of arms shipments to the area, and on collective steps from outside to prevent any border from being changed by military aggression.[20] Such steps might lessen tensions within the region, allow a major shift of local resources from military preparedness to projects that could enhance economic, social, and political stability, lessen the dangers flowing from actual Communist involvement in locally endemic *coups d'état* from reaching the dimensions of a serious crisis, and restrict the possible need for counter-interventions to those more generally acceptable to the international community—namely, to keep neutrals from being subverted from their neutrality.

It would indeed serve to improve international order for us to help all non-Communist states, whether neutralist or not, to cope with the unbalancing forces of uncontrolled social change and so help them lay foundations on which to build independent and responsible foreign and domestic policies. However much we may prefer a policy of close alignment, it might well be acknowledged that the great majority of neutralists in Asia and Africa have demonstrated both the will and the skill to make sure that both the West and the Communist bloc remain on hand competing for advantage among them, each ensuring that the other shall not gain predominance in the area. The interplay of these countervailing forces, and the extraordinary nationalist sensitivity of these new states to any new form of colonialism, constitute powerful new forces at work since the 1950's in restricting the intervention of the Great Powers. The weaker nations of the world are thus for the first time beginning to help define the rules of international relationships.[21]

[20] Between 1956 and 1958, the USSR several times publicly indicated its interest in such a proposal.

[21] In the realm of intervention, as one perceptive member of the Department of State has pointed out, these new rules of the game demand far more skill and prudence than the old. For example, for a Great Power overtly to extend support to any local faction, whether in the government

Among diplomatic initiatives, it might also be worth exploring whether our explicit acknowledgment of the *status quo* in Eastern Europe might have two worthwhile consequences. It could help to institutionalize the rules of the game of intervention. It might also have a more fundamental outcome. By diminishing our pressure on Eastern Europe, we would make it harder for the foes of relaxed controls within the Communist world to justify their position, and thus we might help ultimately both to ease the pressures within the Soviet elite for adventurous interventions abroad and ease pressures for conformity among the satellites. Accepting the *status quo* might thus make changes in the *status quo* more likely—and thus become a most constructive form of intervention.

The USSR is unlikely in the foreseeable future to accept our conception of international order. Though the threat which Soviet behavior thus raises for us may tempt us to copy Soviet techniques, it behooves us instead to work harder by far to attain standards of world law and justice to which the uncommitted might be won, and which the USSR could ignore only at the cost of incurring international sanctions.

This task is no longer as easy as it might have sounded in the 1920's. Today it is painfully apparent that the demands of international law and international justice do not yet coincide—in part, because the old historical order which molded our present standards has become dangerously fragile; in part, because our present standards are not shared by our principal adversary, or even by all the rest of the world. To argue that in such a world our self-interest and what we hold to be our superior values

or the opposition, may in this highly nationalist environment turn out to be the kiss of death. In a world in which the Soviet bloc has become an alternate source of support and supplies, we may also not always be able to afford to let a country that refuses to abide by the conditions of our aid suffer the consequences. But the more moral and more useful course of action has also become clearer: it is no longer enough to pick a strong man and intervene in his behalf. The politics of social change demand intervention in behalf of *programs* relevant to societies in rapid and fundamental transformation.

justify our intervention, however coercive, as long as it succeeds, is to risk the attainment of the surer morality based on
law for the sake of moralism based on power. It would certainly
lead to a conflict with the USSR in which no holds were barred
except on grounds of inefficiency, and hence the present difference in values between us would cease. To argue, on the other
hand, that until intervention achieves in the international order
that lawful status which it now possesses in all domestic societies, there should be a moral and political presumption against
intervention abroad, is to champion law at the expense of justice and ultimately to threaten law itself. Let us observe and
insist on respect for national sovereignty, and try to resolve conflicts through bargaining among these sovereignties. But if
national sovereignty is threatened, or itself clearly threatens
peace, freedom, or justice, wisdom demands intervention, but
in such forms as will best enhance these values and improve the
opportunities for the growth of an international order in which
these values could endure.

VI. *God, Man, and the Purpose of Intervention*

This essay must not end, however, without speaking of two elements which have so far been ignored in this analysis of the
morality of intervention. We have talked only about national
states. We have said nothing about the human being as individual and nothing about God.

The Austrian writer Kraus gave the last line in one of his
plays to God, who, contemplating the destruction of the world
proceeding under his eyes, declared, "I did not will it." A recent
writer in *worldview* has wondered whether nuclear death might
not save more Christian souls for eternal life than life under
atheistic communism. I hesitate to conclude that any man
could know God's earthly preferences with such precision. We
have been given the capacity to distinguish life that is based on
loving one's neighbor from life based on killing him or being
indifferent to him. This is the core of our knowledge and of our

guide to action; the rest is deduction, induction, or dogmatic assertion. We also know how fragile, uncertain, and even absurd this knowledge is, for God has obviously left himself free not only to love but to destroy.

I have therefore spoken in this essay only about our responsibility to act wisely, justly, and with love. I think it is most fortunate for the potentials of justice in international relations that this responsibility arises whether one believes in God or not. It would be fearful if it were not so, for the world which is unlikely to be converted soon to the same view of intervention is even less likely to be converted soon to the same theology. Some men also know how this fits in with God's plans, but I believe that our inescapable ignorance on this subject imposes (as does faith in God) the added responsibility of humility in international relations.

If we commonly err by confusing God's will with our concrete aims in foreign policy, we usually also err by ignoring the existence of concrete individual human beings in discussing the justice of foreign interventions by the abstract collectivity known as the nation-state. If law is not yet an alternative to force in international relations, and indeed requires force, law cannot rest on force alone. The moral individual, however, will not be content with justice; he will prefer a world in which public authority establishes an area of security and justice in which love becomes possible. Instead, he is often confronted by the obvious idiocy of politics in which, to take a recent example, his family is shelled only on odd days on an offshore island that has no military value in preparation for interventions which neither side is in a position to pursue. He knows that interventions are concerned with issues of national power far more often than with poverty, tyranny, or exploitation. As if in compensation for this neglect of the daily concerns of most men, his national leaders make policies based in part on estimates of the personal sincerity or trust or good will of a Nasser or Eden, as if international relations already allowed for more than the identification and enhancement of common national interests. What we share with any rational leaders, whatever their personal morality, is a common interest in the right of their nations to establish foundations which will allow them (and all other nations) to pursue responsibly independent foreign and domestic policies. In such a common interest lie the potentials both for public justice among nations and for personal dignity and love among individuals within nations.

The technicians of power, having shrewdly rejected the illusion that national and individual morality are automatically the same, stop short and do not see that the unfinished task is to relate national purpose to the kind of international justice that gives security and freedom for justice and love to develop among individuals. Indeed, they tend through the prestigious position of their manipulative power to diminish the citizen's concern with love, until he feels embarrassed by the very mention of it in a context of power. In the insecure world in which we live, national loyalty and solidarity have become more precious to most peoples than justice and love. Still, the existence of a nation, any nation, is not justified except as it and its interventions preserve and enhance the individual's capacity to be wise, just, and to love. Mere security can most cheaply be purchased by surrender.

APPENDIX A

International Aspects of Internal War: A Working Paper

☆

BY JAMES N. ROSENAU

THE PURPOSE of this paper is twofold: to clarify what the *international* aspects of internal war are (i.e., into what analytic categories the subject should be divided) and to indicate the directions in which theory and research might be channeled. In pursuing the latter goal, concrete propositions have been presented throughout. These propositions are meant to be only suggestive and would require considerable elaboration in order to be made susceptible to empirical verification.

I

It is doubtful whether a single theory or framework can encompass the international aspects of internal war. If these aspects are to be sought in the behavioral and/or perceptual linkages between a war-torn society and its external environment,[1] these linkages involve too many units acting and perceiving in too many ways to allow for the development of a simple over-all scheme. Hence conceptualization must depend on the action units and the perceptual processes which the observer selects as his foci. In this analysis the flow of action (→) and perception (– – →) across the boundary between a war-torn society and its external environment is viewed as going in two directions, and the units on each side of the boundary are analyzed in both systemic and subsystemic terms. This means that the international system and its national subsystems must be treated as actors on the environment side of the boundary, and that the other side consists of the war-torn society treated as a system and its warring factions treated as subsystems. If these four kinds of actors are viewed as both initiators and recipients of action and/or perception that cross the boundary of a war-torn society, then the sixteen possible linkages between the four initiators and the four recipients

---

[1] A behavioral linkage consists of direct interaction between two or more actors. A perceptual linkage does not involve direct interaction, but consists of an indirect process wherein one of the actors bases his actions on what he perceives to be the capabilities, motives, and/or future behavior of the other actors. In what follows, these linkages are called "actions" and "perceptions."

represent the minimum number of international aspects of internal war that can be identified and studied.[2]

The derivation of these sixteen aspects is most easily seen by positing a simplified model of the international system, one that is composed of three nations (subsystems [A], [B], and [C]), each of which in turn consists of two factions, the "ins" [i] who control the government and the "outs" [o] who do not. Let us further postulate that both [A] and [B] are peaceful nations in which the two factions either are not contesting each other or are doing so through legitimate nonviolent means, but that [C] is a war-torn society in which the ins and the outs have resorted to violence to settle their differences.

When this model is viewed in systemic and subsystemic terms, the four main actors become:

$[C_i]$ and $[C_o]$,	the factions in the war-torn society;
$[C_i \leftrightarrow C_o]$,	the war-torn society treated as a national subsystem;
$[A_{io}]$ and $[B_{io}]$,	the other nations treated as national subsystems;
$[A_{io} \leftrightarrow B_{io}]$ and/or $[AB]$,	the other nations treated as an international system (and consisting of their direct interactions and/or those that occur in international organizations).[3]

If we now introduce the distinction between the boundary-crossing actions and/or perceptions which each of these actors initiate (henceforth called outputs) and those which they experience (henceforth called inputs), the derivation of the sixteen possible international aspects of internal war logically follows, as shown in Figure 1.

II

Before undertaking an analysis of the sixteen linkages, however, we must look at their component parts. Each output or input of an actor is determined by variables within it, as well as by variables in the kind of actor to which the input or output is linked. The impact of a particular internal war on a particular national subsystem, for example, partly depends on the nature of the other society, but it also is a result of the kind of war that is being waged. There are, in other words, independent characteristics of the four actors as initiators and

[2] However, this is not to say that the sixteen aspects are equally interesting or important. For example, several of the sixteen will doubtless be of more interest to students of internal war strategy than to specialists in international politics.

[3] Strictly speaking, nation [C] is also part of the international system and its international organization, but for simplicity in the presentation this point has been ignored.

FIGURE 1

as recipients of action and/or perception that need to be at least briefly noted before we can analyze the linkages between them. To state the problem in terms of Figure 1, while we eventually wish to analyze the different entries in each of the sixteen cells, first we must identify what are likely to be the major phenomena represented by the common symbols on the left-hand side of the four cells in each column and on the right-hand side of the four cells in each row. Let us start with the columns (what can be called, respectively, factional, war, national, and system outputs), and then proceed to the rows (factional, war, national, and system inputs).

Factional Outputs

Whether they are incumbents or insurgents, parties to internal wars are likely to engage in boundary-crossing actions which have perceptions as inputs. Moreover, even when they are inactive in this respect, factions can often serve as the source of perceptions which extend beyond societal boundaries by virtue of their very existence as warring organizations. The likelihood of factional output arises out of a potential or actual necessity for $[C_i]$ and $[C_o]$ to procure support, both moral and substantive, from abroad for their internal war efforts. Although legally only the incumbents are entitled to represent the interests of the war-torn society externally, the insurgents that survive the initial stages of combat can also be expected to develop foreign policies and to maintain foreign relations.

The nature of both the actions and the perceptions initiated by a warring faction will be shaped by several variables such as its present and potential military capacity, its geographic location, its history and traditions, its ideology and war aims, its solidarity and morale, its authority and decision-making structure, and its popularity among the uncommitted elements of the society. The identification and comparison of these variables would make a suitable subject for a separate inquiry. The following are examples of propositions which such an inquiry might explore: Other things (inputs) being equal,

1. Insurgents fighting for civil liberties or other universal values will produce more outputs than those seeking to satisfy local grievances by replacing an unpopular group of insurgents.
2. Incumbents in large countries, feeling they have the resources and ability to maintain control over the course of events at home, will initiate fewer outputs than will their less confident counterparts in small countries.

War Outputs

The most important outputs of war-torn societies treated as national subsystems are, as outlined below, the *perceptions* that flow from the nature and changing state of the hostilities. Yet, note needs to be taken of the possibility that internal wars may also be the source of *action* outputs. At first glance it appears inconsistent to think of war-torn societies engaging in action beyond their boundaries. Such divided societies would seem incapable of acting as units. But it is not difficult to imagine an internal war in which the incumbents and insurgents cooperate sufficiently to produce a common posture toward certain events or trends in the outside world. A war between two strongly anti-Communist factions might be an illustration of this possibility. Without any written or verbal arrangement, both sides might agree that neither would accept or seek outside aid from the Soviet Union. (The longer the war, of course, the less likelihood that the agreement would be maintained.) [4]

While the degree of cooperation between two warring factions can thus be regarded as a war output variable, it is the characteristics of the conflict between them that constitute the main outputs of war-torn societies. For the existence, nature, and course of the war in a nation can produce a variety of perceptions that extend across its boundaries. Two variables stand out as especially important. One involves the state of the war (including its past and potential course through time as well as its present state). Obviously, a stalemated war will have different boundary-crossing consequences than one in which victory for one faction appears imminent.

Perhaps the most important war output involves the purposes for which the hostilities are being waged. Not only do the war goals of the combatants shape the inception, intensity, duration, and termination of the conflict, but they also strongly affect the posture of other actors toward the war. As indicated in Chapter 3, internal wars can be classified in terms of three general types of conflict: personnel, authority, and structural wars. The differences between these types suggest a variety of propositions about war outputs that need to be developed. For example, other things (inputs) being equal, the following two statements seem reasonable:

1. Structural wars (waged for a cluster of universal values) will foster more boundary-crossing perceptions than will authority wars (fought over a single universal value); and the latter will stimulate such perceptions more than will personnel wars (fought over values which are idiosyncratic and local).

2. The closer internal wars come to a conclusion, the more action

[4] An empirical trace of the hypothetical possibility of joint action by $[C_i]$ and $[C_o]$ can be discerned in the meetings that representatives of the warring factions in both Laos and the Congo held on neutral territory. These meetings were primarily concerned with finding a basis for terminating hostilities, but they also seem to have attempted to establish rules for dealing with outside intervention.

outputs they will produce; and the greater the number of values for which a war is being fought, the faster the outputs will mount up. That is, the rate of outputs will be greater in structural wars than in authority wars and in authority wars than in personnel wars.

National Outputs

Since internal wars are characterized by violent and rapid social change, they breed uncertainty as to whether they will adversely affect the welfare of other nations. The latter will therefore be inclined to adopt policies toward the war unfolding in [C] and, even if they do not, the potentiality of their intervention can serve as boundary-crossing outputs.

The size, geographic location, history, foreign policy commitments, political structure, resources, and values of nations [A] and [B] exemplify the kinds of variables which may determine the form and extent of the actions and perceptions which they initiate. The following are illustrative of propositions that might be explored relative to national output variables: Other things (inputs) being equal,

1. Nations located close to [C], having more varied and extensive concerns about its future, will do more to affect the outcome of the war than will more distant nations.
2. Leaders of authoritarian societies, being freer of internal restraints, are more likely to intervene on behalf of an insurgent faction than are leaders in democratic societies.
3. Small nations, having fewer and less complex international responsibilities, are more likely to take an explicit stand toward internal wars than are large nations.

System Outputs

Both actions and perceptions of the international system can flow across the boundaries of war-torn societies. Outputs take the form of action when international organizations become inextricably involved in internal wars. The communiqués of a conference of neutralist leaders, the resolutions of the O.A.S., the decisions of NATO's Council of Ministers, the debates of the U.N. General Assembly, and the actions of its Secretary-General are illustrative of system outputs. They also indicate that system outputs constitute an area in which research could be fruitfully undertaken. For example, propositions such as these might be developed and tested: Other things (inputs) being equal,

1. The more unanimous are the members of an international organization toward events occurring in [C], the greater that organization's outputs will be.

2. If a member of an international organization is experiencing an internal war, the more dominant the role ordinarily played by the war-torn member in the organization's deliberations, the fewer will the outputs of the organization be.

3. The older an international organization is, the fewer its outputs will be.

Perhaps no less important than the actions of international organizations are the boundary-crossing perceptions of the international system. These outputs would seem to be mainly of two kinds: normative and political.

The range of normative outputs is extensive and extends over much of the field of international law. The form of intervention in a conflict, the kind of refuge and assistance provided or denied the insurgents, the activities of diplomats stationed in the war-torn country—these are but a few of the matters in which the behavior of both other nations and the warring factions are influenced by normative limits.

The political outputs of the system can also be of many kinds. Obviously the support which the warring factions are able to procure from the external environment can be shaped in a variety of ways by different systemic states (balance of power, loose bipolar, etc.) and different degrees of stability. It seems reasonable to speculate, for example, that as an internal war becomes increasingly internationalized, there is a point at which it threatens the stability of the system; and thus other nations may tacitly agree to impose limits on their own intervention. Indeed, the same processes whereby limited international wars are contained probably also operate to prevent the escalation of internal wars, and thus an attempt to apply limited war theory to internal wars emerges as another worthwhile undertaking.

Factional Inputs

Any changes in $[C_i]$ or $[C_o]$ which result from the boundary-crossing outputs of other actors are regarded as factional inputs. Such inputs, however, are not entirely determined by the nature of the outputs; they can be shaped at least as much by characteristics inherent in $[C_i]$ or $[C_o]$. Warring factions differ in their military capabilities, geographic locations and physical resources, histories and traditions, ideologies and war aims, solidarities and decision-making structures. Clearly, all of these variables, plus a host of others, can determine how outputs will be translated into factional inputs. It seems likely, for example, that the capabilities of warring factions are more susceptible to change than are their authority structures. The very fact of being engaged in violent battle serves to foster unity and to diminish the disrupting structural effects of external action. This would seem to be particularly true in the case of insurgent groups, although the resistance of the Vietnamese government to U.S.-sponsored structural reforms suggests that incumbents are not much less rigid in this respect. At a more general level, analyses of factional inputs might be concerned with propositions such as these: Other things (outputs) being equal,

1. Incumbent factions, in control of the formal apparatus of the society and thus more bound by legal precedent and historical tradition, will experience fewer inputs than will insurgent factions.

2. The solidarity and morale of insurgent groups, being invigorated by the special risks and rewards involved in a challenge to established authority, will be less vulnerable to inputs than will the cohesiveness and commitment of incumbent factions.

3. Geographically isolated and militarily weak insurgents, seemingly unlikely to take over the reigns of government in the foreseeable future, will be the recipients of fewer inputs than will those who are strong and widely dispersed.

War Inputs

Any alterations in the relationship between $[C_i]$ and $[C_o]$ which stem from boundary-crossing outputs are considered to be war inputs. Shifts in the lines of battle, changes in the intensity and scope of hostilities, and modifications in the prospects and/or processes of negotiations to end the conflict are obvious examples of phenomena which might be linked to external sources and would thus be classified as war inputs. But of course the nature of the inputs is not fully shaped by the outputs to which they are linked. As internal wars near an end, for example, they are probably less susceptible to inputs than they are during the early stages of conflict. The size, geographic location, history, and other characteristics of the war-torn society may also shape the kinds of inputs it experiences. Inquiries into war inputs might thus develop and analyze propositions of this sort: Other things (outputs) being equal,

1. Personnel wars, being fought for a limited set of values, will receive fewer inputs than will authority wars, and the latter will receive fewer than will structural wars.

2. War-torn societies with a long history of personnel wars will experience fewer inputs than will those in which such events have not been a recurring pattern.

3. Authority wars in large countries will absorb more inputs than will such wars in small countries, but structural wars in small countries, involving as they do a wider range of values and a greater potentiality of policy shifts, will experience more inputs than will authority wars in large nations.

296

National Inputs

If outputs crossing the boundary of [C] alter the capabilities, structure, and/or functioning of [A] or [B], these changes are regarded as national inputs. Internal wars, for example, can become hotly contested political issues within [A] or [B]. Relations between the ins and outs in these other countries might be affected to the point of compelling [A_i] or [B_i] to revise their policies toward [C]. National inputs can even take the form of revisions in constitutional structure. As illustrated by the events in Angola during the Algerian war for independence, constitutional structures in other societies can be affected by internal wars in which [C_o] is fighting to alleviate conditions similar to those which prevail for [A_o] or [B_o]. Internal wars, in other words, can be contagious, and the processes by which they are "caught" constitute national inputs. Of course, the nature of the inputs which [A] or [B] experience depends on many variables. Such propositions as the following might be developed with respect to national inputs: Other things (outputs) being equal,

1. The closer a nation is located to a war-torn society, the more will it have a stake in the outcome of the conflict and thus the greater will be the inputs it experiences.
2. Nations with authoritarian political structures contain more disaffected factions that are sensitive to uprisings elsewhere than do democratic nations, and thus the former will be the recipients of more inputs than the latter.
3. The greater the cohesiveness of [A] or [B], the fewer will be the inputs it absorbs, but a well-integrated neighbor of [C] will be host to more inputs than will an equally cohesive nation geographically distant from the war-torn society.

System Inputs

While national inputs refer to relationships *within* [A] and [B] that change as a result of boundary-crossing outputs, system inputs are those alterations that occur in the relations *between* other societies. These inputs can be operative at several levels. Changes can occur in the uninstitutionalized interaction patterns among two or more nations; or they can mark the capabilities, structure, and/or functioning of international organizations; or they can take place at the over-all level of the stability and structure of the international system. These different kinds of inputs are illustrated, respectively, by the impact of the Spanish civil war of 1936–1939 on German-Russian relations, by the impact of the Congo crisis on the United Nations, and by the consequences of the Chinese civil war of 1947–1949 for the structure and stability of the international system.

Analysis of system inputs might yield propositions such as these: Other things (outputs) being equal,

1. The more dissimilar [A] and [B] are in their historical traditions and their political structures, the more likely they are to respond differently to the war in [C], and thus the greater will be the inputs their relationship experiences.

2. The wider the authority possessed by the chief executive officer of an international organization, the more his support will be sought by parties concerned about the course of events in [C], and thus the greater will be the inputs absorbed by the organization.

3. The more tightly the international system is organized along bipolar lines, the greater will be the interdependence of its parts and, consequently, the greater the inputs which the system experiences as a result of internal wars.

III

Having outlined the variables which are operative on both sides of the boundary between war-torn societies and their external environments, we can now analyze their links in behavioral and/or causal sequences. It will be recalled that these linkages are regarded as the international aspects of internal war and that they number sixteen, corresponding to the matrix shown in Figure 1. What follows, however, is not meant to be exhaustive. Rather the purpose is to suggest briefly the kinds of phenomena covered by each aspect and the sorts of propositions that might serve as a basis for investigating them.

I. *Factionally Induced National Changes*
(See Cell I in Figure 1)

Inquiries into this aspect would be mainly concerned with how the varying outputs of different factions give rise to varying perceptions within other societies. As the bifurcation of the arrows in Cell I, Figure 1, suggests, the incumbents and insurgents can seek support from the ins and/or the outs in other societies, and in so doing they can increase the tension and competition between factions abroad. Furthermore, as the dotted arrows indicate, the warring factions could become a source of controversy in [A] even if their actions were directed only toward [B]. Here are some more specific propositions with respect to this linkage:

1. Other nations, mindful of present commitments that limit future opportunities, are likely to be more resistant to the procurement efforts of $[C_i]$ and $[C_o]$ if the war-torn society is a large major power than if it is a small minor one.

2. The values that unite a warring faction will serve as the main

298

determinant of the countries or groups from which it seeks support abroad, but these values will be moderated or minimized if, in so doing, the amount of external support can be substantially increased.

3. In their search for outside support, warring factions will, mainly for logistic reasons, be most active and competitive in neighboring countries, and thus the closer a nation is located to a war-torn society, the more will it experience the internal war as a domestic political issue.

II. *War-stimulated National Effects*
(See Cell II in Figure 1)

This aspect focuses mainly upon the ways in which different types of internal wars, or different stages of the same war, foster varying perceptions within other societies. The course of hostilities may serve to exacerbate or otherwise affect the relations between the ins and outs of other societies. Presumably, for example, there would be serious repercussions for $[A_i]$ if the tide of battle shifted against the warring faction to which it had supplied aid and toward which $[A_o]$ was less favorably inclined. Besides the ebb and flow of battle, its intensity and duration might also serve as stimulants of controversy and change within other societies. Conceivably, the more intensely internal wars are waged, the more will groups in other societies become involved, and the more will they become committed to a particular scheme for ending it. Likewise, the more an internal war drags on, the more may groups abroad become impatient, and the more will both the ins and outs of other societies be inclined to press for some kind of resolution of the conflict. Reactions such as these are also likely to be a function of whether a personnel, authority, or structural war is being waged, so that ultimately analyses of the phenomena covered by this aspect would have to come to grips with propositions such as the following:

1. Personnel wars are less likely to create tension between the ins and outs of other societies than are authority wars, but the latter type will not be as tension-producing as will structural wars.

2. Long and intensely waged personnel wars which do not escalate into other types of conflict will probably stimulate more tension within other societies than will brief *coups d'état*, but the former will not foster as much political dislocation in [A] or [B] as will a short authority or structural war which lasts, say, a week or so.

3. Stalemated structural wars (characterized by uncertainty as to how they will end) will produce more tension within demo-

cratic societies abroad than within authoritarian ones, but such tension will not be fostered by structural wars in which the eventual outcome is fairly clear from the outset.

III. *Factional Sources of System Changes*
(See Cell III in Figure 1)

Analyses of this aspect would concentrate on the ways in which differently located, structured, and motivated factions varyingly affect the structure, functioning, and stability of the international system. For example, warring factions must consider how each procurement effort might have international repercussions affecting their future ability to procure external support. Generally, factional foreign policies can affect international relationships in two ways. First, as indicated in Aspect I, the efforts of $[C_i]$ and $[C_o]$ to obtain support abroad can alter relationships within other societies, and these alterations may in turn require [A] or [B] to adopt new policies toward each other. Increased domestic support for insurgents, for example, may force a nation to modify its policies toward an ally which continues to aid the incumbents. Second, even if relations *within* other societies are not affected by the external actions of the warring factions, relations *between* them can be affected by their differential responses to the solicitations of $[C_i]$ and $[C_o]$. The weakening of the Belgian-American relationship that stemmed from contrary responses to the various warring factions in the Congo is an illustration.

Such considerations can be readily extended to the impact of different kinds of factions on various types of international organizations and on the system in general. Certainly, for instance, the Hungarian insurgents in 1956 rendered the over-all system at least momentarily less stable.

That this aspect encompasses a wide range of linkages that can be fruitfully analyzed is further suggested by such propositions as these:

1. The relationship between [A] and [B], being competitive as well as cooperative, is less likely to be affected if only one of them is the target of factional procurement efforts than if support is sought from both nations.
2. Insurgents, being short on claims to national legitimacy, are much more likely to turn to international organizations for support than are incumbents; and the more the former are fighting for civil liberties, the more will such organizations be affected by the factional procurement efforts.
3. The longer a group of insurgents are able to prosecute their war efforts, the greater will be their claim to legitimacy and thus the greater will be their impact upon the stability of the international system.

IV. *War-induced System Changes*
(*See Cell IV in Figure 1*)

This aspect encompasses the varying ways in which different types of internal wars, or different stages of the same war, affect the structure, functioning, and stability of the international system. For the same reasons that relations among nations are likely to be affected by factional procurement efforts (see Aspect III), the international system will probably be altered by the violent interchange between the factions. If, for example, [A] and [B] have respectively given support to [C_i] and [C_o], their relations with each other are bound to be affected as the tide of battle turns in favor of one of the factions; or, if they value their relationship above the outcome of the war in [C], they may both try to prevent the war from becoming one-sided by pressing the faction which they have backed to negotiate a settlement with the other (this latter consequence is also covered by Aspect XV). Much the same could be said about how international organizations are affected by different stages of internal war. Similarly, the over-all equilibrium of the international system is also subject to variation induced by the progress of the war.

The system changes stemming from the issues over which internal wars are fought can be just as extensive as those fostered by shifts in the lines or stages of battle. Clearly authority or structural wars are likely to produce much wider perceptions than personnel wars. The outcome of authority and structural wars, for example, can involve the loss or gain of an ally to other nations. Thus, as illustrated by recent wars in the Congo, Algeria, Cuba, and Laos, enduring authority and structural wars are almost bound to be disruptive of international stability.

The foregoing are only a few of the possible linkages which this important aspect covers. The following propositions indicate other lines of inquiry which might also be pursued:

1. Irrespective of the issues at stake, the longer an internal war lasts, the greater will be the uncertainty it fosters and thus the greater will be its impact on the international system.
2. Authority and structural wars are more likely to occupy the attention of international organizations than are personnel wars, but the more universal the organization, the greater is the likelihood it will be affected by personnel wars.
3. The more unlike are the historical heritages and political structures of [A] and [B], and the closer they are located to [C], the more is a personnel war in the latter likely to introduce strain into their relationship; but the greater their geographic distance from the war-torn society, or the more common their

heritage, the more their relationship becomes susceptible to the impact of only authority and structural wars.

V. Factional Effects of Factional Procurement Efforts
(See Cell V in Figure 1)

Although perhaps as much an internal as an international aspect of internal war, this linkage calls attention to the fact that warring factions may experience change as a result of their own boundary-crossing outputs. The obligations which factions incur in order to procure external support can become a source of dispute among their members. Whether to seek assistance from [A] rather than [B], whether to accept aid proffered by one or the other of them, whether to press for a revision of the terms under which support has been given or offered, whether to turn to the United Nations for aid, whether to sever relations with a country that has responded favorably to the enemy's procurement efforts—these are but a few of the questions which can, so to speak, create subfactions within factions. Further dimensions of this linkage are illustrated by propositions such as these:

1. The more a faction is hierarchically organized, the less are its subgroups likely to challenge the actions of its leadership, and thus the less will the faction experience divisive effects from its own procurement efforts.

2. Foreign policies which fail to procure moral support (say, from an international organization) will be less consequential for the solidarity and morale of a faction than will those that fail to obtain tangible forms of aid, such as weapons or foodstuffs, that are necessary to the conduct and success of internal warfare.

3. The more commitments a faction makes to [A] or [B] in order to secure support, the more will its subgroups be divided about the wisdom of incurring future obligations and thus the more will the faction experience the effects of its own procurement efforts.

VI. Factional Consequences of War Outputs
(See Cell VI in Figure 1)

This aspect is concerned with the ways in which factions are affected by the international perceptions of the war in which they are combatants. Both the kind of war that is being waged and the stages it passes through foster boundary-crossing outputs which can feed back to factions by several processes. For example, shifts in the lines of battle either facilitate or hinder the procurement of assistance from foreign sources. Another feedback process involves the impact upon factional unity of the effects of the war outputs. As sources of foreign support contract or expand in response to shifts in the prospects of the war, factions may be faced with the question whether to seek or accept assistance from new sources. As noted under Aspect I, such questions can provoke hotly contested issues within a faction, and the resulting controversy can diminish its solidarity and morale. Further elaboration of this aspect might follow along the lines suggested by these propositions:

1. The more one-sided an internal war becomes, the more will subgroups of the losing faction differ on how to turn the tide of battle, and thus the more will the faction be divided by issues involving relations with the international environment.
2. The more one-sided an internal war becomes, the more will the winning faction be inclined to ensure future independence by minimizing the external sources of support and by emphasizing instead that its battle success was due to factional purpose and prowess.
3. The factional feedback of structural wars will be greater than that of authority wars, and the latter will in turn foster more feedback than personnel wars.

VII. *War Consequences of Factional Procurement Efforts*
(See Cell VII in Figure 1)

Perhaps of greater relevance to studies of internal war *per se* than to those of its international aspects, this linkage focuses on the ways in which the course and nature of the hostilities in [C] are affected by the foreign policies of its warring factions. Two dimensions of this linkage are especially noteworthy. One involves the possibility that the type of war may be altered by the contentions and/or commitments which factions make in order to secure external support. It is easy to imagine, for example, a personnel war which escalated into an authority or structural war because one or both of the factions has elevated and dramatized its war aims so as to enlist the aid of [A] or [B]. Second, the procurement efforts of $[C_i]$ and $[C_o]$ can serve to intensify or otherwise alter the conflict as either or both factions are encouraged or discouraged by the prospects of securing outside aid. The effects of this aid itself are covered by Aspects XIII–XVI, but a faction's estimate of the possibility of securing external support, or its calculations as to its enemy's chances in this respect, can feed back as factors in the various stages through which a war passes. Such calculations may also affect the timing, content, and outcome of negotiations to end a war. These additional propositions suggest further refinements of this linkage which might be developed:

1. The more both parties to an internal war estimate that each can obtain as much outside aid as the other, the greater is the likelihood of a negotiated settlement of the conflict; contrari-

wise, the wider the discrepancy between their respective estimates of external procurement ability, the greater is the
likelihood that the war will be waged until one faction capitu-
lates to the other.

2. The more extensive are the external procurement efforts of
$[C_i]$ and $[C_o]$, the more offsetting are their capabilities likely to
become and thus the more the war between them is likely to
move into a stalemate stage.

3. The more a warring faction is ideologically heterogeneous, the
less will its leadership be able to agree on an elevation and
dramatization of its war aims that might yield increased external support, and hence the less is the likelihood that the war
will escalate from one type to another.

VIII. *The Feedback of War Outputs*
(See Cell VIII in Figure 1)

This aspect covers a very limited set of phenomena and is probably
the least important of the sixteen derived from the matrix in Figure
1. It mainly encompasses those rare occasions when the parties to
an internal war tacitly or otherwise agree to a common posture toward some aspect of the international environment, and this agreement then affects the course or nature of the war which they are
waging. If two strongly anti-Communist factions, for instance, are
fighting a personnel or authority war and agree not to seek or accept
aid from the Soviet Union, then the conflict is less likely to escalate
into a structural war than otherwise. Various propositions of this sort
could be developed to analyze other types of tacit or formal agreements to which warring factions might subscribe.

IX. *National Effects of National Intervention*
(See Cell IX in Figure 1)

This aspect focuses on the changes which nations experience as a
result of the actions or policies which they initiate (or fail to initiate)
with respect to the war in $[C]$. As has already been indicated, internal wars can become foci of controversial political issues within $[A]$
or $[B]$. An extreme example of this linkage would be a situation in
which the government of $[A]$ or $[B]$ was forced to resign or was
defeated in a subsequent election as a result of its policies toward
$[C]$. Clearly a host of different and interesting lines of inquiry can
be pursued within the context of this linkage, and the following
propositions suggest only a few of them:

1. The more a nation intervenes in $[C]$, the greater is the likelihood that the intervention will become a source of political dispute among its citizenry.

2. The more a nation is unified by common values, the less will it experience divisive effects of its policies toward [C].

3. A nation located close to [C] is likely to have more varied contacts with the war-torn society than is a geographically distant nation, and thus the former is more likely to be affected by its policies toward the internal war than is the latter.

X. *System-stimulated National Effects*
(See Cell X in Figure 1)

This aspect is concerned mainly with the changes that occur within [A] and [B] as a result of the role that international organizations play in [C]. Just as other nations can experience feedback from their own intervention in internal wars, so can their political life be affected by legal or organizational outputs of the international system which have an impact upon the war-torn society. Whether the U.N. should send troops to maintain order in [C]; whether the Secretary-General should use his good offices to try to settle the conflict; whether an international organization is intervening on the "right" side in the war; whether the precepts of international law are applicable to the events unfolding in [C]—such questions can become controversial issues in other societies, and they can foster changes in [A] or [B]. The role of the U.N. in the Congo, for example, had a discernible impact upon the domestic political scene in the United States. The following propositions suggest other dimensions covered by this linkage:

1. The more extensively an international organization becomes involved in an internal war, the more will its intervention serve as a focus of debate in other countries and the greater will be the salience of events in [C] for factions within [A] or [B].

2. Legislative resolutions about [C] adopted by international organizations, being expressions of attitude more than commitments to action, will not be as divisive for [A] and [B] as will diplomatic or military activities in the war-torn society by their executive officers.

XI. *National Sources of System Changes*
(See Cell XI in Figure 1)

Here attention centers on the ways in which the boundary-crossing outputs of [A] and [B] affect the relationship between them, the structure and functioning of international organizations, and the state of the international system. Just as the policies of a nation toward a war-torn society can become a matter of dispute among its various factions, so can the same policies serve as the source of a hotly contested issue among other nations. Allies of [A] may protest its intervention in the affairs of [C], or neutral nations may condemn the insufficiency of its actions with respect to the internal war; obviously repercussions of this sort can strengthen or diminish the solidarity of the relationships between [A] and other nations. The perceptions of U.S. policies toward internal wars in North Africa during the 1950's are illustrative of this linkage. American avoidance of a commitment with respect to independence movements in Tunisia and Algeria provoked both the allies of the U.S. and the nations of the underdeveloped world, the latter because such a policy seemed supportive of $[C_i]$ and the former because it appeared to aid $[C_o]$. Similarly, as evidenced by events in the United Nations subsequent to Russia's intervention in the Hungarian uprising of 1956, or after participation by the United States in Cuba's internal war of 1961, international organizations can experience feedback from the role played by other nations in war-torn societies. That the over-all state of the international system can also be affected by the intervention of [A] or [B] is well illustrated by the alterations which it underwent (i.e., reduced stability and increased polarization) as a result of the role which all the major nations of Europe played in the Spanish civil war of 1936–1939. The wide scope of this linkage is further indicated by these propositions:

1. The more unlike [A] and [B] are in their historical traditions and their political structures, and the more one of them intervenes in [C], the more will the relationship between them be weakened.

2. The international relationships of a nation located close to [C] are more likely to be affected by whatever policies it adopts toward the internal war than are the relationships of a nation which pursues similar policies but which is geographically far from the conflict.

3. The more a major power intervenes in a geographically distant internal war, the more will the intervention be challenged by other nations, and thus the greater will be the instability of the international system; however, other nations will be more accepting of proximate interventions and, consequently, the stability of the system will only be minimally affected when a major power intervenes in the conflict of an adjacent or nearby society.

XII. *Systemic Effects of System Outputs*
(See Cell XII in Figure 1)

This aspect encompasses two main linkages. One is the consequence for international law of the role it plays in an internal war. International legal norms will be more subject to alteration the more they are involved or invoked in the course of events in [C]. This aspect also focuses on the fact that international organizations, like nations, can experience change as a result of intervening in an internal war. Change in the O.A.S.'s solidarity and effectiveness as a result of its actions toward the Cuban internal war are illustrative, and the impact of the intervention of the U.N. in the Congo upon its structure and functioning is perhaps an even better example. Other dimensions of this aspect are suggested by the following propositions:

1. The greater the regional homogeneity of an international organization, the less will it be affected by its intervention in geographically distant internal wars; in the case of nearby conflicts, however, even regionally homogeneous organizations will experience divisiveness as a consequence of adopting a posture toward the hostilities in neighboring countries.

2. The more the international system is organized along balance of power, rather than bipolar, lines, the less will its stability be affected by boundary-crossing outputs of international organizations.

3. The more an international organization intervenes in an internal war through its executive officers (as distinguished from intervention through legislative resolutions), the less will its actions be based on a consensus of its members and thus the more will the organization experience repercussions of its own boundary-crossing outputs.

XIII. *Nationally Induced Factional Changes* (*See Cell XIII in Figure 1*)

This aspect encompasses phenomena that are the converse of Aspect I. Here inquiries would focus on how the outputs of other nations foster varying consequences for the parties to an internal war. The number of possible forms which this linkage can take is almost incalculable. The capabilities, behavior, and attitudes of $[C_i]$ or $[C_o]$ can be affected in as many ways as $[A]$ or $[B]$ can devise for giving (or withholding) various kinds and amounts of support. Substantial consequences might be induced if $[A]$ and $[C_o]$ are ideologically compatible, thus leading the former to provide the latter with extensive moral and substantive assistance. On the other hand, minimal consequences may result if more weight is attached to capability than to compatibility factors. If, for example, $[C_o]$ is weak and unlikely to survive, $[A]$ may prefer not to involve itself in a losing cause even though it may be sympathetic to the values for which the faction is fighting. Under still other circumstances—say, if $[A]$ attaches conditions to its assistance—changes in the structure as well as the capabilities of a warring faction can occur. Contrariwise, the degree of externally induced change experienced by $[C_i]$ or $[C_o]$ can be a function of their readiness to accept outside aid. One faction, for instance, may be predisposed to accept outside aid on any condition, while another may be receptive to offers of support only from countries with which it is ideologically compatible. The way in which non-Communist insurgent movements cope with offers of aid from the Soviet Union is illustrative in this respect. The resistance of some pro-Western factions to U.S. insistence on the introduction of socio-economic reforms provides another example. In short, depending upon a host of possible output-input combinations, alterations in $[C_i]$ or $[C_o]$ resulting from linkages to $[A]$ or $[B]$ can range from widespread and significant modifications in structure, motivation, and capability to a few changes of a minor nature. Other key points in this range are suggested by these propositions:

1. The more assistance a faction receives from abroad, the more are its external sources of support likely to insist on playing a role in determining the faction's goals, policies, and strategies.
2. The more a faction is committed to an ideological doctrine, the more will it attract external assistance to which stringent conditions are attached.

XIV. System Sources of Factional Changes
(See Cell XIV in Figure 1)

Inquires into this aspect would focus on the ways in which different factions are affected by the varying kinds of equilibria, relationships, and organizational activities which comprise the international system. As shown by the intervention of the U.N. in the Congo or the O.A.S. in the Dominican Republic, international organizations can become extensively involved in efforts to enlarge or restrict the capabilities and/or the goals of warring factions. In the postwar era it has usually been insurgent factions that have attracted either moral or substantive support from international organizations. Indeed, it would appear that the more $[C_o]$ is tyrannized by $[C_i]$, the greater is the likelihood that an international organization will attempt either to reform the structure of the latter or increase the capabilities of the former. Similarly, the aims and abilities of both factions may be affected by shifts in the relationship between $[A]$ and $[B]$. As the two countries become antagonistic, for example, they may wish to avoid a direct clash and instead prefer to express their differences indirectly through aid to the opposing factions in $[C]$. The capabilities and structure of warring factions will likewise be affected by the over-all state of the international system. Presumably $[C_i]$ and $[C_o]$ will attract different degrees and kinds of outside support when a balance of power prevails than when the system is organized along bipolar lines. As these additional propositions indicate, many other lines of investigation could be pursued in the context of this aspect:

1. To the extent that militarily weak factions receive support from international organizations, this is likely to be in the form of endorsing resolutions; but as a faction acquires greater military strength, the support of international organizations is likely to become substantive as well as moral.

2. The more the relationship between [A] and [B] becomes either cordial or hostile, the more will both countries be inclined to supply assistance to ideologically compatible warring factions; however, they will be more disinclined to affect the capabilities of warring factions when their relationship is neither very cordial nor very hostile.

XV. *National Sources of War Changes* (See Cell XV in Figure 1)

Here the main concern is the impact which differently located, structured, and motivated nations have upon the course and conduct of various types of internal wars. Although the goals and structure of a warring faction may, as noted under Aspect XIII, originally stimulate [A] or [B] to intervene in a conflict, these nations must soon become aware that they have a stake in the outcome of the war which may not be identical to the results sought by the faction they are supporting. They may, for example, be just as concerned about the post-conflict stability of a war-torn society as about the triumph of one of its factions. Stated differently, other nations have policies toward internal wars as well as toward particular factions and normally the latter are cast within the framework of the former. Indeed, some outside nations may be exclusively interested in ending hostilities and totally lacking in an identification with one of its factions. Contrariwise, for example, with Communist countries, there may be certain situations in which they are primarily interested in prolonging the conflict and relatively unconcerned about the survival of any of the factions.

It should also be noted that, as the dotted arrows indicate, [A] or [B] can affect the relations between [C_i] and [C_o] even if they do not directly intervene in the conflict. A large nation which has pursued a "hands-off" policy toward a nearby internal war exemplifies this possibility. The course of the conflict might be substantially limited by a recognition (or rumor) that under certain conditions the hands-off policy would be replaced by some form of intervention. Additional dimensions of both the direct and indirect linkages covered by this aspect are suggested by the following propositions:

1. The closer a nation is located to a war-torn society, the more is it likely to be affected by the conflict and thus the more will it press for an early and negotiated settlement of the internal war.

2. [A] and [B] are more likely to search for peace terms that are satisfactory to both parties of a structural war than of an authority or a personnel war.

3. The more intense a conflict and the more fluid its lines of battle, the greater will be the inclination of [A] and [B] to press for a ceasefire or a retreat to the conditions of an earlier stalemate.

4. The longer an internal war persists, the greater will be the efforts of other nations to end it and the less will be their assistance to the warring factions.

XVI. *System-induced War Changes*
(See Cell XVI in Figure 1)

This aspect focuses on the ways in which different international relationships and organizations affect the intensity, conduct, duration, and termination of internal wars. These linkages emphasize the aforementioned point that war-torn societies are parts of larger systems and that considerations pertaining to the stability and persistence of the larger systems may impose limits upon the course and outcome of internal wars. The ties between [A] and [B], for example, may be such that, irrespective of their sympathies for one or another of the warring factions, neither can allow events in [C] to move out of a stalemate stage. Or other international relationships may be so delicate that a continuation of the conflict in [C] cannot be tolerated if the relationship is to endure, with the result that [A] and [B] ignore their sympathies for $[C_i]$ or $[C_o]$ and attempt to end the hostilities as a means of preserving their relationship. Efforts on the part of the United States and the USSR with respect to Laos reflect this process of attaching higher priority to the maintenance of international relationships than to the outcome of internal wars. Depending on the type and scope of the war, on the other hand, the preservation of an international relationship may be less important to [A] or [B] than the triumph of a particular faction in [C]. To cite an obvious illustration from recent history, in 1956 the USSR did not give greater weight to its international relationships when internal war broke out in Hungary.

The foregoing reasoning also applies to the role international organizations play in internal wars. The more a conflict threatens the existence of solidarity of an organization, the greater will be its efforts to bring about a termination of hostilities. The role of NATO in the Indochina settlement of 1954 is illustrative of this process, as is the role of the U.N. in Korea and the Congo. On the other hand, the action undertaken by an international organization will also depend on the type of internal war being waged and on whether organizational solidarity will be undermined to a greater extent by intervention than by abstention. Such variability is suggested by the sharp contrast between the U.N's active participation in the Congo and its minimal role in the Hungarian crisis of 1956. That this aspect subsumes a wide range of possible linkages is further indicated by these additional propositions:

1. The more involved a major power is in an internal war, the greater will be the instability of international organizations in which the major power holds membership and thus the less will such organizations play a role in the conflict.
2. The less the ideological compatibility of [A] and [B], the more will they press for a negotiated settlement of a structural war in [C].
3. The greater the over-all stability of the international system, the more are internal wars likely to be isolated and stalemated.

Contributors

KARL W. DEUTSCH is Professor of Political Science at Harvard University. His many books include *The Analysis of International Relations* (1967), *The Nerves of Government* (1963), and *Nationalism and Social Communication* (1953).

RICHARD A. FALK, Milbank Professor of International Law and Practice at Princeton University, is a Faculty Associate of the Center of International Studies at Princeton. His many writings include *The Status of Law in International Society* (1970), *Legal Order in a Violent World* (1968), and *Law, Morality, and War in the Contemporary World* (1963).

MANFRED HALPERN is Professor of Politics at Princeton University, having previously spent ten years in the Department of State. Among his recent writings is *The Politics of Social Change in the Middle East and North Africa* (1963).

MORTON A. KAPLAN is Professor of Political Science and Chairman of the Committee on International Relations at the University of Chicago. His writings include editorship of *The Revolution in World Politics* (1962) and authorship of *Macropolitics* (1969) and *System and Process in International Politics* (1957).

GEORGE MODELSKI is Professor of Political Science at the University of Washington. He is the author of *A Theory of Foreign Policy* (1962) and *SEATO: Six Studies* (1962).

JAMES N. ROSENAU is Professor of Political Science at Ohio State University, having previously taught at Rutgers University and served as a Research Associate at the Center of International Studies, Princeton University. Among his books are *The Scientific Study of Foreign Policy* (1970), *National Leadership and Foreign Policy* (1963), and *Public Opinion and Foreign Policy* (1961).

ANDREW M. SCOTT is Professor of Political Science at the University of North Carolina. His publications include *The Revolution in Statecraft* (1965) and *The Functioning of the International Political System* (1967).

Index

315